The Imperial Collection Of

AUDUBON ANIMALS

Bust by Joy Buba   *Photo Credit Igor Bakht*

The Imperial Collection Of
AUDUBON ANIMALS

THE
QUADRUPEDS of NORTH AMERICA

Original text by
John James Audubon, F.R.S. and The Rev. John Bachman, D.D.
Edited and with new text by Victor H. Cahalane
Foreword by Fairfield Osborn
Illustrated by John James Audubon and John Woodhouse Audubon

BONANZA BOOKS · NEW YORK

This edition published by Bonanza Books,
a division of Crown Publishers, Inc.
by arrangement with Hammond Incorporated
    e f g h

FOREWORD

The name of Audubon is so universally associated with birds that this remarkable series of paintings of the terrestrial mammals of North America will probably come as a surprise to many people.

The fact that he was able to accomplish this arduous and prolonged task, often under extremely difficult conditions, and after the many years of hardship and the concentrated work he had devoted to completing more than 435 illustrations of THE BIRDS OF AMERICA, exemplifies his boundless energy as well as a passionate interest in animal life. It is strongly recommended that everyone who possesses this book on mammals will read the Introduction that follows, which so vividly portrays the difficulties and trials that had to be overcome in its production.

One or two major incidents occurred, both seemingly accidental, that greatly influenced the development of Audubon's career. The first was that his father happened to be an officer in the French Navy. Among the stations where he served was Les Cayes, Santo Domingo, now Haiti, where Audubon was born. The father subsequently took his son to France where he was educated, including studies in painting. It is sometimes said he studied under J. J. David, an eminent artist of his era, but whether or not this is so, he learned in his youth the techniques of painting including the essential values of perspective and composition, skills that he later developed through his own special talents that resulted in his remarkable accomplishments in this art. Many years later another incident occurred, again seemingly accidental. While passing through Charleston, South Carolina, he met by pure chance a clergyman, John Bachman, who possessed a consuming interest in natural history and indeed, for those days, was extremely well informed concerning both birds and mammals. The two men rapidly formed a deep friendship and regard for each other and decided to collaborate on the preparation of a volume, with Audubon doing the portraiture and Bachman writing the descriptive texts. No partnership could have proved more effective. It survived, in the face of many vicissitudes, over the 15 years that were required to complete the paintings and technical information.

Warm tribute must be expressed to Victor Cahalane who has been responsible for the textual contents of this book. He wisely decided to include key excerpts contained within the first publication of Audubon's paintings that appeared more than 100 years ago. He has accompanied these with separate descriptions expressing present-day scientific knowledge of animal species. Mr. Cahalane is one of today's eminent zoologists whose writings, including his book, THE MAMMALS OF NORTH AMERICA, have become standard reference works.

There are three great values to this book which are rarely combined in the same publication, a fact that makes it unique in many respects. The primary value is, of course, a further demonstration of Audubon's extraordinary talents, frequently supplemented by the work of his son, John, who either assisted in the preparation of or was himself responsible for many paintings. Another value is that this book with its up-to-date revisions of descriptive matter qualifies it is an important and authentic source of information concerning the quadrupeds of this country, enriched, it must be added, by the comparisons of knowledge in this science of more than a century ago to that of today. The richness of the knowledge of people interested in mammalogy in those earlier days is in itself quite extraordinary. Lastly, the original text or, rather, the excerpts therefrom, provide in many instances a revelation of what the United States was in earlier days, thus becoming useful and interesting to the records of early Americana.

FAIRFIELD OSBORN
President, New York Zoological Society

CONTENTS

Foreword v

Introduction ix-xvi

JOHN JAMES AUDUBON

Painted about 1841 by his sons John Woodhouse Audubon and Victor Gifford Audubon.

INTRODUCTION

AN HISTORIC MEETING

The outstanding work on American mammals in the 19th century resulted from a chance meeting of two men. It occurred on October 17, 1831, in Charleston, South Carolina.

John J. Audubon, the famous bird artist and ornithologist, had arrived in town the evening before. With two assistants, landscape painter George Lehman and English taxidermist Henry Ward, he had ridden in stiff-sprung coaches, over rough and potholed roads, from Richmond. The three men were disheveled and weary. Their boardinghouse, when the bill was presented, proved to be too expensive for Audubon. While he had become the talk of natural history circles as the gifted painter of the first folio in a forthcoming series which was to depict all the birds of America, he had had as yet little monetary return. Also, since Audubon and his helpers were on their way to Florida to search for new birds, it was essential to stretch the funds as far as possible.

Consequently, Audubon, with the guidance of a local clergyman named Gilman, was tramping the streets looking for cheaper lodgings. As they proceeded, a man approached on horseback. Recognizing Gilman, the man reined in, dismounted, and was introduced to Audubon as the Reverend John Bachman, pastor of the Lutheran Church. His strong, square face breaking into a warm smile, he greeted the artist. Thus began a deep friendship and eventually a close working and family relationship which was to endure until broken by Audubon's death nearly 20 years later.

Bachman, who had been deeply interested in natural history since boyhood, insisted that his new acquaintance and his helpers should move into the Bachman home for the duration of their stay in Charleston. The minister's family was large — eight children living, in addition to his wife and the latter's sister, Maria Martin. However, the square three-story house was commodious and two rooms were set aside for workshops. During the four weeks that elapsed before the bird men left for Florida, they spent the days traveling about the countryside with Bachman in two carriages provided by him. Notes were taken, birds were collected and preserved as skins, and in the evenings paintings and records were made. Audubon and his host talked natural history far into the night, finding in each other a mutual interest and rapport that developed quickly into affection and a high regard for each other's abilities and attainments.

Following the visit, Bachman wrote Mrs. Audubon: "The last has been one of the happiest months of my life." . . . Audubon was not only an expert, he "was communicative, intelligent and amiable, to an extent seldom found in the same individual . . . we were inseparable." Audubon was indeed an inspiration to Bachman, whose energy and interest were now channeled into effective work in science. For his part, the minister made a deep impression on Audubon.

During the years that followed, Bachman gave Audubon advice and encouragement in completing his great undertaking, *The Birds of America,* and supplied him with numerous specimens which the artist used in painting the plates. In return, during his expeditions Audubon collected mammal skins for his friend's careful study and to add to his already large collection.

At last Audubon completed all 435 paintings for *The Birds of America* and the companion five-volume text, *Ornithological Biographies.* That summer of 1839, although the monumental work was selling but slowly despite much solicitation, the artist's great energies began to overflow. Under the urge of this restlessness and the always pressing need for funds to support his family, he decided to do with the mammals what he had just completed with the birds.

BEGINNING THE QUADRUPEDS

Although the proposed project was actually more difficult than the *Birds,* Audubon assumed that he would collect and identify the specimens as well as paint the portraits and write the text. With typical drive and enthusiasm he proposed to broadcast immediately a printed prospectus announcing the future publication of *The Viviparous Quadrupeds of North America!*

This planned publicity brought a down-to-earth letter from John Bachman: ". . . are you not too fast in issuing your prospectus . . . ? . . . The animals have never been carefully described, and you will find difficulties at every step. Books cannot aid you much. Long journeys will have to be undertaken . . . The Western Deer are no joke (to classify), and the ever varying Squirrels seem sent by Satan himself, to puzzle the Naturalists." Bachman added — also rashly! — "I think that I have studied the subject more than you have . . . Say in what manner I can assist you."

The courteous but sensible advice and perhaps his own second thoughts convinced Audubon that even his great talent should be supplemented by technical assistance. He asked for and received the commitment that Bachman would collaborate as junior author. The latter had not only scientific recognition; he had given his two oldest daughters in marriage to Audubon's sons. By joining the enterprise without personal recompense, Bachman hoped to perhaps provide a future "nest egg" for his children and their families as well as make an important contribution to science.

AN OPEN FIELD

Mammalogy in 1839 was indeed a promising field for a comprehensive publication. The species of eastern and northern America had been investigated by a number of naturalists including Bartram, Rafinesque, Hearne and Richardson, but most of their results had been published here and there in obscure journals and magazines, some of which did not even pretend to be scientific in character. Richardson's *Fauna Boreali-Americana,* printed in 1829, was one of the very few inclusive works on animal life but it was restricted to the northern portion of the continent. DeKay's monumental *Zoology of New York,* which actually attempted to cover a wider area than that State, had not yet appeared. Many original (type) specimens, particularly those representing species in British America, the far west and Mexico, were deposited in European museums and could be studied only by making an expensive and time-consuming journey. American collections of mammals were scarce, poorly housed and all too often subject to loss by fire or to dispersal if the owners went bankrupt. Zoological gardens for live animals were small at best and very few in number. Scant information on possible new species could be gained from them. Libraries of science books were little better; numerous works containing descriptions of American animals were available only in private homes or in Europe.

Finally, much of western America was still poorly known and travel west of the Mississippi River was arduous, dangerous, and restricted largely to the Missouri River and the southern overland route through Santa Fe. Unpredictable and sometimes hostile Indians, and uncertain and often unfriendly international relations with Mexico, discouraged scientific work without an effective military escort.

Bachman had been most conservative in estimating the difficulties of the project.

PLAN OF THE QUADRUPEDS

In establishing the scope of their book, the authors realized that, because nature does not observe political subdivisions, they too should ignore national boundaries. Therefore they resolved to include "the British and Russian possessions in America, the whole of the United States and their territories, California, and that part of Mexico north of the Tropic of Cancer." The illustrations were to be "not only scientifically correct, but interesting to all" readers, in "the varied occupations, expressions, and attitudes" of the animals, "together with the appropriate accessories, such as trees, plants, landscapes, etc." The text would describe the form and color of the subjects, their habits, distribution and relationships ("all of interest"), and methods of hunting for meat, skins, or "to get rid of dangerous or annoying neighbors." (Introduction, p. viii)

During the planning late in 1839, Bachman expressed "doubt that we (will need room for more than one hundred species) unless we include the whales and mammalia of that character." Eventually he described more than double that number of terrestrial mammals, of which the Audubons, father and son, painted 147 species (plus eight separate "varieties") on 150 plates. Bachman continued, "The figures may, I think, be given without reference to any scale, those of a skunk full size, those above as taste or space will dictate." The plate size adopted was 28 by 22 inches.

Audubon envisioned that he would require two years to paint the animal portraits, and that Bachman would need an additional year to complete his field studies and write descriptions. The complete publication, therefore, would be available to the subscribers in three years.

Even the realistic and hardheaded Bachman did not fully realize the magnitude of the task on which they entered with such high hopes. While a few plates were rushed out in 1842 (to impress subscribers), it was not until 1848, eight years after initiation of the project, that the last of the 150 plates came from the press. The third and final volume of text, although writing was finished in the spring of 1852, was not published until 1854, 11 years behind Audubon's "schedule." He himself had died three years previously, after turning his brushes over to his son John in the spring of 1846.

AUDUBON THE INSPIRING FLAME

Even before Bachman committed himself as junior author in January 1840, Audubon was spending every available hour painting mammals and writing for specimens. Through the Christmas holidays he continued to devote long days to the project. Among many correspondents, he wrote to one Thomas McCulloch of Halifax, Nova Scotia: "I wish you to assist me as much as is in your power in the way of procuring specimens for me and paying for them whatever you think proper... I send you now a list of such animals as I think you can get for me." To Increase S. Smith of Hingham, Massachusetts, Audubon sent directions for preserving snowshoe (varying) hares for shipment: "The animals ought to be put in a Keg of Common Yankee Rum, and as soon as possible after death, cutting a slit in the abdomen of not exceeding *Two Inches* in length, and pouring Rum in the apperture until well filled. The Entrails must remain untouched."

Audubon worked rapidly and with great concentration. By mid-August 1841, after painting regardless of cold or heat since the end of the previous year, he had completed 36 plates. (Bachman put this achievement in perspective by pointing out that some 200 more species should have "proper elucidation." He had raised his earlier estimate.) In the autumn, Audubon decided to leave crowded, noisy New York City, which he hated, and he acquired an estate of 30 acres or more a few miles from town. On the western shore of upper Manhattan Island, it afforded a lovely view of the New Jersey Palisades, and fish could be seined from the Hudson River whenever needed for the table. (The two Audubon sons caught an eight-foot, 200-pound sturgeon; such a fish would expire quickly in these present-day polluted waters.) A three-story house was completed in April 1842, giving ample room for the family. Here at "Minnie's Land" (named for his wife) the artist found inspiration for his work and space in which to keep live subjects for his painting and writing — ranging from squirrels and a marten to a pair of elk!

TO THE YELLOWSTONE

When need for specimens and information on western species became pressing in 1842, Audubon went to Washington despite oppressive mid-summer heat to solicit official support for an expedition. In this he failed, but at his hotel he met a fellow-lodger, Col. Pierre Chouteau of the American Fur Company, which traded on the upper Missouri River and its tributaries. Through this acquaintance, Audubon was enabled to travel the next summer on a Company steamboat to Fort Union, a trading post on the Missouri a few miles below the outlet of the Yellowstone River. He was accompanied by a close friend and amateur naturalist, Edward Harris, who rented his farm to help meet one-fifth the cost of the expedition. Expenses included the modest salaries of three assistants who were engaged by Audubon.

The party hunted and made observations at refueling stops on the journey upstream. The 1,400-mile trip from St. Louis took 49 days. At Fort Union, June 12 to August 16, the men sought everything from prairie dogs to bison. Indian and half-breed trappers were hired and given assignments. Audubon sketched and kept a voluminous journal, recording impressions of the strange landscapes, plants and animals, and the white trappers and red Indians. He watched from the sidelines as his companions killed bison, sometimes for their tongues only, and narrowly escaped from an infuriated bull when in the excitement he forgot his limitations of age and approached too closely on foot.

Although Audubon saw many bighorns, he was never able to get near enough to shoot any and the hunters that he sent off usually came back empty-handed. Audubon and his party returned back down the river to St. Louis and thence home. He arrived at Minnie's Land November 6, 1843 with drawings, skins soaked in brine, Indian trophies and a live swift fox, a badger and a mule deer. (Among the Indian gifts were a necklace of grizzly bear teeth and a full-size Indian lodge.) It was Audubon's last field trip. Although his sight was still exceptionally keen, he looked and felt 10 years older than his actual age of 58.

BACHMAN, THE SCIENTIST

The Reverend John Bachman had a dual role in producing the *Quadrupeds*. First, he determined the validity of species or "variety" of the mammals. He wrote all scientific descriptions, compiled the synonymy of species' names, worked out geographic distributions as far as possible from often scanty records, and contributed his personal observations on habits of the animals. Secondly, he acted as scientific editor, revising and fitting together the accounts of habits, hunting anecdotes and other information which he received from the senior Audubon, his son John, and numerous others whose comments were solicited or contributed on their own initiative.

For his time, Bachman was well prepared to undertake the task. He was five years younger than Audubon, of Swiss-German stock, a thorough scholar with a deep and exceptionally broad interest in nature. Although he was isolated from recognized scientific centers of the country, he was accepted as a reputable colleague by naturalists both in America and England. He corresponded with great naturalists of the day and a number of them came to visit him at his home. In 1838, he was invited to deliver an address on natural science in America before a congress of naturalists and physicians in Freiburg, Germany. He used the opportunity while in London to study the notable collection of mammals in the British Museum.

While he was perhaps inclined to be pedantic, Bachman was right in telling Audubon, "You cannot do without me in this business. . . ." He was a friendly, kindly man who was intensely loyal and self-sacrificing. Probably no other naturalist of the period, either amateur or professional, would have carried the project through to completion under the very trying handicaps which beset him during his 12 years of research and writing. Before the invention of the typewriter, every word of copying and manuscript had to be written laboriously with a quill or an "iron" pen.

Because of his churchly obligations, Bachman could rarely give full time to his monumental avocation but he arranged his schedule to the best advantage possible. In the summer of 1842, when Mrs. Bachman's poor health forced her to leave Charleston's heat and humidity, he visited her weekly at her country retreat where he worked on the *Quadrupeds* without interruption. Mrs. Bachman died four years later; this was one of a series of personal catastrophes which included the loss of three children (two of them the daughters who had married Audubon's sons) and of several family servants, as well as his own persistently recurring eye trouble and other infirmities.

Slow communication with the Audubons in New York was frustrating. Mail was two weeks en route; response to a question required a month if given immediate attention. To settle the multitudinous problems of species identification, nomenclature and other points, Bachman needed many reference books which were not in his personal library nor that of the local Natural History Society. He depended largely on the Audubons to obtain those books or to copy pertinent information from them. Engrossed in their own pressing endeavors of finding specimens and painting them, as well as meeting many business obligations, the Audubons sometimes neglected to supply those wants with what Bachman considered reasonable promptness.

At the end of the second year, Bachman was still patient. He declined an offer of the presidency of South Carolina College at three thousand dollars a year, saying that he enjoyed preaching and his hobby, nature, too much to leave Charleston. This decision undoubtedly saved the *Quadrupeds* from foundering, or at best suffering a very long delay.

Difficulties were destined, however, to be compounded. Bachman expected a vast amount of information from the Missouri River expedition — specimens and data for describing new species and "fleshing out" accounts of habits — but he was given only picturesque generalities. When asked for a detailed report, Audubon, well aware that he had accomplished little of scientific value, replied that he had brought back many sketches, and specimens of what he hoped would prove to be 14 new birds and a new type of antelope. Politely, Bachman praised the "grand haul" of birds but advised that the antelope probably had been described earlier. (It had.) Finally, late in 1845, the clergyman traveled to New York where Audubon refused even to show him the notes he had made along the Missouri River. The journal was at long last turned over to Bachman several months later only when he threatened to withdraw completely. Bitterly disappointed that Audubon had brought back so few small mammals, Bachman lamented the amount of time spent watching buffalo-kills, wolves, grizzlies and bighorns. He urged the senior author to write back to Fort Union for specimens, NOT of his "princess brain-eating, horse-straddling squaw" (whom Audubon had painted) ". . . but what is better . . . the Skunk . . . Hares in Winter colors . . . and the Rabbit."

During his visit to Minnie's Land, Bachman became aware that although Audubon's artistic skill was still impressive, his physical and mental capabilities were declining. This explained the increasing frequency of "sad mistakes" in the manuscript pages which were being submitted to the editor. Thereafter, Bachman depended increasingly on the two sons. They, unfortunately, needed "the whip" applied by "the schoolmaster." They failed to send specimens, books, and excerpts from journals which Bachman required. He complained bitterly to a friend, "They have not sent me one single book out of a list of a hundred I gave them, and only six lines copied from a book after my having written them for four years." At one point, Bachman dropped work for almost a year, then resumed when Victor vowed that he and his brother would pay strict attention to directions from Charleston.

The first volume of text which had caused Bachman so much travail was printed in Philadelphia in 1846 and in London the following spring. (This was the end of the "European edition.") With new encouragement, Bachman continued work, even though impaired vision forced him to dictate the final pages to Victor Audubon. In the early spring of 1852 the third and final volume of text was finished.

THREE INDISPENSABLES

John J. and Lucy Audubon reared two sons (two daughters died in early childhood). As men, both sons collaborated with their father and spent much of their lives in his service. The younger, John Woodhouse Audubon (usually called "Johnny" by his father) was quiet, sensitive, gruff with strangers, probably from shyness, but genial and a sparkling conversationalist among friends. With his father's instruction he became an animal painter of some ability, but he did not pretend to be a naturalist. His forte was portraiture and as a young man he painted members of his family and their friends, including Bachman. While in England and Scotland during the 1830's John worked professionally, taking as many as five sittings a day.

This career was stifled by demands of the *Quadrupeds*. Acting from the beginning of the project (late 1839) as assistant artist, secretary and general helper, John was forced to take over more of the work as his father's health declined. His expedition to Texas, November 1845 to April 1846, yielded little that was useful. Shortly after returning from Texas, John spent nearly a year in Europe painting mammals of northern Canada in the British Museum and perhaps other institutions. By the spring of 1846 — midway in the production of folio plates — John was left with sole responsibility in this department. He did at least 72 of the 150 paintings in the imperial folio series, as well as the five "bonus" plates of the octavo edition.

John's older brother (by three years), Victor Gifford Audubon, inherited his father's quick temper and sometimes sarcastic tongue. His artistic talents were in landscapes; his abilities may be measured by his sale of an oil in New Orleans in the fall of 1840 for 150 dollars (perhaps equivalent to five hundred dollars at present). Victor assisted his father in the *Quadrupeds* project by painting backgrounds as well as plants and other accessories to the mammals. His greatest service and most of his time was given to business aspects, especially dealings with the lithographers and printers. To ensure that the original paintings were re-drawn or traced accurately on the stone slabs with the colors reproduced exactly, required constant, careful supervision in the shop while the work was in progress. During the 11 months that his brother was drawing specimens in the British Museum, Victor functioned as overall supervisor for the final preparation of copy for the printer. Costs were mounting, the printer was trying to expedite the work, and to keep him supplied with text for the typesetters Victor edited and condensed copy as it came from Bachman. This did nothing to soothe the latter, who protested alterations and the insertion of still another writing style in the book.

Long years of intensive work and financial worries involved in preparing and publishing the *Quadrupeds,* following equally arduous endeavors in behalf of *The Birds of America,* undoubtedly shortened the lives of Audubon's sons. Victor died in 1860, aged 51, and John in 1862 at the age of 49.

Although she was not mentioned in the Introduction to the *Quadrupeds,* Miss Maria Martin "lightened the labours" of the authors more than all of the "many excellent friends and gentlemen" whose assistance is specifically acknowledged there. The sister-in-law of John Bachman, Miss Martin made fine drawings of mammals, insects and plants as he required them, served as copyist (from books, journals and manuscripts), secretary and editorial assistant, and read to him when his eyes failed from overuse. Two years after the death of the first Mrs. Bachman in 1846, the minister showed his appreciation of Maria Martin's qualities by making her his wife.

OTHER CONTRIBUTORS

By request of the authors or on their own initiative, many persons contributed mammals, or skins and skulls, and information such as field observations. Most of these doctors, surgeons, army officers, farmers, trappers and others are now only obscure names or are completely forgotten. Among the exceptions is Edward Harris who, as a close friend of both Audubon and Bachman, encouraged them, made financial contributions, and settled disagreements when they arose between the two collaborators. John K. Townsend allowed the use of his invaluable field notes and his large collection of mammals, including types of many new species, from the almost unexplored northern Rockies and Pacific Northwest. Spencer F. Baird, later Secretary of the Smithsonian Institution, provided Audubon with numerous mammals, both living and dead, for use in painting; he also searched the literature for descriptions of new species. Sir George Simpson, governor of the Hudson's Bay Company, sent many skins of Arctic furbearers. Pierre Chouteau, famous fur trader, merchant and financier, contributed skins of western mammals and enabled Audubon to make his long-desired trip to the West. These are but examples of the many who became interested in and enhanced the value of *The Viviparous Quadrupeds of North America.*

ABOUT THE PAINTINGS AND TEXT

While Audubon boasted (not with complete accuracy) that he had painted every plate of his *Birds of America* from subjects he had studied in life, he never made a similar claim for the *Quadrupeds.* He used skins and mounted animals at times, and occasionally he resorted to pictures by other artists as a means of refreshing his memory. Occasionally he employed time- and labor-saving expedients or "short-cuts." For example, he traced the figure of an eastern gray squirrel, which he had painted in 1821 and used as an accessory to the Barred Owl in Plate 46 of his *Birds,* to occupy the left side of Plate 7 in the *Quadrupeds.*

Although Audubon gained fame primarily as a painter of birds, he depicted most of the mammals superbly. While his predecessors had posed their subjects woodenly and in conventional postures, he captured life and movement without, in most cases, distortion. He had a fine sense of composition and some of his arrangements are exquisite. His work varies in quality. Some pictures have earned the highest praise of artists and of such noted scientists as Louis Agassiz, Eliot Coues and Thomas Gilliard. Other paintings are less worthy, showing the effects of unfamiliarity with the animal in its natural environment or, too frequently, the pressure under which he worked to meet publication deadlines or financial needs. It must be remembered that many of the plates which the senior Audubon made for the *Quadrupeds* were painted when his physical infirmities were mounting as a result of a lifetime of hardships and stress. One of his last paintings, that of the "Texan" (now hog-nosed) Skunk, Plate 53, appears to be divided in two vertical planes. It was criticized vigorously by Bachman who generally considered his friend's art beyond reproach; the painter, however, could see nothing wrong with it.

John Woodhouse Audubon took over the entire task of painting the mammals early in 1846. Unlike his father who had little formal instruction in art and worked chiefly with chalk, crayon and watercolors, J. W. Audubon had the benefit of considerable training and painted almost entirely in oils. The style of the two men was similar, so alike, in fact, that in some instances it is not possible to credit the paintings with certainty. A number of plates in the imperial folios which bear the name of J. J. Audubon were, in the later octavo edition, assigned to the son. According to the legend on Plate 120, which depicts two lemmings, it was drawn by the senior Audubon. The text, however, states that the drawing was made in London by J. W. Audubon from museum skins obtained in Canada by Drummond. In the subsequent octavo edition the legend was corrected to read, "Drawn from nature (!) by J. W. Audubon." This edition credits the latter with 72 of the original 150 plates, but the actual number may be even larger. Using his father's drawings from the Missouri-Yellowstone trip, the younger Audubon drew most of the larger mammals, as well as the smaller species of the far north. He re-drew all of the imperial folio drawings for the "miniature" edition, a task which must have required many months.

In summary, while John Woodhouse Audubon had less than his father's great ability to portray animals in exciting movement as well as little feeling for design, he has been too deeply shadowed by the senior Audubon's reputation. Indirectly, he has also suffered by the concentration of fame's spotlight on the *Birds* rather than the *Quadrupeds*.

Until the closing stages of work, each species and variety was painted on a separate plate; notable mammals such as white-tailed deer, bison and mountain lion were each given two plates. Even the smallest insectivores and rodents were handled in similar lavish manner. At the end, however, some of the small species were crowded two, three or even four on a single plate.

By agreement of the two authors, the senior Audubon recorded his personal observations on the habits of mammals and sent them to Bachman. The latter edited the manuscript and combined it with his own and sometimes with accounts which were contributed by reliable naturalist-friends or acquaintances. Writing was hard work for him; he labored not only from dawn to dusk but burned a candle for an hour or more at each end of the day. Such a sedentary occupation gave him dyspepsia, and he once wrote to Bachman, "I would rather go without a shirt or any inexpressibles through the whole of Florida swamps in mosquito time than labor as I have hitherto done with the pen."

Nevertheless, Audubon's prose was expressive, complete and even flowery — quite the opposite of the plain style of his co-author. Bachman appears to have been critical at times of these accounts. Possibly he felt that they were unscientific, or improbable, or that the actions of the animals had been misinterpreted. After comparing manuscripts with printed text, some modern writers believe that Bachman's editing and omissions (together with use of the editorial "we") destroyed some of the fine personal qualities in Audubon's prose.

Much to Bachman's distress, it was not possible to give a truly complete account of American mammals — the bats, seals and whales were omitted. The completeness of the other groups — insectivores, rodents, carnivores and hoofed mammals — made the *Quadrupeds* the unquestioned authority in its field. In coverage, scientific accuracy and popular interest, it had no equal at the time of its publication and for a half-century thereafter. Even today the anecdotal flavor of the text and the feel of a lost century make fascinating reading. The delicate design and color of the small animals and the drama of motion and wildness are still exciting.

PUBLICATION

While Audubon mulled over his newly conceived plan for a master work on American mammals, he discussed with Robert Havell, the London publisher, the terms under which he would undertake to produce it. At the time (mid-1839), Havell was thoroughly disgusted by difficulties he had met in printing *The Birds of America*. This expensive publication had been slow to sell and many subscribers had failed to pay promptly. Even people like the Baron Rothschild had canceled their orders. Consequently, Audubon was in arrears for folios as they came from the press and Havell could not meet his payrolls for engravers, lithographers, artists and colorists. (As many as 50 of the latter were employed at one time.) The publisher's reply was negative — his client was too far behind on the old job to talk about another equally expensive project. (Eventually Audubon was able to make full payment.)

On returning to New York in the autumn, Audubon was referred to a Philadelphian, J. T. Bowen.

A skilled lithographer, Bowen had arrived a few years before from his native England. During the post-Jackson depression he had lost most of his savings in the stock market and he was in a receptive mood for any reasonable offer. Accordingly, he entered into successive contracts with Audubon to lithograph and color, first a miniaturized edition of the *Birds,* and later the imperial folio and the octavo edition of the *Quadrupeds.* Actual printing was to be done by other Philadelphia craftsmen, the plates by Bisbaugh and text by Henry Ludwig.

Up to this time, most fine reproductions of paintings had been made from copper engravings. Lithography, a process which was less than 50 years old, had several advantages in addition to economy. Using a grease pencil, the lithographer's artist traced the lines of the original *in reverse* on a smoothly ground, flat slab of fine-grained sandstone. Those portions of the absorbent stone which had been drawn upon would accept ink, and in the press would transfer the ink to paper. The most subtle gradations from deepest black to palest gray were reproduced. After printing, the reproductions on paper were tinted in the proper colors and shades by teams of colorists.

A few of the plates for the imperial folio of the *Quadrupeds* had been rushed to the printer near the end of 1842. As successive plates accumulated, they were bound five in a folio. Volume I, containing the first 50 plates (no descriptions), was published in 1845, Volume II in 1846, and Volume III in 1848. Folios purchased separately cost $10; the three-volume set was $300. As promised, each subscriber to the three volumes of plates also received an equal number of volumes of text which described the species pictured. These were printed in octavo size and were issued as they were completed in 1846, 1851 and 1854. A supplement to the last volume included more text and five "bonus" lithographed plates from paintings by J. W. Audubon. These depicted eight species: a red fox, four tree squirrels, a Harris antelope (ground) squirrel, a California vole and the crab-eating raccoon. The entire work of plates and text bore the imposing title of *The Viviparous Quadrupeds of North America.* Three volumes of an octavo edition combining the text and all 155 plates were published in 1849, 1851 and 1854 respectively. In this smaller edition, the lengthy and ponderous title was appropriately reduced to *The Quadrupeds of North America.*

The United States Congress, in 1857, authorized the payment of $16,000 for 100 copies each of Audubon's *Birds* and of the *Quadrupeds* "to be presented to foreign governments in return for valuable gifts made to the United States."

UPDATING THE QUADRUPEDS

The animals of the imperial folios appeared in the order in which the Audubons painted them. Often the subjects were live animals or fresh carcasses obtained by the Audubons themselves, or by friends or agents. With poor or no refrigeration facilities, it was impossible to hold dead specimens for long during warm weather. The artist propped and wired the body into the desired pose and then worked furiously to complete his painting before the subject disintegrated in putrefaction. Preservation in rum was the only certain means for ensuring that dead animals would reach the artist in usable condition if they were to be shipped from a distance. These bedraggled remains were sketched and painted at the first opportunity and were added to the folios in that sequence.

In the publication, therefore, rodents, carnivores, insectivores and hoofed mammals appeared higgledy-piggledy, one species following another without regard to their natural relationships. The same lack of order was perpetuated in the smaller octavo edition which followed.

In this modern revival, the accounts have been rearranged to follow the accepted zoological sequence beginning with the sole North American (excluding Central American) representative of the marsupials, the opossum. While the sequence of the major groups (Orders) may have little significance for the general reader, this revised arrangement has the practical advantage of bringing together such obviously related mammals as, for example, the 24 species of tree squirrels which Bachman recognized and which are included in this book.

Many of the mammal names in use a century and more ago, including those which were invented by the authors to identify what they believed were new species, are no longer valid. This is true not only of vernacular names, but also of some Latinized (scientific) names. In common with other systematists of his time, Bachman used the binomial system of nomenclature; i.e., the mammal was identified merely by the names of the genus and species to which it belonged. Being acutely aware of variation within species, Bachman usually gave recognition to these differences by creating additional species. (Sometimes he resorted to the term "variety" to differentiate color phases, as in foxes and wolves.) Because individuals of such variants will interbreed in the wild where their geographic territories meet and will produce fertile offspring, these animals could not, by definition, belong to separate *species.*

Today, under the trinomial system of classification, many of the "species" of Audubon and Bachman's time are considered geographic races (subspecies). Other changes in names have been required because some mammals — not a large number — were given names by Bachman not realizing that they had already been identified and named by other zoologists. (Descriptions were often recorded in obscure scientific or literary publications.) Bachman's isolation from large technical libraries and museums, and his difficulties in obtaining records and accurate descriptions of type specimens in the collections of scientific centers such as Philadelphia, New York and London, were large factors in the errors that were made. Under modern rearrangement, his 147 "different species" depicted in the imperial folios have been reduced to 119, including one, the "Wooly Squirrel," which is unidentifiable.

In view of the many handicaps under which Bachman worked, his determination of the status of most mammals was remarkably sound. He described and named many new species; his Latin names for most have survived.

Each of the 147 "species" and an additional eight "varieties" were depicted on 150 plates in the imperial folios. Each plate, with the principal mammal described, is given two pages in this book. On the left-hand page are excerpts from that portion of the original text which described the habits of the animal. These excerpts have been chosen not only for interesting and usually accurate information on the life history of the species portrayed, but for colorful anecdotes and personal experiences of one or more of the authors. Material from books, articles or letters of explorers, frontiersmen, or other naturalists which Audubon and Bachman sometimes quoted at length have not been used except when their own observations were scanty.

Editorial comments have been made on unusual or obscure statements. Individual authors of interesting anecdotes have been identified, and other information has been added which might make the original text more meaningful to the modern reader. Errors have been pointed out either here or in the updated life-history accounts on the opposite page. Because the authors usually mentioned naturalists or other persons only by their surnames, the given name and a brief identification have been furnished on the first appearance of these names in the excerpts. Modern synonyms for the common and scientific names which the authors applied to plants and animals have been inserted, and vernacular names have been located. These insertions have been indicated by the use of oblique lines.

On the right-hand page the reader will find, under the illustration, the modern name (including the trinomial scientific name) of the animal, followed by a brief account of the *species'* habits as they have been revealed by modern field research. When two or more of the original "species" are now classified as subspecies of a single (modern) species, the account is continued on the following pages. Because of space limitations, usually no attempt has been made to describe *subspecific* distinctions of the animal or its biology. The information is presented to supplement and round out the text from the original *Quadrupeds* which appears opposite.

The illustrations have been prepared from photographs on Ektachrome film of the 150 imperial folio plates in the collection of the Kennedy Galleries, New York City. The photography was done under the direction of John Lowell Pratt.

ACKNOWLEDGMENTS

I want to express my gratitude especially to my wife, for invaluable assistance in research and editorial matters, and to the following: Mrs. Eileen Coulston, formerly of the New York State Museum and now of the New York State Library, for obtaining reference material; Edward H. Dwight, Munson-Williams-Proctor Institute, for information concerning Audubon and Bachman; E. Raymond Hall and José Alvarez, Natural History Museum of the University of Kansas, for assistance with the nomenclature; Emmet T. Hooper and William P. Harris, Jr., University of Michigan Museum of Zoology, for advice on the status of tropical squirrels and certain other mammals; David H. Johnson, U. S. National Museum, for assistance in species identification; Joseph Curtis Moore, Field Museum of Natural History, for advice on nomenclature of the sciurid squirrels; J. Lowell Pratt and the staff of Hammond, especially Executive Editor Ashley F. Talbot, for their understanding and assistance in the preparation of the book; Mrs. Helen Sellner and Mrs. Doris Brown, for typing manuscript; Stanley Jay Smith, New York State Museum, for updating the botanical nomenclature; Mason Tolman and members of the staff, New York State Library, for advice and the loan of indispensable reference works; Richard G. Van Gelder, of the Department of Mammalogy, American Museum of Natural History, for advice on the classification of the skunks; The American Philosophical Society and the Museum National d'Histoire Naturelle (Paris) for furnishing an Audubon letter with permission to quote from it; and many other persons and institutions which have helped in numerous ways.

The Imperial Collection Of
AUDUBON ANIMALS

DIDELPHIS VIRGINIANA, PENNANT.
VIRGINIAN OPOSSUM.

... We can imagine to ourselves the surprise with which the Opossum was regarded by Europeans when they first saw it. Scarcely any thing was known of the marsupial animals, as New Holland had not as yet opened its unrivalled stores of singularities to astonish the world. Here was a strange animal, with the head and ears of the pig, sometimes hanging on the limb of a tree, and occasionally swinging like the monkey by the tail! Around that prehensile appendage a dozen sharp-nosed, sleek-headed young, had entwined their own tails, and were sitting on the mother's back! The astonished traveller approaches this extraordinary compound of an animal and touches it cautiously with a stick. Instantly it seems to be struck with some mortal disease: its eyes close, it falls to the ground, ceases to move, and appears to be dead! ...

The whole structure of the Opossum is admirably adapted to the wants of a sluggish animal. It possesses strong powers of smell, which aid it in its search after food; its mouth is capacious, and its jaws possessing a greater number and variety of teeth than any other of our animals, evidencing its omnivorous habits; its fore-paws, although not armed with retractile claws, aid in seizing its prey and conveying it to the mouth. The construction of the hind-foot with its soft yielding tubercles on the palms and its long nailless opposing thumb, enable it to use these feet as hands, and the prehensile tail aids it in holding on to the limbs of trees whilst its body is swinging in the air; in this manner we have observed it gathering persimmons with its mouth and fore-paws, and devouring them whilst its head was downwards and its body suspended in the air, holding on sometimes with its hind-feet and tail, but often by the tail alone. ...

The gait of the Opossum is slow, rather heavy, and awkward; it is not a trot like that of the fox, but an amble or pace, moving the two legs on one side at a time. Its walk on the ground is plantigrade, resting the whole heel on the earth. When pursued, it by no means stops at once and feigns death, as has often been supposed, but goes forward at a rather slow speed, it is true, but as fast as it is able, never, that we are aware of, increasing it to a leap or canter, but striving to avoid its pursuers by sneaking off to some thicket or briar patch; when, however, it discovers that the dog is in close pursuit, it flies for safety to the nearest tree, usually a sapling, and unless molested does not ascend to the top, but seeks an easy resting place in some crotch not twenty feet from the ground, where it waits silently and immoveably, till the dog, finding that his master will not come to his aid, and becoming weary of barking at the foot of the tree, leaves the Opossum to follow the bent of his inclinations, and conclude his nightly round in search of food. Although a slow traveller, the Opossum, by keeping perseveringly on foot during the greater part of the night, hunts over much ground, and has been known to make a circle of a mile or two in one night. ...

The habit of feigning death to deceive an enemy is common to several species of quadrupeds, and we on several occasions witnessed it in our common red fox *(V. Fulvus).* But it is more strikingly exhibited in the Opossum than in any other animal with which we are acquainted. When it is shaken from a tree and falls among grass and shubbery, or when detected in such situations, it doubles itself into a heap and feigns death so artfully, that we have known some schoolboys carrying home for a quarter of a mile an individual of this species, stating that when they first saw it, it was running on the ground, and they could not tell what had killed it. We would not, however, advise that the hand should on such occasions be suffered to come too familiarly in contact with the mouth, lest the too curious meddler should on a sudden be startled with an unexpected and unwelcome gripe. ...

The young, when first born, are naked and flesh-coloured; the eyes, together with the ears, are covered by a thin integument through which these organs and the protuberances of the ears are distinctly visible. The mouth is closed, with the exception of a small orifice, sufficiently large to receive the teat, which is so thin and attenuated that it seems no larger than the body of a pin. Length of body, 7–12ths of an inch; of tail, 2–10ths. The nails, which can be seen with the naked eye, are very distinct when viewed with a microscope, and are of a dark brown colour, small and much hooked. The nostrils are open; the lungs filled with air, and when placed in water, the young float on the surface. ...

OPOSSUM

Didelphis marsupialis virginiana Kerr

Only one of the marsupials (pouched mammals) lives in North America. This is the opossum — often called "possum" for short.

In Audubon's time, many naturalists believed that opossums were born clinging to the mother's teats like fruit on a stalk (a "mammary rather than uterine gestation"). Common folk thought that opossums copulated through the nose and that later the female blew the tiny young into her pouch. Being skeptical of these and other theories, Bachman made careful investigations and experiments.

Opossums are sexually mature when only six to eight months old. Following mating in the usual manner, the fertilized eggs develop for 13 days in the uterus. Just before the young are born, the female cleans out the fur-lined pouch with her tongue.

At birth, which usually takes place in a grass-lined burrow or hollow log, the undeveloped, transparent young weighs only about 1/270th ounce. Even the maximum brood of 18 could easily be contained in a teaspoon. Each sightless embryo crawls by a swimming motion of the forelegs across the two-inch expanse of hair to the entrance of the mother's pouch. Once inside, the tiny creature attaches itself to a nipple and either nurses or has the milk injected into its mouth. Some young may fail to reach the pouch; others will find that there are not enough nipples (average number 13) to go around. Of the eight to 18 young born, only about seven survive to be weaned at 3½ months of age.

The opossum's defense act of "playing possum" is not "feigning death so artfully" as Bachman and many later naturalists believed. It is an involuntary act controlled by the nervous system — rather like shock or temporary paralysis. Foraging within about 50 acres, the opossum is omnivorous but prefers animal food.

The opossum is 24 to 34 inches long, including the 10- to 13-inch tail, and weighs 4 to 14 pounds. It occurs from tropical South America north to central New Hampshire, southern Ontario and Wisconsin. In the early 1900's, it was introduced by man to the Pacific Coast.

SOREX LONGIROSTRIS, BACH.
LONG-NOSED SHREW.

We possess very little knowledge in regard to the habits of this little Shrew. The first specimen we saw was obtained in the swamps that border the Santee River, by Dr. ALEXANDER HUME; his labourers found it whilst digging a ditch through grounds nearly overflowed with water. Another was obtained in a singular manner. Whilst we were at the house of Major LEE in Colleton district, his huntsman brought in some wild ducks, and among the rest a hooded merganser *(Mergus cucullatus).* There was a protuberance on the throat of this bird, appearing as if it had not fully swallowed some article of food at the time it was shot. On opening the throat, it was found to contain this little Shrew, which was fresh, and not in the least mutilated.

We saw two or three Shrews in the same vicinity which we think were of this species, coming out of a bank on the edge of a rice field and swimming in the canal at the dusk of the evening. From the above circumstances we are induced to think that this quadruped prefers low swampy situations, and is to a certain extent aquatic in its habits. We more recently obtained a specimen from Col. W. E. HASKELL, of St. Paul's parish, South Carolina, which was a shade lighter, and a little larger, than others in our possession, but presented no specific differences.

Fig. 1

Fig. 2

Fig. 4

Fig. 3

SOUTHEASTERN SHREW

Sorex longirostris longirostris Bachman

Short-legged and long-snouted, all species of shrews are tiny, very active and extremely nervous animals. When excited, their hearts may beat 1,200 times a minute and they are often literally scared to death by loud noise or capture. Noses and vibrissae twitching constantly, they rush jerkily about and devour enormous amounts of food. They attack their prey and their competitors with high-pitched squeaks and great ferocity. Born blind and hairless, but with permanent teeth, most of them probably die before they are 18 months old.

The southeastern shrew is sometimes called "Bachman's Shrew" after its discoverer. Even now, 130 years after identification, there may be no more than a hundred examples of this species in study collections in all the museums of the country.

Little is known of its life. Usually found in damp, even wet places which are overgrown densely by blackberry briars, honeysuckle vines and cattails, it is occasionally located in dry woods and grassy glades in forests. During dry weather or on arid ground, the animal uses underground rather than surface runways.

A very few nests have been recorded; these contained two to five young. Two of the nests, which were made of leaves, were in rotting logs.

In addition to the specimen which Bachman obtained from the throat of a hooded merganser (see opposite page), at least one southeastern shrew has been taken from the stomach of a barred owl. Undoubtedly, the species has numerous other enemies, but most shrews have a strong odor which seems to make them distasteful to many predators. Domestic cats, for example, may kill shrews but after playing with the bodies usually abandon them uneaten. On the other hand, in a study of bobcats in Minnesota, hunger had apparently made the shrews of some importance in the predators' winter diet.

Hunting alone, usually in darkness, the southeastern shrew devours insects, some centipedes, worms, and such members of its own kind, as well as mice, as can be overcome in chance encounters.

If it is seen at all by a person who happens to disturb it, the shrew would probably be recalled only as a tiny flash with a long snout. The shrew has minute eyes which are so weak that they may register little more than daylight. Total length is 3 to 4 inches, of which 1 to 1½ inches is tail; weight is about ¼ ounce. Although local in distribution, the southeastern shrew ranges from Maryland to central Florida near the Atlantic Coast and westward to northern Illinois, southeastern Missouri and northeastern Louisiana.

[The Audubon plate above also illustrates three other species, De Kay's shrew (Fig. 2), the silvery shrew-mole (Fig. 3) and the southeastern pocket gopher (Fig. 1). Text references for theses species may be found on pages 8, 17 and 141, respectively. Fig. 4 illustrates the species described above, the southeastern shrew.]

SOREX PALUSTRIS, RICH.

AMERICAN MARSH SHREW.

The habits of all Shrews (except those of the kind described by SHAKESPEARE) must necessarily be little known. These animals are so minute in the scale of quadrupeds that they will always be overlooked, unless sought after with great zeal, and even then it is often difficult to meet with or procure them. It may be said that it is only by chance that one is seen and taken now and then, even where they are known to exist. We have not seen more than five or six alive during several years, although dead ones have been found by us more frequently, and upon one occasion we found two that appeared to have recently died, lying close to each other. No wonder, then, that they may escape the observation of the most persevering student of nature, as their instinctive caution would, by causing them either to fly to some little hole or tuft of grass, or to remain still, when danger was near, render their discovery more than doubtful; or, if seen, it would be only for a moment. Not the least singular circumstance connected with the family of Shrews is the fact that they can exist in extremely cold climates, and move about in winter, when the snow covers the ground. In his article on *Sorex palustris* Dr. /John/ RICHARDSON /Scottish naturalist and explorer of the Canadian Arctic/ says it "most probably lives in the summer on similar food with the Water Shrew, but I am at a loss to imagine how it procures a subsistence during the six months of the year in which the countries it inhabits are covered with snow. It frequents borders of lakes, and /Samuel/ HEARNE /British fur trader and explorer in Canada/ tells us that it often takes up its abode in beaver houses."

We might easily make some probable speculations as to the manners and customs of the present species, but prefer not doing so farther than to say that it very likely feeds on seeds, insects, and on the carcases of any small birds or other animals it finds dead in the fields, that in winter it has a store of provision laid by, only coming to the snow-covered surface on fine days for the purpose of getting a little fresh air, and that from the number of tracks sometimes seen at one place we consider it partly gregarious in its habits.

Our drawing was made from a specimen in the British Museum at London.

WATER SHREW

Sorex palustris palustris Richardson

The water shrew runs along the top of the water as well as on the bottom of lakes and streams. A fringe of stiff hairs around the outer margin of each hind foot holds a bubble of air, and surface tension does the rest. Captive shrews will skim across the top of a pan of water just for fun. In the water, the little animal twists, turns, and dives, with great dexterity. On the ground, it runs along using the same swimming motion of the feet and legs. Its fine, velvety fur is highly resistant to wetting but, when it does become damp, the creature retreats to shore and dries it thoroughly with rapid motions of the hind foot. The hair fringe acts as a comb.

One of the lesser known inhabitants of cold and high mountain regions, the water shrew lives in wooded bogs and marshes and the wet borders of watercourses. Always it likes a protective cover of sedges, alders or other shrubs. Its runways are inconspicuous and it often uses the trails of mice and other small creatures.

Hunting by day as well as at night, it is active throughout the year, although it may stay under dense vegetation during severe weather. The diet is chiefly insects — adults and larvae of May flies, caddis flies, bugs and beetles — snails, leeches and, occasionally, salamanders and small fishes. Possibly it catches small mammals at times. Prey is tracked by smell and touch-vibration senses; sight is very poor. Much of the shrew's hunting is done in darkness or deep gloom, underground or beneath snow and ice where sight would not be an advantage to the animal.

The breeding season lasts from March until early fall. Gestation requires 21 days and four to eight (normally about five) young comprise the litter. The female has more than one brood in a season. Weasels, the mink and predacious fishes such as pike, pickerel, bass and trout, are perhaps the shrew's most serious enemies. Probably few water shrews live more than two years.

Total length of the water shrew is 5½ to 6 inches, of which the tail makes up 2½ to 2¾ inches; the weight is 2/7 to ½ ounce. Individuals in northeastern America are black all over; elsewhere they have gray or grayish-brown underparts. The range is eastern Labrador and New England (except south in the Appalachians to the Great Smokies), west through southern Canada to Great Slave Lake and Cook Inlet, Alaska; south in the western United States to northern New Mexico and, in the Sierra Nevada, Sequoia National Park.

SOREX CAROLINENSIS, BACH.

CAROLINA SHREW.

It it difficult to know much of the habits of the little quadrupeds composing this genus. Living beneath the surface of the earth, feeding principally on worms and the larvae of insects, shunning the light, and restricted to a little world of their own, best suited to their habits and enjoyments, they almost present a barrier to the prying curiosity of man. They are occasionally turned up by the plough on the plantations of the south, when they utter a faint, squeaking cry, like young mice, and make awkward and scrambling attempts to escape, trying to conceal themselves in any tuft of grass, or under the first clod of earth that may present itself. On two occasions, their small but compact nests were brought to us. They were composed of fibres of roots and withered blades of various kinds of grasses. They had been ploughed up from about a foot beneath the surface of the earth, and contained in one nest five, and in the other six young. In digging ditches, and ploughing in moderately high grounds, small holes are frequently seen running in all directions, in a line nearly parallel with the surface, and extending to a great distance, evidently made by this species. We observed on the sides of one of these galleries, a small cavity containing a hoard of coleopterous insects, principally composed of a rare species *(Scarabaeus tityus)* /now *Dynastes* sp./, fully the size of the animal itself; some of them were nearly consumed, and the rest mutilated, although still living.

/Editor's Comment: The paragraphs below were written by the authors concerning "DeKay's Shrew," pictured with other species in Plate 150, page 5. It was described by Bachman in 1837 under the scientific name Sorex dekayi *in honor of the New York naturalist. The specimen on which Bachman based his description was captured in the garden of the Audubons' estate, Minnies Land, in what is now upper New York City. The paler, somewhat yellowish tinge of the gray fur led him to regard it as a species separate from his "Carolina Shrew." Today, "DeKay's Shrew" is classified as a subspecies of the short-tailed shrew,* Blarina brevicauda./

We have always found it difficult to obtain satisfactory information as to the habits of the smaller quadrupeds, from the fact that many of our farmers and their men are unacquainted with the generic and even specific names, and consequently often mistake the habits of some genus or species for those of a very distinct one. The various species belonging to the genera *Scalops* /eastern moles/, *Condylura* /star-nosed mole/, and *Sorex* /long-tailed shrews/, are in most cases called (and considered to be) "ground moles," and thus are represented as all possessing the same habits. The gardener who caught for us the two specimens above described, said they were ground moles. On showing him that they were smaller, and had very different feet from those of any animal belonging to the genus *Scalops*, he said "they were only young ones, that their feet would become large by next year." On asking him about their nests, he said they were not old enough as yet to have young. When we requested him to show us their holes he first directed us to the ridges made in the soil by the ground mole.

After a careful examination, however, we ascertained that DeKay's Shrew burrows deeper in the earth than *Scalops* /Scalopus/ *aquaticus* /eastern mole/. The galleries of *S. DeKayi* /now the short-tailed shrew/ run along at the depth of about a foot from the surface, and have apertures leading up to the open air at short distances from each other, by which the animals have ingress or egress. Ground moles seek worms and insects in the earth, whereas the Shrews come abroad on the surface, and run over the ground at night in quest of food, a habit in which the mole does not appear to indulge.

SHORT-TAILED SHREW

Blarina brevicauda carolinensis (Bachman)

A powerful poison is secreted by the salivary glands of this shrew. When it bites a victim, the poison flows between the large lower incisors into the wound. The heart and breathing of the prey slow down, paralysis sets in, and the prey is quickly devoured. A short-tailed shrew carries enough poison to kill two hundred mice.

Although quick, nervous and irritable, it is not as prone to shock as most members of the family. Experiments indicate that it may also be slightly more social and may occasionally mate for life. It is exceedingly strong and muscular for its size.

The short-tailed shrew burrows readily (many other shrews do not). It climbs once in a while and can swim well although slowly. The animal trots with apparently great speed but, with its tiny legs, the rate is only two or, at most, three miles per hour.

It sees, smells and hears little. With its sensitive snout and quivering vibrissae, it finds quantities of food — insects, earthworms, snails, slugs, centipedes, millepedes, spiders, occasionally disabled or young mice and birds, snakes and salamanders. Some vegetable food (nuts, seeds and roots) is taken, mostly during fall and winter. Short-tailed shrews eat the equivalent of one-third to one-half of their own weight daily. (At this rate, a 200-pound man would eat 70 to 100 pounds every day!) In captivity, treated with special delicacies provided by man, a long-tailed shrew (a close relative of this species) once ate three times its weight every day for a week.

Short-tailed shrews live in almost any type of damp habitat from forest to grassland. The individual territory may be as small as 100 feet across when food is ample, up to 500 feet when scarce. Populations of areas fluctuate widely, perhaps as much as 25 specimens to one or more.

The nest is located under a rock or stump. Two or more tunnels radiate to foraging areas, usually four to ten inches below ground, and to surface runways.

The mating season continues from March to fall with two and sometimes three litters annually. The gestation period is about 21 days. A litter may have as many as 10 young (average five or six). They reach half size when two weeks old and disperse a few days later.

Weighing ¾ to 1 ounce, they are 3¾ to 5¼ inches long, including the ¾- to 1-inch tail. The range is extensive: the Atlantic Coast from Prince Edward Island to the Florida Keys, west to central Saskatchewan, northeastern Colorado and southeastern Texas.

SOREX PARVUS, SAY,

SAYS LEAST SHREW.

This little creature, to which the above name was attached by /Thomas/ SAY /American entomologist; co-founder of the Philadelphia Academy of Sciences/, was first captured by Mr. TITIAN R. PEALE /animal painter/, during LONG's Expedition to the Rocky Mountains, at Engineer Cantonment /a few miles north of present-day Omaha, Nebraska/ on the Missouri, where it was found in a pit-fall excavated for catching wolves.

Look at the plate, reader, and imagine the astonishment of the hunter on examining the pit intended for the destruction of the savage prowlers of the prairies, when, instead of the game that he intended to entrap, he perceived this, the Least Shrew, timidly running across the bottom.

The family to which this Shrew belongs, is somewhat allied in form and habits to the mole, but many species are now probably extinct.

We have seen a fragment of a fossil remainder of the tooth of a Sorex, found by our young friend Dr. LECONTE /John LeConte, amateur naturalist/, of New-York, in the mining region adjoining Lake Superior, from the size of which, the animal must have been at least a yard long, and no doubt was, with its carnivorous teeth, a formidable beast of prey; whether it had insects and worms of a corresponding size to feed upon, in its day and generation, is a matter of mere conjecture, as even the wonderful discoveries of geologists have thrown but little light on the modes of life of the inhabitants of the ancient world, although some whole skeletons are found from time to time by their researches.

The Least Shrew feeds upon insects and larvae, worms and the flesh of any dead bird or beast that it may chance to discover.

It also eats seeds and grains of different kinds. It burrows in the earth, but seeks its food more upon the surface of the ground than the mole, and runs with ease around its burrow about fences and logs. Some birds of prey pounce upon the Shrew, whilst it is playing or seeking its food on the grass, but as it has a musky, disagreeable smell, it is commonly left after being killed, to rot on the ground, as we have picked up a good many of these little quadrupeds, which to all appearance had been killed by either cats, owls or hawks. This smell arises from a secretion exuded from glands which are placed on the sides of the animal (Geoffroy, Mem. Mus. Hist. Nat., Vol. i., 1815), This secretion, like that of most animals, varies according to the age, the season, &c., and prevails more in males than females.

Of the mode in which the Least Shrew passes the winter we have no very positive information. It is capable of sustaining a great degree of cold. We have never found one of these animals in a torpid state, when examining burrows, holes, or cavities in and under rocks or stones, &c., for the purpose of ascertaining, if possible, the manner in which they passed the winter. We have seen minute tracks on the surface of the snow where it was four feet in depth in the Northern parts of New-York, which we ascertained were the foot-prints of a Shrew which was afterwards captured, although we cannot be certain that it was this species. It had sought the dried stalks of the pig weed *(chenopodium album)* on which the ripened seeds were still hanging and upon which it had evidently been feeding.

We are unacquainted with any other habits of this minute species.

LEAST SHREW

Cryptotis parva parva (Say)

Counting its tail, the least shrew, sometimes called the short-tailed shrew, is the shortest of the shrews (and of all American mammals). Although nervous and rather belligerent, it is much more sociable toward its own kind than are other species of shrews. Not uncommonly, four to ten of the little animals live together under a log, and several adults may occupy a single baseball-size grass nest. These shrews are only 3 to 3½ inches long, including the ½- to 9/10-inch tail, and they weigh .15 to .2 ounce.

The least shrew attacks larger insects like crickets, and even small frogs by "hamstringing" or biting the joints of the jumping legs — crippling them for easy eating. Large quantities of food are required (the equivalent of half the animal's own weight daily); digestion is accomplished in one and one-half to four hours.

At birth, the blind, hairless shrew weighs only one-hundredth of an ounce. The litter numbers three to six (average about five). In two weeks their eyes are open, they are furred, and as big as their mother. The females probably mate at three months or earlier, and produce young in only 15 days. Several broods are reared in the breeding season, which is year-long in the south and from March to November in the north. The life-expectancy is less than two years.

Least shrews are eaten, at least occasionally, by hawks, owls, snakes, weasels, both gray and red foxes, domestic cats and by their larger relative, the "big" short-tailed shrew *(Blarina brevicauda)*. These predators must have strong stomachs or a shortage of appetizing food for, in addition to the odoriferous flank glands mentioned by Bachman, the least shrew has on its belly a large gland which gives off an equally strong odor.

Because sight, smell and hearing are poor, the shrew depends on its very sensitive snout and vibrissae to find food. Active at any time of day or night throughout the year, it darts along its own trailways and tunnels or those of mice and other shrews, or it burrows stoutly through the upper soil. Worming its way through loose dirt, it uses its flexible snout to open a passage and pushes on to leave a tunnel about a half-inch in diameter. The food is mostly small insects and their larvae, slugs, snails, earthworms, centipedes, spiders, salamanders and any carrion that is encountered.

The least shrew lives in dry, grassy or weedy fields and meadows; only occasionally is it found in damp places. The geographic range extends from the Atlantic Coast between western Connecticut and southern Florida, westward to western Nebraska, central Texas and northeastern Mexico.

SCALOPS TOWNSENDII, BACH.

TOWNSEND'S SHREW MOLE.

We were informed by /Thomas/ NUTTALL /Anglo-American botanist and ornithologist/ and /John Kirk/ TOWNSEND /naturalist and discoverer of many mammals and birds of the northwestern United States/, who mistook this species for our common Shrew-Mole *(Scalops aquaticus)* /now *Scalopus aquaticus,* the eastern mole/, that they dug and formed galleries, and threw up little mounds of earth precisely in the manner of that animal. They are well known to the farmers and settlers in the valleys of Oregon, as they traverse their fields and gardens, cutting up the ground in some places to an injurious extent.

TOWNSEND'S MOLE

Scapanus townsendii (Bachman)

Moles look somewhat like oversize shrews with their long naked snouts and their short "plush" hair that won't be disturbed whether the animals go backward or forward in tight fitting burrows. Their eyes are quite tiny; in fact, those of some moles are covered over by skin and fur.

Moles like to tunnel extensively and spend most of their lives below ground. Accordingly, they have undergone several major modifications of body structure: their shoulders are heavy and powerful, and their front feet are greatly enlarged and permanently turned outward for digging.

As they go through the tunnel, or even above ground, the palms of the "hands" are not flat on the ground but turned edgewise. Thrust outward and backward like a man swimming with a breast stroke, the hands push aside loose soil or propel the body through an already constructed tunnel. They have no external ears (which would collect dirt) and most species are blind, or nearly so. In compensation, they are sensitive to vibration and have a good sense of direction. The snout is not used to dig, but to feel. Like shrews, most moles have a strong, musky odor which may discourage attack. Many predators will not eat moles after killing them.•

Townsend's mole is the largest of the American moles.

The center mole (in plate above) which John W. Audubon painted in an upside down position, was a partial albino.

Even living underground, this mole is active mostly at night. Because it needs large tunnels, the surface ridges of the upper shafts and the mole hills thrown out from the lower galleries are very conspicuous. (One Townsend's mole piled up 302 mounds on a quarter-acre field in 77 days!) These excavations and the animal's habit of eating bulbs, roots, tubers and large seeds in addition to the usual animal food, make Townsend's mole distinctly unpopular with gardeners and farmers.

After gestation of about 30 days, the young, usually two or three to a litter, are born in March or early April. As with all moles, there is only one litter a year. The low rate of reproduction indicates that predators are not a serious factor in survival of the race.

This mole is found from sea level to the coldest mountain tops on the Pacific Slope, from extreme southwestern British Columbia to northern California, and inland from the coast as much as 150 miles.

Weighing 4 to 6 ounces, it is 7¾ to 9½ inches long, including the 1¼ - to 2-inch tail.

13

SCALLOPS BREWERII, BACH.

BREWER'S SHREW MOLE.

In a collection of the smaller rodentia procured for us in New England by our friend THOMAS M. BREWER, Esq. an intelligent naturalist /of Boston/, we were surprised and gratified at finding this new species of shrew mole; the specimen having been obtained by Dr. L. M. YALE, at Martha's Vineyard, an island on the coast of New England. In its habits it approaches much nearer the star-nosed mole (*Condylura cristata*) than any species of shrew mole. Its burrows are neither as extensive or so near the surface of the earth as those of the common shrew mole. We observed that the meadows in the valleys of Virginia, where this species is found, seldom exhibited any traces of their galleries, which are so conspicuous where the common species exists. We only possessed one opportunity of seeing this species alive. It ran across the public road near the red sulphur springs in Virginia /now West Virginia/; in its mode of progression it reminded us of the hurried, irregular and awkward manners of the common shrew mole. It had, as we ascertained, pursued its course under ground, at about five inches from the surface, until it reached the trodden and firm gravelly road, which it attempted to cross and was captured. It evidenced no disposition to bite. From the fact of our having seen three specimens, which were accidentally procured in a week, we were led to suppose that it was quite common in that vicinity. We have not found its nest, and regret that we have nothing farther to add in regard to its habits.

HAIRY-TAILED MOLE

Parascalops breweri (Bachman)

Except for its well-furred tail and slightly coarser and much darker fur, this mole is not markedly different from the eastern mole. White spots often occur on the lower surface of the hairy-tailed mole (rarely on the eastern) and an old hairy-tailed may have an all-white snout, tail and feet. It has no external ears and its eyes are almost hidden in the fur. When pursued, it may take to the water to escape. Not a good swimmer, the animal tires quickly.

Because it prefers damp but well-drained woods and gets into adjacent fields only incidentally, this mole is of little economic concern and is one of the less-known members of the family. Local in distribution, it sometimes becomes rather numerous in especially favorable places. Here the tunnels, which may be used for years, are extended to crisscross and interlock with the passages of other hairy-tails. Apparently, however, the various owners remain solitary and have nothing to do with each other outside of the March-April mating season. A high population density of 11 animals per acre has been reported; ordinarily, it would not exceed two.

Like other moles, the hairy-tailed mole has two systems of tunnels. The shafts constructed just below the ground surface may extend over an area 100 feet in diameter. These are used mostly in summer and during warm periods in winter. Less extensive tunnels for cold weather are dug below the usual frost line.

How does one know if a mole is in residence? Cut into a ridge; if the mole is there, the break will soon be repaired. The owner is active day and night searching for insects and their larvae, as well as earthworms. Mice and shrews often use these tunnels, but only the owner repairs them. At night the hairy-tailed mole is likely to forage on the surface where it may be caught by a cat, owl or other nocturnal hunter.

The four or five young are born in April, May or early June, after a gestation period of 28 to 42 days, in a grass-lined nest which is six inches in diameter and located about a foot below ground level in the winter tunnel. They are naked at birth and weigh about one-half ounce.

Adults are 5½ to 7 inches in total length, including the thick, fleshy tail 1 to 1½ inches long. The weight is 1.4 to 3 ounces. The range extends from southwestern New Brunswick to Sault Saint Marie, Ontario, thence southeast ward through much of New England, the Middle Atlantic states and Ohio to the Great Smoky Mountains, being absent from coastal areas south of Cape Cod.

SCALLOPS AQUALICUS, LINN.

COMMON AMERICAN SHREW MOLE

Whilst almost every farmer or gardener throughout the Northern and Eastern States is well acquainted with this curious animal, as far as the mere observation of its meandering course through his fields and meadows, his beds of green peas or other vegetables, is concerned, but few have arrived at proper conclusions in regard to the habits of the Shrew Mole; and it is generally caught and killed whenever practicable; the common idea being, that the Mole feeds on the roots of tender plants, grasses, &c.; while the fact that the animal devours great quantities of earth-worms, slugs, and grubs, all hurtful to the fruit trees, to the grasses, and the peas and other vegetables, seems to be unknown, or overlooked.

In justice to the farmer and gardener, however, we must say, that the course taken occasionally by this species, directly along a row of tender plants, throwing them out of the earth, as it does, or zig-zag across a valuable bed or beautiful lawn, is rather provoking, and we have ourselves caused traps to be set for moles, being greatly annoyed by their digging long galleries under the grass on our sloping banks, which during a heavy shower soon filled with water, and presently increased to large gutters, or deep holes, requiring repairs forthwith. At such times also, a Mole-track through loose soil where there is any descent, will be found by the gardener, perchance, to have become a miniature ravine some twenty or thirty yards in length, and a few (anticipated) bushels of carrots are destroyed. . . .

When this Mole was fed on earth-worms, *(Lumbricus terrenus,)* as we have just related, we heard the worms crushed in the strong jaws of the animal, with a noise somewhat like the grating of broken glass, which was probably caused by its strong teeth gnashing on the sand or grit contained in the bodies of the worms. These were placed singly on the ground near the animal, which after smelling around for a moment turned about in every direction with the greatest activity, until he felt a worm, when he seized it between the outer surface of his hands or fore-paws, and pushed it into his mouth with a continually repeated forward movement of the paws, cramming it downward until all was in his jaws. . . .

This species whilst beneath the earth's surface seems to search for food with the same activity and untiring perseverance that are observable in animals that seek for their provender above ground. It works through the earth not only in a straight-forward direction, but loosens it to the right and left, beneath and above, so that no worm or insect can escape it. When in contact with any one of the objects of which it has been in search, it seizes it with remarkable quickness both with its fore-feet and its sharp teeth, drawing itself immediately backward with its prize, upon which it begins to prey at once. The Shrew Mole passes through loose soil with nearly the same ease and speed that it displays in running, or "scrabbling" along above ground. It moves backward almost as rapidly as it goes forward. The nose is often seen protruded above the surface of the ground.

The snout of this species, although apparently delicate, is most powerfully muscular, as well as flexible; the animal can turn it to the right or left, upward or downward, and at times inserts it in its mouth, as if for the purpose of cleansing it, and then suddenly withdraws it with a kind of smack of its lips; this habit we observed three times in the course of a few minutes. The Shrew Mole is exceedingly tenacious of life; it cannot easily be put to death, either by heavy pressure or strangling, and a severe blow on the head seems to be the quickest mode of despatching it. . . .

The Shrew Moles are able to work their way so rapidly, that in soft or loamy soil it is almost impossible for the most active man to overtake and turn them out with a spade, unless he can see the spot where they are working by the movement of the earth, in which case they can be thrown out easily by sticking the spade in front of them or at one side of their gallery, and with a quick movement tossing them on to the surface. . . .

We had an opportunity on two different occasions of examining the nests and young of the Shrew Mole. The nests were about eight inches below the surface, the excavation was rather large and contained a quantity of oak leaves on the outer surface, lined with soft dried leaves of the crab-grass, *(Digitaria sanguinalis.)* There were galleries leading to this nest, in two or three directions. The young numbered in one case, five, and in another, nine. . . .

EASTERN MOLE

Scalopus aquaticus aquaticus (Linnaeus)

The eyes of the eastern mole are covered with skin and hair, and there are no external ears. The species name *aquaticus* refers to the slight webbing of all toes, not to any aquatic skill. In an emergency it can swim; usually there is no need.

The generic name of the eastern mole comes from two Greek words: *skalops,* which means "digger," and *pous* meaning "foot." The animal is well named for with its large, flattened front feet turned outward, it can tunnel in porous surface soil as fast as one foot a minute. In harder subsoil, it digs at the rate of 10 to 15 feet an hour. One individual dug nearly 100 feet of shallow tunnels in a day.

Except for very rare, brief forays on the surface, the eastern mole spends its life in its series of underground galleries. The permanent tunnels are below frost level, where the owner has its nest and obtains most of its winter food. Upper foraging tunnels may be used repeatedly or only at long intervals. The tunnel system is usually limited to less than one acre, but if food is scarce it may be two or three times as large.

The diet of the eastern mole is about 85 percent animal matter — mostly earthworms but also including insects and their larvae, spiders, snails and, rarely, young mice and small snakes. This mole also eats starchy seeds and tubers such as potatoes, sunflowers and peanuts. In captivity the eastern mole may eat the equivalent of half its own weight daily.

Two or three of these moles may use a large tunnel system together. Usually they are solitary except during the mating season between mid-February and mid-April. After a gestation period of about 45 days the two to five (usually four) hairless young are born. The young probably leave the mother when a month old and breed the following spring.

Although these moles may disfigure lawns and fields, they also are a boon, as they aerate the soil and devour vast numbers of destructive insects.

Adults are 5 to 8 inches long, including the ¾ - to 1½- inch tail, and weigh 1½ to 5 ounces. Eastern moles occur from Massachusetts to southeastern Wyoming, southward to the tip of Florida and the mouth of the Rio Grande in Texas.

* * * *

The "Silvery Shrew-Mole" which appears with other species in Plate 150 (p. 5) is a subspecies of the eastern mole; it ranges from the Lake States to western Tennessee.

CONDYLURA CRISTATA, LINN.

COMMON STAR-NOSE MOLE.

As far as we have been able to ascertain, the habits of this species do not differ very widely from those of our Common Shrew Mole. We doubt, however, whether its galleries ever run to so great a distance as those of the latter animal, nor does it appear to be in the habit of visiting high grounds. It burrows and forms galleries under ground, and appears to be able to make rapid progress in soft earth. Its food is of the same nature as that of the Common Mole, and it appears to prefer the vicinity of brooks or swampy places, doubtless because in such localities earth worms and the larvae of various insects are generally abundant.

The proper use of the radiating process at the end of the nose has not been fully ascertained, but as the animal has the power of moving these tendrils in various directions, they may be useful in its search after worms or other prey, as is the moveable snout of the Shrew Mole. When confined in a box, or on the floor of a room, this Mole feeds on meat of almost any kind. It is not as strong as the Common Mole, nor as injurious to the farmer, since it avoids cultivated fields, and confines itself to meadows and low swampy places.

During the rutting season the tail of the Star-nosed Mole is greatly enlarged, which circumstance caused Dr. /Richard/ HARLAN /Philadelphia physician and zoologist friend of J. J. Audubon/ to describe a specimen taken at that season as a new species, under the name *Condylura macroura*.

Dr. /John Davidson/ GODMAN's /American naturalist and anatomist/ account of the abundance of this species does not coincide with our own experience on this subject. He says, "In many places it is scarcely possible to advance a step without breaking down their galleries, by which the surface is thrown into ridges and the surface of the green sward in no slight degree disfigured." We have sometimes supposed that he might have mistaken the galleries of the Common Shrew Mole for those made by the Star-Nose, as to us it has always appeared a rare species in every part of our Union.

In a few localities where we were in the habit, many years ago, of obtaining the Star-nosed Mole, it was always found on the banks of rich meadows near running streams. The galleries did not run so near the surface as those of the Common Shrew Mole. We caused one of the galleries to be dug out, and obtained a nest containing three young, apparently a week old. The radiations on the nose were so slightly developed that until we carefully examined them we supposed they were the young of the Common Shrew Mole. The nest was spacious, composed of withered grasses, and situated in a large excavation under a stump. The old ones had made their escape, and we endeavoured to preserve the young; but the want of proper nourishment caused their death in a couple of days.

The specimen of the Star-nosed Mole, from which our plate was drawn, was sent to us by our highly esteemed friend JAMES G. KING, Esq., having been captured on a moist piece of ground at his country seat in New Jersey, opposite the city of New-York.

STAR-NOSED MOLE

Condylura cristata cristata (Linnaeus)

The "star," consisting of 22 pink tentacles arranged around the nose of this animal, sets it apart from all other mammals in the world. Constantly in motion when looking for food, the "star" clamps together when the mole is eating.

Although the star-nosed sometimes occurs in damp uplands, it normally lives in swamps, marshes and moist swales and meadows. Rather gregarious, the species may be numerous in small areas and rare or absent for miles around. Within the colonies, the shallow burrows wander erratically with numerous crossings. Sometimes the tunnels drop abruptly to a foot or two in depth and rise again elsewhere. In places the tunnels are flooded and they often open below the surface of streams and pools.

This mole swims rapidly and expertly, staying under water for minutes at a time, propelling itself by alternate movements of fore and hind feet and the sculling of its long tail. Its rather coarse fur coat is waterproof.

The star-nosed mole is active throughout the year. In winter, it swims under the ice and may burrow through snow, or run about on the surface. It is abroad by day as well as night, but prefers rainy or cloudy periods to sunshine. A poor digger by comparison with most members of the family,

the star-nosed mole has been timed to burrow at only eight feet an hour. Because of its surface life, it can be captured by hawks, owls, skunks, cats and dogs. While swimming, it may fall prey to the mink or large predacious fish such as the black bass.

The activity of the fleshy tentacles on the animal's nose may help to locate the worms, snails, crustaceans and insects which make up the mole's diet. Three-quarters of its prey is aquatic. Fat is stored in the coarsely-haired tail which swells in winter to the diameter of a lead pencil.

Star-nosed moles are believed to pair in autumn and, unlike most or all other moles, to stay together until the young arrive in spring. After a probable gestation period of 45 days, the three to seven (usually six) young are born in the dry leaf-grass nest in the underground den. They are pink, naked and about three inches long (large in comparison with the mother) and the nose "star" is already developing. They disperse when about a month old.

Adults are 7 to 8¼ inches long, including the 2¼- to 3¼-inch tail, and weigh 1½ to 3 ounces. They occur from Labrador west to Manitoba and North Dakota, south to Georgia and South Carolina.

DASYPUS PEBA, DESM.

NINE-BANDED ARMADILLO.

This singular production of nature, it might be said, resembles a small pig saddled with the shell of a turtle; it is about the size of a large opossum; the head is small, and greatly elongated, and the neck can be retracted so far as to entirely withdraw the head under the shell. . . . the covering of the head may be compared to a helmet, and that of the shoulders and on the hind parts to breast-plates and thigh-pieces, the whole forming an almost impenetrable coat-of-mail. . . .

The Armadillo is not "a fighting character," but on the contrary is more peaceable than even the opossum, which will at times bite in a sly and treacherous manner, quite severely. Indeed nature, whilst giving to the Armadillo a covering of horn-plates or scales, which serve to protect it from many of its foes, has not supplied it, as she has other non-combating animals — the porcupine for instance — with sharp-pointed quills or spines, and its only means of aggression are its claws, which although large are better adapted for digging than aught else. The animal, however, sometimes has been known when caught by the tail, to kick rather hard with both fore and hind-legs, so that its captor was glad to let go, for it possesses great strength in the limbs. A friend of ours who formerly resided in South America had a pet Armadillo in his bed-chamber, where it generally remained quiet during the day, but in the dark hours was active and playful. One night after he had gone to bed, the Armadillo began dragging about the chairs and some boxes that were placed around the room, and continued so busily engaged at this occupation that our friend could not sleep. He at length arose and struck a light, when to his surprise he found boxes he had supposed greatly too heavy for such an animal to stir, had been moved and placed together so as to form a sort of den or hiding-place in a corner, into which the animal retreated with great apparent satisfaction, and from whence it could only be drawn out after a hard struggle, and the receipt of some severe strokes from its claws. But in general the Armadillo does not evince any disposition to resent an attack, and in fact one of them when teased by a pet parrot, struck out with its claws only till pressed by the bird, when it drew in its head and feet, and secure in its tough shell, yielded without seeming to care much about it, to its noisy and mischievous tormentor . . .

But when the Armadillo has a chance of escape by digging into the ground, it is no sluggard in its movements, and progresses towards the depths of the soil with surprising rapidity. This animal however on being much alarmed rolls itself up, and does not attempt to fly, and it is chiefly when it has been digging, and is at or near the mouth of a hole, that it tries to escape; preferring generally, to be kicked, tumbled about with a stick, or be bitten at by a dog, to making an effort to run. . . .

. . . They are said to dig down in a straight direction when they discover a subterranean colony of ants, without beginning at the mouth or entrance to the ant-hole. There are two favourite species of ant with the Armadillo in Nicaragua, one of which makes nests in the forks of trees in the forests. The tree ants are white, the others small and black. The Armadillos keep about the roots of the trees in order to feed upon the former, and as we have already said, dig for the latter. . . .

It has been assured us that when a line of ants (which may sometimes extend some distance in the woods) are busily engaged in carrying provision to the general storehouse, they scatter in every direction at the instant the Armadillo begins to dig down towards their stronghold, evidently having some communication from head-quarters equivalent to "sauve qui peut."

The gait of these animals when not alarmed is like that of a tortoise, and about as fast. They have nails powerfully organized for digging, whilst their legs are only long enough to raise the body from the ground. The holes the Armadillo excavates in the earth for its own purposes, are generally dug at an angle of forty-five degrees, are winding, and from six to eight feet long.

The Armadillo is generally much darker in colour than the specimen we figured, which having been a pet, was washed and clean when we drew it. When in the woods these animals partake more or less of the colour of the soil in which they find their food, as some of the dirt sticks to their shell. Those that have been domesticated prefer sleeping above ground, but this animal when wild lives in burrows, holes in the roots of trees, or under rocks. . . .

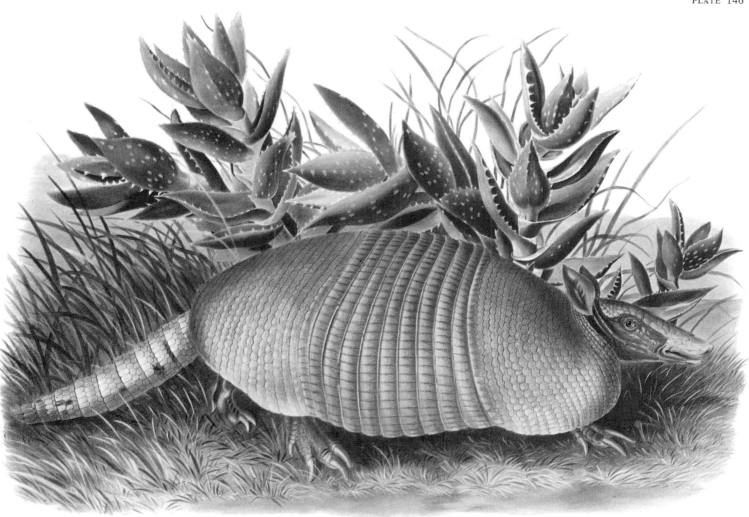

NINE-BANDED ARMADILLO

Dasypus novemcinctus mexicanus Peters

In spite of its heavy coat of armor reaching from head to end of tail, the armadillo can swim. By gulping air into its stomach and intestines, it decreases its specific gravity from 1.06 to .92 and dog paddles for some distance. Even easier, because it can undergo considerable exertion for at least six minutes without breathing, it walks submerged across the bottom of small streams and ponds.

The armadillo has neither incisor nor canine teeth, but its long tongue can sweep in from 60 to 70 insects at one lick. The powerful arms with strong claws dig burrows, anchor the animal to the ground, if attacked, and enable it to fight, when necessary.

The animal is normally solitary, although several of the same sex are sometimes found in one of the four or five burrows or ledge crevices which the average animal maintains. The home den contains a nest made of half a bushel of dry grass and leaves, while the other burrows serve as emergency shelters. The tunnels are only 10 to 15 feet long and generally have one entrance under a stump.

After sundown, and sometimes on rainy or dark days, the owner goes forth for insects, arthropods and earthworms. It rambles erratically, unhurriedly, with numerous grunts, over its home range of five to ten acres. Occasionally it rears

up on its hind legs to sniff for danger. It has a keen sense of smell but poor sight. Unlike some foreign armadillos, the one North American species cannot roll up into a ball to protect its soft underparts from attack. However, its tough armor is proof against most enemies except dogs, men and automobiles. Because of its nervous habit of jumping up in the air when scared, it is often killed by cars that would otherwise pass over it. In thick growth, the armadillo can often out-dodge and out-run dogs and men.

The armadillo female almost invariably produces four young of the same sex in each litter. This results from division of a single egg. Although mating season is late summer to early fall, implantation is delayed as much as four months and birth occurs in February to May. The young leave the mother two months later.

Armadillos are 24 to 32 inches long, including the 10- to 15-inch tail, and weigh 10 or 12 to a maximum of 17 pounds. The species is found from northern Argentina through Central America to Mississippi, Kansas and western Texas. By human means, the armadillo has reached Alabama and most of peninsular Florida. The range has expanded northward some 700 miles in the past century, but cold winter temperatures seem to limit further advance of this furless creature.

LAGOMYS PRINCEPS. RICHARDSON.

LITTLE CHIEF HARE.

Little is known with regard to the habits of this animal.

The following extract is made from the Fauna Boreali Americana:

"Mr. /Thomas/ DRUMMOND /British fur trader in Great Lakes region and western Canada/ informs me, that the Little-Chief Hare frequents heaps of loose stones, through the interstices of which it makes its way with great facility. It is often seen at sunset, mounted on a stone, and calling to its mate by a peculiar shrill whistle. On the approach of man, it utters a feeble cry, like the squeak of a rabbit when hurt, and instantly disappears, to reappear in a minute or two, at the distance of twenty or thirty yards, if the object of its apprehension remains stationary. On the least movement of the intruder, it instantly conceals itself again, repeating its cry of fear; which, when there are several of the animals in the neighbourhood, is passed from one to the other. Mr. DRUMMOND describes their cry as very deceptive, and as appearing to come from an animal at a great distance, whilst in fact the little creature is close at hand; and if seated on a grey limestone rock, is so similar, that it can scarcely be discovered. These animals feed on vegetables. Mr. DRUMMOND never found their burrows, and he thinks they do not make any, but that they construct their nests among the stones. He does not know whether they store up hay for winter or not, but is certain, that they "do not come abroad during that season."

To the above account, it affords us pleasure to annex the extract of a letter, which we received from Mr. NUTTALL on the same subject.

Of this curious species of Lepus, (L. princeps of RICHARDSON), we were not fortunate enough to obtain any good specimens. I found its range to be in that latitude (42°) almost entirely alpine. I first discovered it by its peculiar cry, far up the mountain of the dividing ridge between the waters of the Columbia and Colorado, and the Missouri, hiding amongst loose piles of rocks, such as you generally see beneath broken cliffs. From this retreat I heard a slender, but very distinct bleat, so like that of a young kid or goat, that I at first concluded it to be such a call; but in vain trying to discover any large animal around me, at length I may almost literally say, the mountain brought forth nothing much larger than a mouse, as I discovered that this little animal was the real author of this unexpected note."

PIKA

Ochotona princeps princeps (Richardson)

"Little Chief Hare" is a "book name" which was popular in the day of Audubon and Bachman but is rarely used today. The modern term "pika" is from the language of the Tungus of northeastern Siberia. The proper pronunciation is "peeka" but in western America where it lives, it is usually called "pika." Its sharp bark and short whistle has given rise to the Old World names of "whistling hare" and "piping hare." Another pika call is a harsh "kaach" or a repeated "ka." These sounds are ventriloquial and with each exclamation the animal jerks forward and upward.

The pika belongs to the rabbit-hare order, but it has many differences. It has little eyes, small, rounded ears and no visible tail. It is colonial and diurnal rather than solitary and nocturnal. It stores food which rabbits do not. Like the rabbits and hares, its incisor teeth continue to grow as long as it lives. (They wear down with constant use.)

Although it dwells in a colony and collects forage in the communal pasture, each animal maintains its own small range around its nest deep in the talus (broken rock). Here, from distances up to a hundred yards, the pika carries food in its mouth. The many kinds of herbs and clippings from vines, shrubs and lower branches of trees are piled in shallow layers for the sun to cure. Even if the pile is as much as a bushel and weighs up to 50 pounds, the pika will keep moving it to dry in the sun or to shelter when rain threatens.

Within the breeding season from March to August, two litters are probable. The two to five young are born, after a 30-day gestation, naked and helpless, weighing approximately one-third ounce each. Weaned when about one-quarter grown, they reach adult size when two months old.

Except for weasels and martens, pikas have little to fear from four-footed or winged enemies. Their grayish to brownish color (more buffy or tawny in summer than winter) closely matches the rocks where they live. In their remote mountain habitat, American pikas never conflict with man's agricultural enterprises.

Pikas are 6½ to 8½ inches long and weigh 3½ to 4½ ounces. The range extends from northern New Mexico and the Sierra Nevada of California north to central British Columbia and the Rocky Mountains of Alberta; a northern species occurs from western Mackenzie District west to Mount McKinley.

LEPUS BACHMANI, WATERHOUSE.

BACHMAN'S HARE.

The manners of this pretty Hare, as observed in Texas by J.W. Audubon, appear to assimilate to those of the common rabbit *(Lepus sylvaticus)* /now *Sylvilagus floridanus mallurus* (Thomas)/, the animal seldom quitting a particular locality, and making its form in thick briar patches or tufts of rank grass, keeping near the edges of the woody places, and being seen in the evenings, especially for a short time after sunset, when it can be easily shot.

We have been favoured with the following particulars as to the habits of this Hare by our esteemed friend Captain J.P. McCown of the United States Army:

"This Hare is deficient in speed, and depends for its safety upon dodging among the thick and thorny chaparals or nopal clusters *(cacti)* which it inhabits, never venturing far from these coverts.

"Large numbers can be seen early in the morning or late in the evening, playing in the small openings or on the edges of the chaparals, or nibbling the tender leaves of the nopal, which seems to be the common prickly pear of our country, only much larger from congeniality of climate."

"The principal enemies of these Hares in Texas are the cat species, hawks, and snakes."

During the war with Mexico, some of the soldiers of our army who were stationed on the Mexican frontier had now and then a sort of battue, to kill all the game they could in their immediate vicinity; and by surrounding a space of tolerably open ground, especially if well covered with high grass or weeds, and approaching gradually to the centre, numbers of these Hares were knocked down with clubs as they attempted to make their escape, as well as occasionally other animals which happened to be secreted within the circle. We were told that a raw German recruit, who had once or twice before been made the butt of his comrades, having joined only a few days, was invited to partake of the sport, and as the excitement became quite agreeable to him, was amongst the foremost in knocking down the unfortunate Hares, as they dashed out or timidly squatted yet a moment, hoping not to be observed; when suddenly one of his companions pointed out to him a *skunk,* which, notwithstanding the din and uproar on all sides, was very quietly awaiting the course of events. The unlucky recruit darted forward: — we need say nothing more, except that during the remainder of the war the skunk was, by that detachment, known only as the "Dutchman's rabbit."

This Hare so much resembles the common rabbit, that it has been generally considered the same animal; and this is not singular, for the gray rabbit /eastern cottontail/ does not extend to those portions of our country in which Bachman's Hare is found, and few, save persons of some observation, would perceive the differences between them, even if they had both species together so that they could compare them.

/Editor's Comment: Unfortunately, the above information which was gathered in Texas by J. W. Audubon not only "assimilated" to the eastern cottontail — it actually was about the eastern cottontail. The species which was named in honor of Dr. Bachman (from a specimen in the Zoological Society of London) is confined to the Pacific Coast region, from the Columbia River to the southern tip of Baja California. Its closest approach to Texas is nowhere more than 175 miles from the Pacific Ocean. In extenuation for the error, it may be pointed out that "Bachman's Hare," now called "brush rabbit," looks like a small, dark-colored eastern cottontail./

BRUSH RABBIT

Sylvilagus bachmani bachmani (Waterhouse)

The Romans called all rabbits and hares by one name, "Lepus," and the world followed this practice until 1867 A.D. Then scientists divided the animals into two groups: *Lepus* (hares) and *Sylvilagus* (rabbits).

Strictly speaking, "hare" should be applied to those species which nearly always use surface "forms" where the young are born in the open, well-furred, eyes open and able to run about only a few hours later. Rabbits have shorter gestation periods, use burrows at times and prepare fur-lined nests to receive the young which arrive naked (or thinly haired), blind and helpless. Larger than rabbits, hares run faster and further, and rarely or never seek refuge in burrows.

Both hares and rabbits have a characteristic which is unusual among mammals — females are generally larger than males. Both groups have sensory pads on each side of their nostrils (origin of the human term "hare lip"). Both also re-eat one type of their pellets (droppings) to regain lost vitamins.

During courtship, male hares and rabbits flag their tails, caress females (hares are rougher and kick and bite) and, standing upright, they box and kick their rivals. Both genera send warnings by drumming on the ground with their hind feet. Many scream when terrified; in this way a cottontail scared away my neighbor's overgrown son — 14 years old!

In Audubon's day most hares and rabbits were called "hares." Today most of them are commonly called "rabbits," in spite of scientific distinction.

* * * *

The brush rabbit was given its name because it never goes more than a few yards from dense brush cover. Instead of burrows, it uses forms (like the hares). From each form radiates an inter-connecting labyrinth of runways which are veritable tunnels through the brush.

While not gregarious, intrusion on a neighbor's grazing does not necessarily cause a fight. During daylight, food is obtained under cover; in dusk or darkness, the animals move out three to 15 yards from the thicket edge.

Adults pair briefly during January-to-June. The two to five young have a thin coat of fine hair and their eyes open a week to 10 days after birth. They leave the grass nest when they are about two weeks old, and attain maturity in four to five months.

Small to medium in size, with rather short ears and hind legs, the brush rabbit is 12 to 15 inches long, including the ¾- to 1¼ inch tail, and weighs 1 1/5 to 1¾ pounds. It is found on the western slope of the Sierra Nevada from desert scrub, near sea level, to the yellow-pine belt at 5,000 feet.

LEPUS PALUSTRIS. BACHMAN.

MARSH HARE.

The Marsh-Hare chiefly confines itself to the maritime districts of the southern States, and is generally found in low marshy grounds that are sometimes partially inundated, near rivers subject to freshets that occasionally overflow their banks, or near the large ponds called in Carolina "reserves," which are dammed up or otherwise made to retain the water intended to flood the rice-fields at the proper season.

In these situations — to which few persons like to resort, on account of the muddy nature of the ground, and the many thorny and entangling vines and other obstructions that abound near them; and which, besides, continually exhale from their stagnant waters a noxious vapour, which rapidly generates disease — surrounded by frogs, water-snakes and alligators, this species resides throughout the year, rarely molested by man, and enabled by its aquatic habits to make up for any want of speed when eluding the pursuit of its enemies.

It winds with great facility through miry pools, and marshes overgrown with rank weeds and willow bushes, and is quite at its ease and at home in the most boggy and unsafe parts of the swamps.

We have met with this animal a few miles from Columbia, South Carolina, one hundred and twenty miles north of Charleston, along the muddy shores of the sluggish rivers and marshes; but on arriving at the high grounds beyond the middle country, where the marshes disappear, it is no longer to be found.

In its movements it is unlike most of our other hares; it runs low on the ground, and cannot leap with the same ease, strength and agility they display. From the shortness of its legs and ears, and its general clumsy appearance as we see it splashing through the mud and mire, or plunging into creeks or ponds, it somewhat reminds us of an over-grown Norway rat endeavouring to escape from its pursuers.

The Marsh-Hare is so slow of foot, that but for the protection afforded it by the miry tangled and thorny character of its usual haunts, it would soon be overtaken and caught by any dog of moderate speed. We have observed the negroes of a plantation on a holiday, killing a good many of them by first setting fire to the half-dried grasses and weeds in a marshy piece of ground during a continued drought, when the earth had absorbed nearly all the moisture from it, and then surrounding the place, with sticks in their hands, and waiting until the flames drove the hares from their retreats, when they were knocked down and secured as they attempted to pass. Several gray-rabbits /eastern cottontails/ ran out of this place, but the men did not attempt to stop them, knowing their superior speed, but every Marsh-Hare that appeared was headed, and with a loud whoop set upon on all sides and soon captured. . . .

We kept an individual of this species in confinement, which had been captured when full-grown. It became so gentle in a few days that it freely took its food from the hand. It was fed on turnips and cabbage-leaves, but preferred bread to any other food that was offered to it. In warm weather it was fond of lying for hours in a trough of water, and seemed rest-less and uneasy when it was removed: scratching at the sides of its cage until the trough was replaced, when it immediately plunged in, burying the greater part of its body in the water. . .

The Marsh-Hare deposits its young in a pretty large nest, frequently composed of a species of rush, (Juncus effusus,) growing in convenient situations. The rushes appear to be cut by it into pieces of about a foot in length. We have seen these nests nearly surrounded by, and almost floating on the water. They were generally arched by carefully bending the rushes or grasses over them, admitting the mother by a pretty large hole in the side. A considerable quantity of hair was found lining them, but whether plucked out by the parent, or the re-sult of the natural shedding of their coat, (it being late in the spring when these animals shed their hair,) we were unable to ascertain.

The young number from five to seven. They evidently breed several times in the season, but we have observed that the females usually produce their young at least a month later than the gray rabbit /eastern cottontail/. Twenty-one specimens were obtained from the 9th to the 14th day of April; none of the females had produced young that season, although some of them would have done so in a very few days. On one occasion only, have we seen the young in March. They bear a strong resemblance to the adult, and may almost at a glance be distinguished from those of the gray rabbit /eastern cottontail/.

MARSH RABBIT

Sylvilagus palustris palustris (Bachman)

This animal is easily distinguished from the ubiquitous eastern cottontail, being darker and duller in coloration. It even lacks the conspicuous white tail which is the badge of most of the rabbit family. The marsh rabbit runs in a jerky, uncertain and erratic manner. On being startled by an enemy, it scuttles into cover, turns at right angles and, if not closely followed, moves furtively back toward its starting point. It is probably the slowest and least graceful runner of its tribe. Instead of the soft, fluffy fur which is common to the majority of the group, the coat of the marsh rabbit is coarse, stiff and harsh to the touch.

Bachman and some later writers have cited numerous instances of the aquatic habits of this species. Other reputable observers, however, state without hesitation that while it lives near water, it keeps to the drier areas and enters water only as a last resort. Once there, it is neither a strong nor rapid swimmer. It is indeed an inhabitant of the lowland and rarely or never occurs more than 500 feet above sea level.

The marsh rabbit spends the daylight hours sitting in a well-hidden form, coming out at dusk to feed. The leaves of ca brier and centella are favorite foods in Florida, but the diet includes a wide variety of trees, shrubs, woody vines and herbaceous plants. The animal spends its adult life in a small area, usually less than 300 yards across. Water is always close by and is used for shower-bathing as well as for drinking.

Except during the breeding season (February to March), marsh rabbits are unsociable and fight off intruders of their own species. A biologist who kept several of these rabbits in cages reported that they maintained a similar attitude toward him. Unlike Bachman's pet, "None of them grew tame or reconciled to human presence."

The female bears three or four young. These rabbits fall prey to alligators, snakes (rattlers and water moccasins), carnivorous mammals and birds. Being active at night, they are particularly likely to become the victims of the great horned and other large owls. Marsh rabbits are host to botfly larvae, fleas, ticks and numerous internal parasites.

Because of their short legs, these rabbits look smaller but are actually about the same size as the eastern cottontails. They are 17 to 18 inches long, including the 1¼- to 1½-inch tail. The range covers the Atlantic coastal plain, from southeastern Virginia to southern Florida (except for an area on the southeastern coast) and west along the Gulf Coast to Mobile Bay, Alabama.

LEPUS SYLVATICUS, BACHMAN
GREY RABBIT.

This species abounds in our woods and forests, even in their densest coverts; it is fond of places overgrown with young pines thickly crowded together, or thickets of the high bush-blackberry, *(Rubus villosus;)* and is also fond of frequenting farms and plantations, and occupying the coppices and grassy spots in the neighbourhood of cultivation, remaining in its form by day, concealed by a brush-heap, a tuft of grass, or some hedgerow on the side of an old fence; from which retreat it issues at night, to regale itself on the clover, turnips, or corn-fields of the farmer. It not unfrequently divests the young trees in the nursery of their bark; it often makes inroads upon the kitchen-garden, feasting on the young green peas, lettuces, cabbages, &c., and doing a great deal of mischief; and when it has once had an opportunity of tasting these dainties, it becomes difficult to prevent its making a nightly visit to them. Although the place at which it entered may be carefully closed, the Rabbit is sure to dig a fresh hole every night in its immediate vicinity; and snares, traps, or guns, are the best auxiliaries in such cases, soon putting an end to farther depredations.

This animal, when first started, runs with greater swiftness, and makes fewer doublings than the Northern /snowshoe/ hare, *(L. Americanus;)* having advanced a hundred yards or more, it stops to listen; finding itself pursued by dogs, should the woods be open and free from swamps or thickets, it runs directly toward some hole in the root of a tree or hollow log. In the lower parts of Carolina, where it finds protection in briar patches, and places thickly overgrown with smilax and other vines, it continues much longer on foot, and by winding and turning in places inaccessible to larger animals, frequently makes its escape from its pursuers, without the necessity of resorting for shelter to a hollow tree.

The Gray Rabbit /eastern cottontail/ possesses the habit of all the other species of this genus with which we are acquainted, of stamping with its hind feet on the earth when alarmed at night, and when the males are engaged in combat. It is also seen during the spring season, in wood-paths and along the edges of fields, seeking food late in the mornings and early in the afternoons, and during the breeding season even at mid-day: on such occasions it may be approached and shot with great ease. This species, like all the true hares, has no note of recognition, and its voice is never heard except when wounded or at the moment of its capture, when it utters a shrill, plaintive cry, like that of a young child in pain; in the Northern hare this cry is louder, shriller, and of longer continuance. The common domesticated European rabbit seems more easily made to cry out in this way than any other of the genus.

. . . In autumn, the greater portion, if not all, the summer fur drops off in spots, and is gradually replaced by the winter coat. In this state, as there are shades of difference between the summer and winter colours, the animal presents a somewhat singular appearance, exhibiting at the same time, like the Northern /snowshoe/ hare, (although far less conspicuously,) patches of different colours. The Gray Rabbit /eastern cottontail/, although it breeds freely in enclosed warrens, seldom becomes tame, and will probably never be domesticated. When captive, it seems to be constantly engaged in trying to find some means of escape; and though it digs no burrows in a state of nature, yet, when confined, it is capable of digging to the depth of a foot or more under a wall, in order to effect its object. We, however, at the house of Dr. DE BENNEVILLE at Milestown, near Philadelphia, saw five or six that were taken from the nest when very young and brought up by hand, so completely tamed that they came at the call and leapt upon the lap of their feeder; they lived sociably and without restraint in the yard, among the dogs and poultry. . . .

The Gray Rabbit /eastern cottontail/ is one of the most prolific of all our species of this genus; in the Northern States it produces young about three times in the season, from five to seven at a litter; whilst in Carolina its young are frequently brought forth as early as the twentieth of February, as late as the middle of October, and in all the intermediate months. Nature seems thus to have made a wise provision for the preservation of the species, since no animal is more defenceless or possesses more numerous enemies. Although it can run with considerable swiftness for some distance, its strength in a short time is exhausted, and an active dog would soon overtake it if it did not take shelter in some hole in the earth, heap of logs, or stones, or in a tree with a hollow near its root; in these retreats it is often captured by young hunters. . . .

EASTERN COTTONTAIL

Sylvilagus floridanus mallurus (Thomas)

The geographic term "eastern" as applied to this cottontail is only relative, for the range extends from southern Ontario and Quebec and the Atlantic Coast across the Great Plains, and from northern Manitoba south through Central America to Costa Rica, and possibly to Panama.

Millions of these rabbits with the powder puff tails are shot every year. Over a vast region, including the most densely populated portion of industrial and agricultural America, they are the most abundant of all game mammals. Because of their importance in sport and economics, they have been the subject of intensive study and of probably thousands of pages in publications.

Most cottontails are killed before they are a year old. To cope with this high death rate, females mate promiscuously from early February through August, or even October in the Gulf States. The gestation period is 29 or 30 days and three to four (rarely six) litters are produced annually. Each litter contains three to six (usually five) young which at birth are blind, sparsely furred, with ears undeveloped and a weight of about one ounce. At two weeks of age, they can move about and nibble foliage near the nest and, in another two or three weeks, they are weaned and independent. (If it is not winter, the mother is about to give birth to the next

litter.) The juveniles are physically mature as early as five months, but the relatively few survivors do not breed until the following season.

The normal home of a cottontail is a "form" — a flattened resting place in a brush pile or copse. However, an abandoned burrow of woodchuck or skunk may be used during severe weather or as an escape when closely pressed by an enemy. Cottontails are solitary but the ranges of neighbors frequently overlap. A cottontail requires one to 10 acres and up to 40 acres if food is scarce.

When feeding, cottontails hop along slowly (hind feet together) and stop frequently to sample plants or sit erect to look for one of the numerous enemies among the carnivorous mammals, birds and snakes. Their only defenses are keen hearing, smell, sight and speed, which can reach a maximum of 18 miles an hour for distances up to half a mile.

In summer, cottontails eat a great variety of succulent herbs; during winter they must resort to the buds, twigs and bark of woody shrubs and trees. Sometimes great damage is inflicted on orchards, plant nurseries and crops.

Varying with the subspecies, cottontails measure from 15 to 19 inches long, including the 1½- to 2¾-inch tail, and weigh 2 to 5 (rarely 5½) pounds.

LEPUS ARTEMESIA, BACH.

WORM WOOD HARE.

Mr. TOWNSEND, who procured this species at Fort Walla-walla /near the present town of Wallula, Southeastern Washington/, remarks, "it is here abundant but very shy and retired, keeping constantly in the densest wormwood bushes, and leaping with singular speed from one to another when pursued. I have never seen it dart away and run to a great distance like other Hares. I found it very difficult to shoot this animal, for the reasons stated. I had been residing at Fort Walla-walla for two weeks, and had procured only two, when at the suggestion of Mr. PAMBRUN, I collected a party of a dozen Indians armed with bows and arrows, and sallied forth. We hunted through the wormwood within about a mile of the Fort, and in a few hours returned bringing eleven Hares. The keen eyes of the Indians discovered the little creatures squatting under the bushes, where to a white man they would have been totally invisible. This Hare, when wounded and taken, screams like our common species /presumably the eastern cottontail/.

NUTTALL'S COTTONTAIL

Sylvilagus nuttallii nuttallii (Bachman)

This species is not really "diminutive" as Dr. Bachman first described it. (For explanation, see following account.) Actually, Nuttall's cottontail is somewhat above average size for its group (genus); it has rather long hind legs with broad, very hairy feet, and medium long ears. The coat is pale gray to buffy brown; the shade depending on the individual, the subspecies and the season of year.

Nuttall's cottontails are rather solitary, congregating only where food is especially attractive such as in grassy clearings. As a rule, they feed during the hours around sunrise and sunset, principally on sagebrush, western juniper and grasses.

The breeding season is limited to spring and early summer, when one to two litters of four to eight young (average six) are the normal quota per female. In dense thickets, the young are reared in a shallow depression which is lined and covered with grass and with fur which the mother pulls from her abdomen. If brush is sparse, the nest is located in a burrow or under broken rocks. The young are born blind but with a pelage of short, fine hair.

When startled, Nuttall's cottontails run only 20 to 50 feet, then pause facing away from the intruder. If disturbed further, the animals hop off through the thickets on a circular course to throw off pursuit. The principal enemies are coyotes, bobcats, hawks and owls.

This species lives on rocky hills and in canyons which are thick with sagebrush and other shrubs; it stays away from open plains where it would have little protection. In the south, it resorts to brushy, rocky slopes among the yellow pines. When cover is sparse, the cottontails spend the day in burrows or rock crevices; in dense thickets, aboveground forms suffice.

The species' range is extensive: southern British Columbia, Alberta and Saskatchewan south to central New Mexico, Arizona, Nevada and the southern Sierra Nevada of California.

Its size is within the lower limits of the eastern cottontail in being 14 to 15½ inches long, including the 1¾- to 2-inch tail; its weight is 1¾ to 2½ pounds.

LEPUS NUTTALLII, BACH.

NUTTALL'S HARE.

The only information which we have been able to obtain of the habits of this diminutive species is contained in the following note from Mr. NUTTAL, which accompanied the specimen.

"This little Hare we met with west of the Rocky Mountains, inhabiting thickets by the banks of several small streams which flow into the Shoshonee and Columbia rivers. It was frequently seen, in the evening, about our encampment, and appeared to possess all the habits of the *Lepus Sylvaticus* /now *Sylvilagus floridanus,* the eastern cottontail/."

NUTTALL'S COTTONTAIL

Sylvilagus nuttcllii nuttallii (Bachman)

The specimen on which Bachman based his description cf a "diminutive" new species and named it "Nuttall's Hare," (see account of preceding painting) was actually only one-quarter grown. It had been sent to him by the famous naturalist, Thomas Nuttall, who collected it in 1834 probably near the mouth of the Malheur River in eastern Oregon.

Two years later Bachman obtained another specimen of the same species from Old Fort Walla Walla, Washington. Because this one was adult, he was misled by its age differ-

ences of size, color and other characteristics and described it as another new species. Since its collector, J. K. Townsend, noted that he found it constantly in "worm-wood" (better known under its common name of sagebrush), Bachman named it "Worm-wood Hare."

This species is now known as Nuttall's cottontail. "Sage-brush cottontail" would have been a more descriptive common name but since "Nuttall's" had scientific priority it had to be continued.

LEPUS AQUATICUS, BACH.

SWAMP HARE.

The habits of this animal are very singular, differing in one remarkable peculiarity from those of any other species of hare yet known, with the exception of the marsh-hare. /For "marsh-hare" and "swamp-hare," read "marsh rabbit" and "swamp rabbit," respectively./ Although the Swamp-Hare is occasionally seen on high grounds in the dense forest, it prefers low and marshy places, or the neighbourhood of streams and ponds of water, to which it is fond of resorting. It swims with great facility from one little islet to another, and is generally found seeking its food in wet places, or near the water, as it subsists on the roots of various kinds of aquatic plants, especially on a species of iris growing in the water.

Persons who have given us information on the subject of this hare, inform us, that when first started, and whilst running, its trampings are louder, and can be heard at a greater distance, than those of any other hare.

As it suddenly leaps or bounds from its hiding place ere it is seen, it is apt to startle the rambler who has intruded upon its solitary retreat, and he may be impressed with the belief that he has started a young deer. When chased by dogs, the Swamp-Hare runs with great swiftness, and is able to escape from them without difficulty; but it almost invariably directs its flight towards the nearest pond, as if led by instinct to seek an element in which all traces of its scent are soon lost to its eager pursuers. There is a specimen of the Swamp-Hare, which we added to the collection of the Academy of Natural Sciences, Philadelphia, considerably larger than the Northern hare /snowshoe hare/; this individual, on being pursued by hounds, swam twice across the Alabama river, and was not captured till it had finally retreated to a hollow tree.

We have been informed that it is a very common habit of this species when pursued, to swim to the edge of some stream or pond, retreat beneath the overhanging roots of the trees that may be growing on its border, or seek for a secure shelter under the hollows made by the washing of the banks. The swiftness of foot possessed by this Hare, and the stratagems to which it is capable of resorting, might easily enable it to elude pursuit but for this habit of seeking for shelter as soon as it is chased, which is the cause of its being frequently captured.

When the waters in the swamps are low, it seeks the first hollow tree, where it is easily secured. In this manner, Major LEE informed us, that in his vicinity the boys and the domestics caught thirty or forty in three days.

The young of this hare are frequently found in nests formed of leaves and grasses, placed on hillocks in the swamps, or in the hollow of some fallen tree. We have been informed that it produces young at least twice in a season, and from four to six at a litter.

SWAMP RABBIT

Sylvilagus aquaticus aquaticus (Bachman)

As Bachman described, and as both its common and scientific names indicate, this rabbit lives in swamps and along the banks of rivers and ponds. It is the largest of all the true rabbits (not counting the jack rabbits because they are actually hares). It also runs and swims much better and longer than the marsh rabbit. It can hide in the water by remaining almost submerged with its head above the surface in a clump of brush or floating debris. On land, if hard pressed, the swamp rabbit may take refuge in a hole in the ground or a hollow tree. Strictly solitary, it permits no other member of its own species to share its range. Like all rabbits and hares, it prefers to escape detection by sitting motionless on its form among tangled vegetation.

The grass nest is lined with fur from the mother's abdomen and is built in the abandoned burrow of some other animal or on the surface in dense cover. More rarely the female may select a hollow log or a tree cavity near the ground. The gestation period is 39 to 40 days and the litter has one to six (usually two or three) young. At birth, unlike most other rabbits, the swamp rabbits are well developed, furred and have their eyes open. They can walk when only two or three days old. The breeding season extends from January through August with the peak in February to March. It is presumed that the female produces two litters annually.

The swamp rabbit often perches on stumps, logs, low tree-crotches and other lookouts to see if there are any enemies around. Apparently, however, it depends more on scent than sight. The diet includes many sedges, grasses, aquatic herbs and cane. (In Georgia, this rabbit is called "cane-cutter.") During winter, twigs and bark of other shrubs are eaten

The swamp rabbit is 19 to 22 inches long including the 2- to 3-inch tail, and weighs 3 to 6 pounds. It is essentially a resident of the western Gulf States with range limits in northwestern South Carolina, southern Illinois and Missouri and central Oklahoma and Texas, thus inhabiting the lower Mississippi River basin.

LEPUS AMERICANUS. ERXLEBEIN.

NORTHERN HARE. Summer.

...The Northern Hare /snowshoe hare/, like most others of the genus, seeks its food only by night or in the early part of the evening. To this habit it is more exclusively confined during autumn and winter, than in spring and summer. In the latter seasons, especially in spring, these animals are frequently observed in the morning, and as the sun is declining, in the afternoon, cautiously proceeding along some solitary by-path of the forest. Two or three may often be seen associated together, appearing full of activity and playfulness. When disturbed on these occasions, they stamp on the ground, making a noise so loud that it can be heard at some distance, then hopping a few yards into the thicket, they sit with ears erect, seemingly listening, to ascertain whether they are pursued or not. This habit of thumping on the earth is common to most hares and rabbits. We have particularly noticed it in the domesticated rabbit (*L.* /now *Oryctolagus*/ *cuniculus*), and in our common gray rabbit. They are more particularly in the habit of doing it on moonlight nights; it is indicative either of fear or anger, and is a frequent action among the males when they meet in combat. During cold weather this Hare retires to its form at early dawn, or shelters itself under the thick foliage of fallen tree tops, particularly those of the pine and hemlock. It occasionally retires to the same cover for a number of nights in succession, but this habit is by no means common; and the sportsman who expects on some succeeding day to find this animal in the place from which it was once started, is likely to be disappointed; although we are not aware, that any other of our species of hare are so attached to particular and beaten paths through the woods, as the one now under consideration. It nightly pursues these paths, not only during the deep snows of winter, but for a period of several years, if not killed or taken, wandering through them even during summer. We have seen a dozen caught at one spot in snares composed of horse-hair or brass wire, in the course of a winter, and when the snow had disappeared and the spring was advanced, others were still captured in the same way, and in the same paths.

The period of gestation in this species is believed to be, (although we cannot speak with positive certainty,) about six weeks. Two females which we domesticated, and kept in a warren, produced young, one on the tenth and the other on the fifteenth of May; one had four, and the other six leverets, which were deposited on a nest of straw the inside of which was lined with a considerable quantity of hair plucked from their bodies. They succeeded in rearing all their young but one, which was killed by the male of a common European rabbit. They were not again gravid during that season. Ill health, and more important studies, required us to be absent for six months, and when we returned, all our pets had escaped to the woods, therefore we could not satisfactorily finish the observations on their habits in confinement, which had interested and amused us in many a leisure hour.

We, however, think it probable that the females in their wild state may produce young twice during the season. Those referred to above were much harassed by other species which were confined in the same warren, and might therefore have been less prolific than if they had enjoyed their liberty undisturbed, amid the recesses of their native woods. We have frequently observed the young of the Northern Hare in May, and again in July. These last must have been either from a second litter, or the produce of a young female of the previous year. The young, at birth, were able to see. They were covered with short hair, and appeared somewhat darker in colour than the adults, at that season. They left their nest in ten or twelve days, and from that time seemed to provide for themselves, and to derive little sustenance or protection from their mothers. The old males at this period seemed to be animated with renewed courage; they had previously suffered themselves to be chased and worried by the common English rabbit, and even retreated from the attacks of the gray rabbit /eastern cottontail/; but they now stood their ground, and engaged in fierce combats with the other prisoners confined with them, and generally came off victorious. They stamped with their feet, used their teeth and claws to a fearful purpose, and in the fight tore off patches of skin and mutilated the ears of their former persecutors, till they were left in undisturbed possession of the premises! ...

Fig. 1

Fig. 2

SNOWSHOE HARE

Lepus americanus americanus Erxleben

This is the first of the true hares *(Lepus)* described in this book. Hares are easily distinguished from rabbits by generally larger size, longer ears, and longer hind legs well adapted for swift running. (For other distinctions, see page 25.) Hare populations are cyclic, alternating between scarcity and abundance over periods of seven to ten years.

Because of its speed and tendency to circle back to the point where it was first startled, the snowshoe hare (often called snowshoe rabbit and varying hare) has been a favorite winter game animal since colonial times. The authors knew it well and except for a few details, their account can hardly be improved more than a century later.

A solitary creature, the snowshoe hare is shy and equipped with keen hearing, sight and scent to detect enemies. Its typical habitat is northern evergreen forests and swamps. There, in a patch of dense brush, the hare spends the day motionless on its form. For a few hours following the first evening dusk and before full morning daylight, it moves slowly and soundlessly to feed. At the first indication of danger, the hare slinks silently to cover. Unless flushed by dogs, it is seldom seen by the average person. Then it may

spring in five-foot jumps and, on good footing in fairly open places, reach a speed up to 25 miles an hour. Ordinarily, the animal spends its life in an area 300 yards in diameter.

Snowshoe hares mate for the first time early in their second year of life, during March or April. The young are born after a gestation period of 36 or 37 days (a little shorter than Bachman supposed) in the form or wherever the female happens to be. Like newborn of all hares, they are well furred, their eyes are open and in a few hours they are crawling about the spot.

The mother can breed on the same day and may have as many as four litters during the season although two or three are normal. At birth the three or four young (sometimes one to seven) are about 4 inches long and weigh 2 to 3½ ounces. Some green food is nibbled at ten days and weaning is completed a month after birth. Young hares are fully grown at five months of age. Losses are high; at least one-third of the young die within the first twelve months of life and only a few attain what is considered old age at five years.

For additional information, see the following pages.

LEPUS AMERICANUS, ERXLEBEIN.
NORTHERN HARE.

. . . It depends on its long legs, and on the thickness of the woods, to aid it in evading the pursuit of its enemies. When hunted, it winds and doubles among thick clusters of young pines and scrub-oaks, or leads the dogs through entangled patches of hemlock and spruce fir, until it sometimes wearies out its pursuers . . .

In deep snows, the animal is so light, and is so well supported by its broad furry-feet, that it passes over the surface making only a faint impression, whilst the hounds plunge deep into the snow at every bound, and soon give up the hopeless pursuit. It avoids not only open grounds, but even open woods, and confines itself to the densest and most impenetrable forests. Although it wanders by night in many directions in search of its appropriate food, we have scarcely ever seen its tracks in the open fields; it seems cautiously to avoid the cabbage and turnip fields of the farmer, and seldom even in the most retired places makes an encroachment on his cultivated grounds.

The food of this species in summer consists of various kinds of juicy and tender grasses, and the bark, leaves, and buds, of several small shrubs; and these Hares seem to be particularly fond of the young twigs of the wild allspice *(Laurus /now Lindera/ benzoin),* but in winter, when the earth is covered with snow, they gain a precarious subsistence from the buds and bark of such trees as are suited to their taste. Sometimes they scratch up the snow to feed on the leaves and berries of the various species of *Pyrola* /wintergreen/, found in the Northern States. The bark of the willow, birch and poplar, and the buds of young pines, are sought after by them with avidity. . . .

The Northern Hare seems during summer to prefer dry and elevated situations, and to be more fond of grounds covered with pines and firs, than of those that are overgrown with oak or hickory. The swamps and marshes soil their feet, and after having been compelled to pass through them, they are for hours employed in rubbing and drying their paws. In winter, however, when such places are hardened by the frost, they not only have paths through them in every direction, but occasionally seek a fallen tree-top as a hiding or resting place, in the centre of a swamp. We have observed them in great numbers in an almost impenetrable thicket of black larch, or hackmatack, *(Larix pendula,)* /now *L. laricina*/ considerable portions of which were during summer a perfect morass. In what are called the "bark clearings," places where hemlock trees have been cut down to procure tan bark, this species is sometimes so abundant that twenty or thirty of them may be started in a day's walk. . . .

Sometimes we have found these Hares dead in the woods after the melting of the snow in the Spring, and on examination we found they were entangled in portions of wire snares, frequently entwined round their necks, from which they had been unable to extricate themselves.

This species when caught alive cannot be taken into the hand like the gray rabbit /eastern cottontail/, with impunity; the latter, when seized by the ears or hind-legs soon becomes quiet and is harmless; but the Northern Hare struggles to escape, and makes a formidable resistance with its teeth and nails. On one occasion a servant who was expert at catching the gray rabbit in traps, came to us with a rueful countenance holding a hare in his hands, exhibiting at the same time sundry severe scratches he had received, showing us his torn clothes, and a place on his leg which the animal had bitten, and declaring that he had caught "a rabbit as cross as a cat." We ascertained it to be a Northern Hare in its summer dress, and although its captor had not been able to distinguish it from the gray rabbit by its colour, he certainly received a practical lesson in natural history which he did not soon forget.

A living individual of this species, which we /Bachman/ have in Charleston in a partially domesticated state, for the purpose of trying to ascertain the effect of a warm climate on its changes of colour, is particularly cross when approached by a stranger. It raises its fur, and springs at the intruder with almost a growl, and is ready with its claws and teeth to gratify its rage, and inflict a wound on the person who has aroused its ire. When thus excited, it reminded us by its attitudes of an angry racoon. . . .

SNOWSHOE HARE

Lepus americanus americanus Erxleben

This painting of the snowshoe hare is in striking contrast to that of the same animal in summer coat (preceding account). Except in the humid lowlands of western Washington and Oregon, snowshoe hares change in autumn from the brownish or dusky grayish summer coat to all-white winter pelage. Appropriately, the name "varying hare" is sometimes used. The more widely known name, "snowshoe hare," comes from the large hind feet which in winter are widened by long, thick hair and enable the animal to walk or run on crusted and even soft snow. The seasonal change takes 75 to 80 days and follows a definite pattern. In fall (October) different hair roots produce white hair on the ears and feet, then on the legs, chest and abdomen, and eventually on the back. In spring (March) the process is nearly reversed -- brown hairs appear first on the forehead, then on the body and last on the ears and feet.

Sometimes a weather aberration plays a mean trick, and the still-brown hare becomes conspicuous against an early autumn snowfall, or the white coat shows up in the brown woods during a mid-winter thaw. However, there seems to be a good correlation between pelage color and *average* climatic conditions. The color change is tripped off by some mechanism within the animal, for captive hares kept in heated quarters turn white in fall on the same schedule as their fellows in the wild.

Although wild hares violently resist capture, they are ordinarily extremely shy. The aggressive behavior of Dr. Bachman's hare was extraordinary.

Snaring, a general practice in Bachman's day, is now generally prohibited by law as "unsportsmanlike." The method is highly effective because the animal is prone to follow its trails in the snow and attempts to push through rather than go round any flimsy obstruction such as a wire snare.

Snowshoe hares measure 14½ to 21 inches long, including the 1- to 2¼-inch tail. They weigh 2½ to 4½ pounds. The range is transcontinental south of the tree line, south to the northern United States and, in the mountains, to northern Georgia, northern New Mexico and east-central California.

LEPUS GLACIALIS, LEACH.

POLAR HARE.

It is to the cold and inhospitable regions of the North, the rugged valleys of Labrador, and the wild mountain-sides of that desolate land, or to the yet wilder and more sterile countries that extend from thence toward the west, that we must resort, to find the large and beautiful Hare we have now to describe; and if we advance even to the highest latitude man has ever reached, we shall still find the Polar Hare, though the mercury fall below zero, and huge snow-drifts impede our progress through the trackless waste.

Both Indians and trappers are occasionally relieved from almost certain starvation by the existence of this Hare, which is found throughout the whole range of country extending from the Eastern to the Western shores of Northern America, and includes nearly thirty-five degrees of latitude, from the extreme North to Newfoundland.

In various parts of this thinly inhabited and unproductive region, the Polar Hare, perhaps the finest of all the American hares, takes up its residence. It is covered in the long dark winter with a coat of warm fur, so dense that it cannot be penetrated by the rain, and which is an effectual protection from the intense cold of the rigorous climate.

Its changes of colour help to conceal it from the observation of its enemies; in summer it is nearly of the colour of the earth and the surrounding rocks, and in winter it assumes a snow-white coat. The changes it thus undergoes, correspond with the shortness of the summers and the length of the Arctic winters. . . .

The eye of the Polar Hare is adapted to the twilight that reigns during a considerable part of the year within the Arctic circle; in summer it avoids the glare of the almost continual day-light, seeking the shade of the little thickets of dwarfish trees that are scattered over the barren grounds, the woods that skirt the streams, or the shelter of some over-hanging rock.

In addition to the circumstance that the eye of this Hare is well fitted for seeing with a very moderate light, it may be remarked that in winter the frequent and long continued luminous appearance of the heavens caused by the aurora borealis, together with the brightness of the unsullied snow, afford a sufficient degree of light for it to proceed with its customary occupations.

During the summer this species is found on the borders of thickets, or in stony or rocky places. In winter it is often seen in the barren and open country, where only a few stunted shrubs and clumps of spruce fir *(Abies rubra)* /now *Picea mariana,* the black spruce/ afford it shelter, differing in this habit from the Northern /snowshoe/ hare, which confines itself to thick woods throughout the year . . .

The Polar Hare is not a very shy or timid animal, but has on being approached much the same habits as the Northern /snowshoe/ hare. "It merely runs to a little distance, (says RICHARDSON,) and sits down, repeating this manoeuvre as often as its pursuer comes nearly within gun-shot, until it is thoroughly scared by his perseverance, when it makes off. It is not difficult to get within bow-shot of it by walking round it and gradually contracting the circle — a method much practised by the Indians." HEARNE had previously made the same observations; he says also, "the middle of the day, if it be clear weather, is the best time to kill them in this manner, for before and after noon the sun's altitude being so small, makes a man's shadow so long on the snow as to frighten the Hare before he can approach near enough to kill it. The same may be said of deer /caribou/ when on open plains, which are frequently more frightened at the long shadow than at the man himself."

All travellers concur in stating the flesh of this animal to be of a finer flavour than that of any of our other hares. We /Audubon/ obtained one while at St. George's Bay, in Newfoundland, and all our party made a meal of it; we pronounced it delicious food. . . .

The specimen we procured in Newfoundland weighed seven and a half pounds; it was obtained on the 15th August, in the midst of summer, when all hares are lean. It was at a period of the year also, when in that island they are incessantly harassed by the troublesome moose-fly Deer, hares, &c., and even men, suffer very much in consequence of their attacks. The Indians we saw there, although tempted by a high reward, refused to go in search of these Hares, from a dread of this persecuting insect . . .

ARCTIC HARE

Lepus arcticus arcticus Ross

Throughout the long, dark winter, the white Arctic hares assemble in bands of up to 100. At this season, by moving quietly, men have caught them in their hands. When frightened, the hares run up (never down) the slopes, jumping along high up on the toes of their hind feet while their forelegs are held against the chest or dangle in the air. Dancing about in this upright position, they swivel their ears and sniff vigorously. Their hearing and sense of smell is excellent, but sight is rather poor. Once they have located their enemy, they drop to normal running position.

Largest of all hares in North America, the Arctic hare lives on rocky hills and uplands where fierce winds blow the snow into hollows, leaving nearly bare ridges with food plants somewhat exposed. In most severe weather, the hare may retreat temporarily to low tundra. The dense, woolly coats of the more southerly hares change to a smoky gray for two or three summer months; those of the Greenland, Ellesmere Island and northern Baffin Island hares remain white throughout the year.

As with other hares, the population fluctuates widely every nine or 10 years. This hare is an important food of Eskimos and predators (chiefly Arctic fox, wolf, snowy owl and gyrfalcon); they all suffer severely in times of hare scarcity. Eskimos use the skins for making stockings and sleeping bags.

Near winter's end, in late April and early May, the bands of hares break up. The animals pair briefly and are very wary throughout the summer. Litters appear from May to early July and may contain from four to eight young (usually six).

While eating, the hares crouch, hunched up, their ears and eyelids drooping as if they were half asleep. The diet includes many dwarf plants, particularly willow (leaves, buds, bark and even roots), crowberry, saxifrage, mountain sorrel and grasses. Hares locate food under snow by their sense of smell. When necessary, they break the crust by hammering with their front feet. The more northern subspecies have extraordinarily long, projecting incisors.

Arctic hares are 19 to 27 inches long, of which the tail makes up 1¼ to 3¼ inches. They weigh 6 to 13 pounds. They occur across Canada, from near the tree line northward to the northern islands and the coasts of Greenland.

* * * *

Arctic hares in Alaska are now called Alaskan hares by the scientists. Classified as a separate species, the Latin name is *Lepus othus*.

LEPUS TOWNSENDII BACH.

TOWNSEND'S ROCKY MOUNTAIN HARE

We subjoin the following note, received from the original discoverer (J. K. Townsend) of this Hare . . . when we arrived at /Fort/ Walla-Walla /near present town of Wallula, southeastern Washington/, in September /1836/, we found the Indians and the persons attached to the fort using it as a common article of food. Immediately after we arrived we were regaled with a dish of hares, and I thought I had never eaten anything more delicious. They are found in great numbers on the plains covered with wild wormwood, *(Artemesia.)* /sagebrush/ They are so exceedingly fleet that no ordinary dog can catch them. I have frequently surprised them in their forms and shot them as they leaped away, but I found it necessary to be very expeditious and to pull trigger at a particular instant, or the game was off among the wormwood and I never saw it again. The Indians kill them with arrows by approaching them stealthily as they lie concealed under the bushes, and in winter take them with nets. To do this, some one or two hundred Indians, men women and children, collect, and enclose a large space with a slight net about five feet wide, made of hemp; the net is kept in a vertical position by pointed sticks attached to it and driven into the ground. These sticks are placed about five or six feet apart, and at each one an Indian is stationed with a short club in his hand. After these arrangements are completed a large number of Indians enter the circle and beat the bushes in every direction. The frightened hares dart off towards the net, and in attempting to pass are knocked on the head and secured. . . .

To the above account we (J. J. Audubon) added some farther information on our last visit to the far West. On the 8th June 1843 whilst our men were engaged in cutting wood and bringing it on board the steamer Omega, it being necessary in that wild region to stop and cut wood for fuel for the boat every day, one of the crew started a young Hare and after a short chase the poor thing squatted and was killed by a blow with a stick. It proved to be the young of *Lepus Townsendii,* was large enough to have left its dam, weighed rather more than one pound, and was a beautiful specimen. Its irides were pure amber colour and the eyes large, its hair was slightly curled. This Hare was captured more than twelve hundred miles east of the Rocky Mountains. On the next day in the afternoon one of the negro fire-tenders being out with a rifle, shot two others, both old individuals; one of them was how-ever cut in two by the ball and left on the spot. The hair, or fur, of this individual was slightly curled, as in the young one, especially along the back and sides, but shortly after the skins had been prepared this character disappeared. These specimens are now in our collection.

Pursuing our journey up the tortuous and rapid stream, we had not the good fortune to see any more of these beautiful animals until after our arrival at FORT UNION /in eastern Montana/ near the mouth of the Yellow Stone river, where we established ourselves for some time by the kind permission of the gentlemen connected with the fur trade.

On the 29th of July on our return from a buffalo-hunt, when we were some forty or fifty miles from the fort suddenly a fine hare leaped from the grass before us and stopped within twenty paces. Our friend, EDWARD HARRIS, Esq., /New Jersey amateur naturalist and close friend of J. J. Audubon/, was with us but his gun was loaded with ball and ours with large buck-shot intended for killing antelopes; we fired at it but missed: away it went, and ran around a hill . . .

This species, like all others of the same family, is timid and fearful in the extreme. Its speed, we think, far surpasses that of the European hare, *(L. timidus.)* /now *L. europaeus*/

If the *form* is indicative of character, this animal, from its slender body long hind legs and great length of tarsus must be the fleetest of the hares of the West.

These hares generally place or construct their forms under a thick willow bush, or if at a distance from the water-courses on the banks of which those trees grow, or when they are in the open prairie, they place them under the edge of some rock, or seek the shelter of a stone or large tuft of grass.

The Rocky Mountain Hare produces from four to six young in the year. As far as we have been able to ascertain it has but one litter. The young suck and follow the dam for about six weeks after which she turns them off and leaves them to provide for themselves. The flesh of this species resembles in flavour that of the European hare . . .

WHITE-TAILED JACK RABBIT

Lepus townsendii townsendii Bachman

Although all jack rabbits are technically hares *(Lepus)*, even scientists call them "jack rabbits."

The white-tailed jack rabbit is named for its tail that stays white the year round — in spite of its brown summer coat. The tips of its ears remain black, winter and summer. In the north and on high mountains the white-tailed jacks become all white in winter. During the summer they are protectively colored like the soil.

Like most hares and rabbits, this jack conceals itself by spending the day crouched motionless against a tussock of grass or even in the open. Only if almost stepped upon, will it make four or five hops on its hind feet and then bound away on all fours in leaps that span 12 to 18 feet. It has been clocked at speeds up to 40 miles an hour. The ordinary gait is not a walk but a series of slow hops of one to three feet.

White-tailed jack rabbits have keen sight and hearing and a highly developed sense of smell that, with protective coloration and speed, help them to escape from coyotes, foxes, golden eagles, great horned owls, and the larger hawks. Human hunters prefer these jack rabbits because they provide faster sport, their flesh is tasty and they are larger than the other jacks.

Mating for this rather solitary hare, in April or May, is a brief and cursory affair. Born like all hares, furred and open-eyed, the young become interested in plant food when two weeks old, but are not weaned until about two weeks later when they are one-quarter grown. They disperse at two months of age, and for a time they may use brush piles or abandoned burrows for shelter. Exceptional adult females may mate again and produce a second litter the same season.

The white-tailed jack moves about at dawn and dusk — also during the night hours, especially by moonlight. In summer the diet includes many herbaceous plants, wild and cultivated; in winter the food is chiefly the bark, twigs and buds of shrubs and trees. Sagebrush (as Townsend remarked — see opposite page) and ocean spray are important items.

Measuring 22 to 26½ inches in total length, including the 2¾- to 4½-inch tail, white-tailed jack rabbits weigh 5 to 10 pounds (average about 8, rarely to 14).

Grassy plains and open slopes of the western mountains up to 14,000 feet elevation are the home of the white-tailed jack. The range extends from southwestern Ontario and Wisconsin to Washington and eastern California, and from southern Alberta to northern New Mexico.

LEPUS CALIFORNICUS, GRAY.

CALIFORNIAN HARE.

The habits of all hares are much the same; and this family is a general favourite for the beauty, timid gentleness, and fleetness its various species exhibit, although some of them are annoying to the gardener. In America, however, many species of Hare inhabit territories too far from cultivated fields or gardens for them to be able to nibble even at a cabbage plant.

Many pleasant evening hours have we passed, walking through forest-shaded roads in the last rays scattered here and there by the sinking sun, observing the playful "rabbits" leaping gracefully a few paces at a time, then stopping and looking about, ignorant of our proximity and unconscious of danger. But we are now to give the habits of the Californian Hare /now black-tailed jack rabbit/, for which take the following account of the animal as observed by J. W. AUDUBON /in California/:

"The Californian Hare appears to possess just brains enough to make him the greatest coward of all the tribe I have seen, for, once startled he is quite as wild as a deer, and equally heedless as to the course he takes, so that as he has not the keen sense of smell of the deer to warn him of danger in any direction, he sometimes makes a great fool of himself in his haste, and I have had these Hares run to within three feet of me, before I was seen, even where there was no cover but a sparse prairie grass."

"It was after toiling night and day through the sands of the Colorado desert, and resting afterwards at Vallecito and San Felipe, while marching along the streams through the rich fields of Santa Maria, that I saw the first Californian Hare. I knew him at sight: he showed no *white tail* as he ran, and looked almost black amongst the yellow broom-sedge as he divided it in his swift course. His legs seemed always under his body, for so quick was the movement that I could not see them extended, as in other Hares, from one bound to another; he seemed to alight on his feet perpendicularly at each leap, with a low-squatting springy touch to the earth, and putting his enormously long ears forward, and then back on his neck, and stretching out his head, appeared to fly over the undulating ridges of the prairie as a swallow skims for insects the surface of a sluggish river in summer."

Very few of these Hares were seen by J. W. AUDUBON's party until they had travelled some distance further north, and it was only after they had left the plains of the San Joaquin for the mines that they became a common animal, and in fact often their sole resource for the day's meat.

J. W. AUDUBON says that a single Hare of this species, with a little fat pork to fry it with, often lasted himself and a companion, as food when travelling, for two days. Nearly every miner has eaten of this fine Hare, which is well known in all the hilly portions of Upper /now State of/ California.

The Californian Hare brings forth about five young at a time, which are generally littered in the latter part of April or beginning of May. J. W. AUDUBON says: "I shot a female only a few days before her young would have been born: she had five beautiful little ones, the hair and feet perfect, and a white spot on the forehead of each was prominent. I never shot another afterwards, and was sad at the havoc I had committed."

We do not know whether this species breeds more than once in the year or not, but it probably does, as Mr. /Titian R./ PEALE /animal painter, and naturalist of the U.S. Exploring Expedition/ says: "A female killed on the twenty-fourth of September was still suckling her young."

The Californian Hare is more frequently met with in uplands, on mountain sides, and in bushy places, than in other situations. During the rainy season it was not seen by J. W. AUDUBON in low and wet grounds, although it doubtless resorts to them during the dry weather of summer.

Mr. PEALE says, these Hares "when running, carry the ears erect, and make three short and one long leap; and that the Indians catch them by setting hedges of thorny brush, with openings at intervals, in which they set snares, so constructed as to catch the Hares when passing, without the use of springes; the noose is made of a substance like hemp, very strong and neatly twisted with cords."

BLACK-TAILED JACK RABBIT

Lepus californicus californicus Gray

The "Californian hare" which J. W. Audubon found on his way to the Sierra gold mines still belongs to the *Lepus californicus* species, but its common name has been changed to "black-tailed jack rabbit." As we find so often with Audubon and Bachman's *Quadrupeds,* the scientific names have changed less than the common names during the last one hundred years.

The black-tailed jack rabbit was named obviously for the black upper surface of its tail. Unlike the white-tailed jack, it does not have a white coat during winter. The black-tailed jack scratches a form in the ground, usually under a mesquite or other shrub. Ten to 18 inches long, six to eight inches wide, it may be two to four inches deep under the animal's hindquarters. This "home" may be used only once or on many successive days.

During some years, 90 percent of these black-tailed jacks have died of tularemia. Prolific, like all hares and rabbits, they soon come back to peak numbers. Foraging chiefly in the evening and early morning, the jack may travel as much as a mile to a choice feeding place. Except for other black-tailed jack rabbits which may move into the same area to feed, the species is solitary within its home range of one-half to two square miles.

This jack must have open or semi-open land. Aside from the scattered mesquite, sagebrush or other shrubs that provide food, shade and protection from enemies, the ground cover can be no more than a few inches high. The species will thrive on seriously over-grazed plains, but it will languish and die if the area is converted to an unbroken stand of grass two feet or more tall!

The range of the species is vast — western Missouri to the Pacific Coast, and from South Dakota and central Washington south to Querétaro State and the tip of Baja California in Mexico. It is adapted to a wide variety of climates and altitudes, from searing heat below sea level in Death Valley to sub-zero cold at 13,000 feet in the Sierra Nevada.

* * * *

Audubon's "Californian hare," now a subspecies of the black-tailed jack rabbit, occurs through the western half of California and southwestern Oregon.

Information on the black-tailed jack rabbit continues on the next page under "Texian Hare," another subspecies.

LEPUS TEXIANUS, AUD. & BACH.

TEXIAN HARE

This Hare received from the Texans, and from our troops in the Mexican war, the name of Jackass rabbit, in common with *Lepus callotis,* the Black-tailed Hare /which is actually a separate species, the white-sided jack rabbit, *Lepus callotis;* see following account/. . . . It is the largest of three nearly allied species of Hare which inhabit respectively New Mexico, Texas, Mexico, and California, viz. the present species, the Black-tailed and the Californian Hare. It is quite as swift of foot as either of the others, and its habits resemble those of the Black-tailed Hare in almost every particular. The young have generally a white spot on the middle of the top of the head, and are remarkable for the rigidity of the fringe of hairs which margins the ears. The feet of this species do not exhibit the red and dense fur which prevails on the feet of the Black-tailed Hare (and from which it has sometimes been called the Red–footed Hare).

The Mexicans are very fond of the flesh of this animal, and as it is widely distributed, a great many are shot and snared by them. It is very good eating, and formed an important item in the provisions of JOHN W. AUDUBON'S party whilst passing through Mexico, they at times killing so many that the men became tired of them.

Fabulous stories similar to those related of many other animals of which little was formerly known, have been told us of this Hare, which has been described as enormously large, and was many years ago mentioned to us as equal in size to a fox. Of course we were somewhat disappointed when we procured specimens, although it is a fine large species. . . .

BLACK-TAILED JACK RABBIT
Lepus californicus texianus Waterhouse

Audubon and Bachman named specimens of jack rabbits which were sent to them from Texas, appropriately, "Texian hares." Their remarks on the resemblance of these hares to their "Californian hare" were proven sound. Today both the "Californian" and "Texian" hares are combined in cne species and called black-tailed jack rabbits.

The "Texian" subspecies occurs from southern Utah and Colorado south through New Mexico and western Texas into northern Mexico. The hares in this region, living under more desert conditions than those in the coastal region of California, are paler in color; otherwise the two black-tails are quite similar in appearance and habits.

In warmer parts of their range, black-tailed jacks breed during most months of the year; in colder regions, pairing begins in spring. Gestation requires 41 to 47 days and a female will produce one to four litters annually. The average number of young per litter is two to four, with extremes of one to eight. At birth the furred, wide-eyed hares are six to eight inches long and weigh two to six ounces. They leave the mother when about a month old and are full grown at the age of two to three months.

During the juvenile period, natural enemies include most carnivores down to the weasel in size, as well as snakes and birds of prey. As adults, the black-tails contend chiefly with coyotes, foxes, golden eagles and large hawks and owls. To detect these foes, jacks depend upon their keen sight, hearing and smell. (On these points, J. W. Audubon was mistaken; see page 44.) Like all hares and rabbits, the black-tail has an excellent nose. Its sight, too, is exceptionally good for moving objects, but apparently it has poor perception of objects at rest.

In a chase, the jack's powerful hind legs make a top speed of 30 to 35 miles an hour for short distances. Dodging among scattered shrubs or over open plains, the animal races in a series of easy bounds five to 10 feet long, or even up to 20 feet under extreme stress. Every four to six jumps, it hops about five feet off the ground to get a clear view of its pursuer and the surroundings.

Black-tailed jacks, and sometimes other species of jack rabbits, may become serious pests at times on the western range. It has been estimated that, in forage consumption, 30 rabbits eat as much as one sheep. Dense rabbit populations, however, are not the primary cause of range depletion; they merely profit from it.

Black-tailed jacks are large. Males are 18½ to 25½ inches long, including the tail which may be up to 4½ inches, and they weigh from 4½ to more than 6 pounds. As with the rest of the family, the females are somewhat larger.

LEPUS NIGRICAUDATUS, BENNET,

BLACK-TAILED HARE.

Our account of this species is principally derived from the journals of J.W. AUDUBON, kept during his journey through part of Texas, made for the purpose of procuring the animals of that State, and obtaining some knowledge of their habits for our present work, in 1845 and 1846, with an extract from which we now present our readers.

"One fine morning in January, 1845, at San Antonio de Bexar, as I mounted my faithful one-eyed chesnut horse, admiring his thin neck and bony legs, his delicate head and flowing flaxen tail and mane, I was saluted with a friendly good morning by Mr. CALAHAN, then holding the important office of mayor of the little village . . .

Mr. CALAHAN having mounted, we set out, and after about an hour's hard work, occupied in crossing one of the thickest covers near the town, gained the broad and nearly level prairie beyond, across which to the west we could see varied swelling undulations, gradually fading into the faint outline of a distant spur, perhaps of the rocky chain of mountains that in this latitude lie between the water courses flowing toward the Gulf of Mexico, and the streams that empty into the Gulf of California: so far away indeed seemed these faint blue peaks that it required but a little stretch of the imagination to fancy the plains of California but just at the other side. I was enchanted with the scene, scarcely knowing whether the brilliant fore-ground of cacti and tropical plants, the soft indefinite distance, or the clear summer blue sky, was most beautiful. My companion observing my enthusiasm, warmed into praises of his adopted country he had, he said, fought hard for it, and exclaimed, it is a country worth fighting for; when my reply, of whatever nature it might have been, was prevented, and all ideas of blue mountains, vast rolling prairies, &c., were cut short by a jackass rabbit bounding from under our horses' feet; he was instantly followed by my worthy friend the mayor at full speed on his white pony, to my great annoyance, for otherwise he would have stopped in a hundred yards or so. Away they went, and as my friend's horse was a running nag, he doubtless expected to overtake the Hare, which had only gained about fifty yards start during our momentary surprise. The Hare, as I quickly observed, did not make much shorter leaps than the horse. I could see it at each bound appear like a jack-o'-lantern floating with the breeze over a swamp, but in less time than I have taken to write this, they had ran a mile, the Hare doubled and was a hundred yards in advance, but could not stop and look behind, for he had such a race that he knew well no time was to be lost in gaining some bed of cactus or chapparal. . . . We had not the good fortune to start another of these hares that day.

Some time afterwards while at Castroville, a little place of about a dozen huts and one house, this Hare was procured by a party of Indians and brought to J.W. AUDUBON, who writes: "I chanced to be visited by some of the Shawnee Indians who were in the neighbourhood on a hunting expedition. They were highly astonished and pleased with my drawings, which I exhibited to them while trying to explain what animals I wanted. I made a hasty sketch of a hare with immensely long ears, at which I pointed with an approving nod of the head, and then made another sketch smaller and with shorter ears, at which last I shook my head and made wry faces; the Indians laughed, and by their gutteral eugh, haugh, li, gave me to understand that they comprehended me; and in a day or two, I had a beautiful specimen of the Black-tailed Hare brought to me, but with the head shot off by a rifle ball. The Indians were quite disappointed that it did not answer my purpose, and smoothed down the fur on the body, which is the only part of the skin they generally preserve, and what they thought I wanted.

The specimen I drew from was shot by POWEL, one of Colonel HAYS' rangers, from whom I received many attentions and who acted most kindly while with me on one of my excursions from San Antonio. This Hare is so rare in those parts of Texas that I visited, that I can say little of its habits. It appears to be solitary, or nearly so, fond of high open prairie with clumps of trees, or rather bushes and thickets about them, trusting to its speed for safety and only taking cover from hawks and eagles. Near San Petruchio, as I was informed, this Hare is more abundant than in this vicinity, and two or three of them can occasionally be started in a morning's ride." . . .

WHITE-SIDED JACK RABBIT

Lepus callotis callotis Wagler

The "black-tailed hare" *(Lepus callotis)* of Audubon and Bachman's original *Quadrupeds* is now called the white-sided jack rabbit, although the scientific name of their time remains the same.

Unfortunately, the specimens that J. W. Audubon collected in southeastern Texas and sent to his father as study skins for the above painting were not of this species, *L. callotis* (which is Mexican and does not exist in Texas nor within 100 miles of that boundary). Instead, they were what is known today as black-tailed jack rabbits, *L. californicus texianus*. Thus the above painting and J. W. Audubon's account on the opposite page are *not* of their "black-tailed hare" (now called the white-sided jack rabbit). Bachman's description (not quoted here), however, is correct for the latter species. This is an example of the difficulties under which the *Quadrupeds* was put together over 100 years ago.

The white-sided jack rabbit is different from all other jack rabbits for two reasons. It is "white-sided" and has no black ear tips. The white on the underparts extends from the belly well up on its sides from shoulder to rump. When the animal is startled, the skin of either side is jerked upward by involuntary contraction of the muscles until the upper margin of white fur reaches almost to the backbone. In bright sunlight, this white flank flashes first on one side and then on the other as the rabbit zigzags away. Presumably this is a protective mechanism which helps to confuse the pursuer as to the actual course of the fleeing prey. Speed is the jack's only defense; in a fair race, it can outdistance practically any four-footed carnivore except a band of coyotes which are clever enough to chase in relay.

The habitat — mesquite-grassland with numerous dense thorn thickets — is a protection but it also helps skulkers like the bobcat to ambush and pounce upon the jack rabbit in its form. There the hare sits crouched throughout most of the day, coming out when shadows lengthen to feed on herbs and the buds, twigs and bark of shrubs and trees.

Offsetting losses to natural predators and man, white-sided jack rabbits rear several litters of young each year. The number and size of litters vary with food supply, being higher when adequate rainfall renews the succulent vegetation than during years of drought. Generally, the young are two to four, born in a shallow nest on the ground.

When adult, white-sided jack rabbits are 18 to 22 inches in total length, including the 2½- to 3-inch tail. Almost entirely Mexican in distribution, they live from extreme southwestern New Mexico to Oaxaca.

APLODONTIA LEPORINA, RICH.

THE SEWELLEL.

LEWIS and CLARK, who discovered this species during their journey across the Rocky Mountains to the Pacific, give us the following account of it:

"Sewellel is a name given by the natives to a small animal found in the timbered country on this coast. It is more abundant in the neighbourhood of the great falls and rapids of the Columbia than on the coast. The natives make great use of the skins of this animal in forming their robes, which they dress with the fur on, and attach them together with the sinews of the elk or deer. The skin when dressed is from fourteen to eighteen inches long, and from seven to nine in width: the tail is always separated from the skin by the natives when making their robes."

"This animal mounts a tree, and burrows in the ground, precisely like a squirrel. The ears are short, thin, and pointed, and covered with a fine short hair, of a uniform reddish-brown; the bottom or the base of the long hairs, which exceed the fur but little in length, as well as the fur itself, are of a dark colour next to the skin for two thirds of the length of this animal; the fur and hair are very fine, short, thickly set, and silky; the ends of the fur and tip of the hair are of a reddish-brown, and that colour predominates in the usual appearance of the animal. Captain LEWIS offered considerable rewards to the Indians, but was never able to procure one of these animals alive."

Mr. /James/ DOUGLAS /of the Hudson's Bay Company/ gave Dr. RICHARDSON an Indian blanket or robe, formed by sewing the skins of the Sewellel together. This robe contained twenty-seven skins, selected when the fur was in fine order. They are described by Dr. RICHARDSON as all having the long hairs so numerous as to hide the wool or down at their roots, and their points have a very high lustre. The doctor appears to think there were skins of two species of Sewellel in this robe. We did not hear of this animal ever being found to the east of the Rocky Mountains. Our figure was drawn from a fine specimen in London.

We are inclined to think from the form of the Sewellel that it is a great digger; but LEWIS' account of its mounting a tree seems to us to require some modification; the Maryland marmot /woodchuck/, to which it is somewhat allied in form and in the shape of its claws, when hard pressed will mount a tree for a little distance to avoid the pursuit of a dog, but is very awkward and soon descends; we presume the climbing properties of the Sewellel can scarcely be greater than those of the marmot.

From the number of mammae exhibited in the female, we conclude that it produces five or six young at a time, and from the nature of the animal, these are probably brought forth, like those of the marmots, in nests within their burrows.

MOUNTAIN BEAVER

Aplodontia rufa rufa (Rafinesque)

Audubon's name of "sewellel" had probably been given this animal by Lewis and Clark because they mistook the Chinook Indian term for fur robes (made from the animal's pelts) for the animal itself. Some fifteen English names have been applied including "whistler" and "boomer," although the animal neither whistles nor booms. Today, "mountain beaver" is most widely used although again it is not a beaver and only occasionally a mountaineer. Of all living rodents, this is the oldest. Its ancestors appeared on our continent at least 60 million years ago.

Mountain beavers tunnel in wet but well-drained slopes under moist, dense undergrowth, usually in coniferous forest at lower elevations but occasionally as high as 9,000 feet. Solitary, each animal digs its own extensive system of shallow tunnels 4 to 8 inches in diameter. Some exits are plugged, but most are indicated by fans of excavated earth. When rivulets pour through the runways, in and out of the numerous openings, the animals splash right along, their long vibrissae guiding them in darkness. Although somewhat more active by night, mountain beavers also forage in daylight, especially in autumn.

With many shrill noises and gratings of teeth, they cut and gather a great variety of leaves, stems and roots (even nettles and skunk cabbage) and canes of blackberry and devil's club. Climbing rather clumsily along branches up to 20 feet above ground, they clip twigs of Douglas fir, western hemlock and lodgepole pine. Much of this material is spread on logs to dry, and then stored underground. In winter, mountain beavers tunnel under the snow and occasionally emerge to feed on tree bark and evergreen foliage of salal and Oregon grape. Their cheek teeth continue to grow throughout their short lives.

Mountain beavers mate at two years of age during a late winter-early spring period of about six weeks. After a 30-day gestation, the two or three (occasionally four or even six) young are born in an underground nest, lined with dry vegetation, 18 inches in diameter. Blind for about 10 days, the young are weaned when two to three months old and disperse.

Occasionally these animals tunnel into dams and roadbeds or damage crops but usually they are too remote to affect man's interests.

Weighing two to four pounds, the mountain beaver is 12½ to 18¾ inches long, including the 1-inch tail which is hidden in the short, coarse fur. The species is limited to the humid Pacific Coast belt from southern British Columbia to San Francisco Bay and in the Sierra Nevada of California.

TAMIAS LYSTERI. RAY.

CHIPPING SQUIRREL. HACKEE &c.

The Chipping Squirrel . . . is found in most parts of the United States, and being beautifully marked in its colouring, is known to every body. From its lively and busy habits, one might consider it among the quadrupeds as occupying the place of the *wren* among the feathered tribes. Like the latter, the Ground Squirrel /chipmunk/, full of vivacity, plays with the utmost grace and agility among the broken rocks or uprooted stumps of trees about the farm or wood pasture; its clucking resembles the chip, chip, chip, of a young chicken, and although not musical, like the song of the little winter wren, excites agreeable thoughts as it comes on the air. We fancy we see one of these sprightly Chipping Squirrels as he runs before us with the speed of a bird, skimming along a log or fence, his chops distended by the nuts he has gathered in the woods; he makes no pause till he reaches the entrance of his subterranean retreat and store-house. Now he stands upright, and his chattering cry is heard, but at the first step we make towards him, he disappears. Stone after stone we remove from the aperture leading to his deep and circuitous burrow; but in vain is all our labour — with our hatchets we cut the tangled roots, and as we follow the animal, patiently digging into his innermost retreat, we hear his angry, querulous tones. We get within a few inches of him now, and can already see his large dark eyes; but at this moment out he rushes, and ere we can "grab" him, has passed us, and finds security in some other hiding place. . . .

. . . we /Bachman/ obtained in the State of New-York five or six young ones almost half grown. We removed them to Carolina, where they were kept during winter and spring. They were somewhat more gentle than those we had formerly possessed, occasionally took a filbert or a ground-nut from the fingers, but never became tame enough to be handled with safety, as they on more than one occasion were disposed to test the sharpness of their teeth on our hand.

The skin which covered the vertebrae of their tails was so brittle that nearly all of them soon had mutilated them. They appeared to have some aversion to playing in a wheel, which is so favourite an amusement of the true squirrels. During the whole winter they only left their nest to carry into it the rice, nuts, Indian corn, &c., placed in their cage as food. . . .

This species is to a certain extent gregarious in its habits. We had marked one of its burrows in autumn which we conceived well adapted to our purpose, which was to dig it out. It was in the woods on a sandy piece of ground and the earth was strewed with leaves to the depth of eight inches, which we believed would prevent the frost from penetrating to any considerable depth. We had the place opened in January, when the ground was covered with snow about five inches deep. The entrance of the burrow had been closed from within. We followed the course of the small winding gallery with considerable difficulty. The hole descended at first almost perpendicularly for about three feet. It then continued with one or two windings, rising a little nearer the surface until it had advanced about eight feet, when we came to a large nest made of oak leaves and dried grasses. Here lay, snugly covered, three Chipping Squirrels. . . .

Several species of hawks are successful in capturing the Chipping Squirrel. It furnishes also many a meal for the hungry fox, the wild cat, and the mink; but it possesses an enemy in the common weasel or ermine, (*mustela erminea*) more formidable than all the rest combined. This blood-thirsty little animal pursues it into its dwelling, and following it to the farthest extremity, strikes his teeth into its skull, and like a cruel savage of the wilderness, does not satiate his thirst for blood until he has destroyed every inhabitant of the burrow, old and young, although he seldom devours one fifth of the animals so wantonly killed. We once observed one pursue a Chipping Squirrel into its burrow. After an interval of ten minutes it reappeared, licking its mouth, and stroking its fur with its head by the aid of its long neck. We watched it as it pursued its way through a buckwheat field, in which many roots and stumps were yet remaining, evidently in quest of additional victims. On the following day we were impelled by curiosity to open the burrow we had seen it enter. There we found an old female ground squirrel and five young, half-grown, lying dead, with the marks of the weasel's teeth in their skulls.

EASTERN CHIPMUNK

Tamias striatus lysteri (Richardson)

This curious but wary neighbor flashes out of sight at any sudden movement. Its speed has been clocked at 11 feet per second. A loud trilled "chip!", a "chip-chip-chip" rattled off at about 130 notes a minute, or a slower, low-pitched "chuck" expresses light-heartedness or concern.

It can climb for seeds, or swim if necessary. The home range ordinarily covers one-half to three acres in deciduous forest borders and brushy, rocky areas.

Its home tunnel drops down to perhaps three feet and may extend 30 feet. Often storing more than it needs, the chipmunk fills its storerooms and even piles food under its nest in a chamber that may be 17 or more inches in diameter and 14 inches high.

The usually solitary chipmunk becomes torpid in severe weather but, during warm periods, it eats the stored food and may emerge briefly. Breeding begins in March and gestation takes 31 days. The one or two litters a year average four or five with extremes of one to eight young. A few females breed at three months; most wait until the following year. Populations fluctuate widely. The average chipmunk lives about two years.

The long, dexterous fingers of the chipmunk help to remove the shells of many tiny seeds and to fill the capacious cheek pockets. Each cheek may be stuffed until it is almost as big as the animal's head. The diet chiefly consists of buds, seeds, roots, berries and some animal matter including insects, snails, salamanders, young mice, birds' eggs and nestlings.

Eastern chipmunks are 8 to 12 inches long, including the 2½- to 4½-inch tail, and weigh 2 to 5 ounces. The species occurs from Cape Breton Island off Nova Scotia south to Virginia and westward to southern Manitoba, the Great Plains and southeastern Louisiana.

TAMIAS TOWNSENDII. BACHMAN.

TOWNSEND'S GROUND SQUIRREL.

No doubt the different species of this genus are as uniform in their habits as the true squirrels. They are usually found seated low, on stumps or rocks, at the roots of or near which they have their burrows. Their cheek-pouches enable them to carry to these hiding-places, nuts, grains, &c., to serve them for food in winter. Mr. TOWNSEND, who procured the specimens from which we have drawn up our description, observes, "This pretty little fellow, so much resembling our common *T. striatus, (Lysteri,)* /i.e., the eastern chipmunk/ is quite common; it lives in holes in the ground; running over your foot as you traverse the woods. It frequently perches itself upon a log or stump, and keeps up a continual clucking, which is usually answered by another at some distance, for a considerable time. Their note so much resembles that of the dusky grouse, *(Tetrao* /now *Dendragopus/ obscurus,)* that I have more than once been deceived by it."

TOWNSEND'S CHIPMUNK

Eutamias townsendii townsendii (Bachman)

The some 16 species of chipmunks in western America tend to be smaller than the one species in the east. Their dark stripes, from shoulder to rump, alternate with white instead of the eastern chipmunk's gray or brown. The Greek prefix *eu* (meaning "true" or "most typical") has been added to their genus name of *tamias* ("storer") since the time of Audubon.

Townsend's chipmunk is one of the largest of the western chipmunks. Compared to its sleek relatives, this species has a rather loose, shaggy coat. In temperament, it is much less nervous and active than other chipmunks and so gives an impression of fewer numbers. At any rate the species never appears to be abundant.

An adept climber, this animal seems to spend much time in trees, particularly in autumn when gathering seeds. It inhabits thickets and clearings in coniferous forests, from dripping-wet coastal valleys of the Olympic Peninsula to the cold, dry passes at 9,000 feet elevation through the Sierra Nevada. Being well protected from avian predators by its brushy habitat, its chief enemies are probably various species of weasel and the mink.

Its home range is about one and a half acres. The unbranched burrow is two inches in diameter and relatively short (about five feet). It terminates in a seven-inch diameter nest chamber which is filled with grass and moss. Three young have been found in such a nest. One Townsend's chipmunk, identified by an ear tag, lived at least seven years in the wild.

Total length of this chipmunk is 9 to 11 inches, including the 3½- to 5-inch tail. Adult males weigh about 3 ounces. The range of the species extends from central California to extreme southern British Columbia; the eastern limit is rarely more than 200 miles from the Pacific Coast.

* * * *

Although Audubon and Bachman recognized the scientific distinction, they frequently referred to chipmunks as "ground squirrels" and occasionally as "squirrels." Among the more obvious differences — chipmunks have striped cheeks, while ground squirrels and squirrels do not. Some of the ground squirrels and most chipmunks climb readily and go high into the trees for food. Not even the chipmunks, however, have the tree squirrels' agility to jump from limb to limb.

TAMIAS QUADRIVITTATUS, SAY.

FOUR-STRIPED GROUND SQUIRREL.

This pretty little species was discovered by Mr. SAY, during Colonel /Stephen H./ LONG's /explorer of the Rocky Mountain region/ expedition. Mr. SAY does not however appear to have seen much of its habits, and gives us but the following short account of them:—

"It does not seem to ascend trees by choice, but nestles in holes, and on the edges of rocks. We did not observe it to have cheek-pouches. Its nest is composed of a most extraordinary quantity of the burrs of the cactus, and their branches, and other portions of the large upright cactus, and small branches of pine trees and other vegetable productions, sufficient in some instances to fill an ordinary cart. What the object of so great and apparently so superfluous an assemblage of rubbish may be we are at a loss to conjecture; nor do we know what peculiarly dangerous enemy it may be intended to exclude by so much labour. Their principal food, at least at this season, is the seeds of the pine, which they readily extract from the cones."

We /John J. Audubon/ met with this species as we were descending the Upper Missouri river in 1843; we saw it first on a tree; afterwards we procured both old and young, among the sandy gulleys and clay cliffs on the sides of the ravines near one of our encampments.

These Ground Squirrels /chipmunks/ ascend trees when at hand and offering them either shelter or food, and seem to be quite as agile as the common species *Tamias Lysteri /T. striatus,* the eastern chipmunk/.

Dr. RICHARDSON, who found this Ground Squirrel during his long and laborious journeyings across our great continent, says of it — "It is an exceedingly active little animal, and very industrious in storing up provisions, being very generally observed with its pouches full of the seeds of leguminous plants, bents and grasses. It is most common in dry sandy spots, where there is much underwood, and is often seen in the summer, among the branches of willows and low bushes. It is a lively restless animal, troublesome to the hunter, and often provoking him to destroy it, by the angry chirruping noise that it makes on his approach, and which is a signal of alarm to the other inhabitants of the forest. During winter it resides in a burrow with several openings, made at the roots of a tree; and is even seen on the surface of the snow. At this season, when the snow disappears, many small collections of hazel-nut shells, from which the kernel has been extracted by a minute hole gnawed in the side, are to be seen on the ground near its holes."

Dr. RICHARDSON further informs us that on the banks of the Saskatchewan, the mouths of the burrows of this species are not protected with heaps of vegetable substances, as described by Mr. SAY, and we have no doubt the animal adapts its nest (as many of our birds do) to the locality and circumstances that surround it.

These animals bite severely when captured, and probably resemble *Tamias Lysteri /T. striatus,* the eastern chipmunk/ in their general habits and mode of living.

COLORADO CHIPMUNK

Eutamias quadrivittatus quadrivittatus (Say)

Like most of its relatives, the Colorado chipmunk is a sleek, brightly patterned, agile little rodent. It is almost as much at home in trees as on the ground. Rarely found away from broken rock, it prefers scattered woodland or sunny openings in the forest where windfalls or rock outcrops offer elevated perches and protective cover.

Colorado chipmunks are fairly social although not gregarious. They are strictly diurnal and seem to be always busy looking for food: a great variety of fruits, seeds, nuts, bulbs, tubers, tender shoots, flowers, mushrooms, cactus fruits, many insects and spiders. Surplus food is carried in their large cheek pouches and stored in the burrow which is usually longer and more elaborate than that of Townsend's chipmunk. Winter is spent below ground in a drowsy state. At intervals, the animal rouses to eat stored food and during mild periods it even comes out on the snow briefly.

The female may have two litters of about five young each annually. They are born hairless and remain in the protective custody of the mother for at least six weeks. The adult Colorado chipmunk is 8 to 9½ inches in length, including the 3½ - to 4½ -inch tail, and it weighs 1¾ to 2½ ounces.

* * * *

Except for Say's report, the accounts on the opposite page do not apply to the Colorado chipmunk. (Alas, even Say erred; the nest he described is clearly that of a wood rat!)

The Colorado chipmunk (called "four-striped" in the original *Quadrupeds*) does not exist on the upper Missouri where J. J. Audubon thought he saw it, nor farther north as reported by Richardson.

The animal they described must have been the least chipmunk *(Eutamias minimus)*. The mistake is understandable. The two species look so much alike that the subject in the painting above could be either animal, and they have similar habits and habitat. The least chipmunk occurs almost everywhere that the Colorado chipmunk is found — northern New Mexico, adjacent Arizona, eastern Utah and most of Colorado except the eastern plains. The least chipmunk, however, is much more widespread — west to California, north to Yukon Territory, and east to Ontario and western Quebec.

ARCTOMYS MONAX GMEL.

MARYLAND, MARMOT, WOODCHUCK, GROUNDHOG.

...We kept two of these animals alive for several weeks, feeding them on different grasses, potatoes, apples, and other fruits and vegetables. We found them to be very active at times, though fond of placing themselves in an erect posture, sitting on their rump, and letting their fore-legs and feet hang loosely down in the manner of our squirrels.

The old female, when approached, opened her mouth, showed her teeth, and made a rattling or clattering noise with the latter, evidently in anger. Neither the female nor the young appeared to become in any degree tame during the period we kept them. The former frequently emitted a shrill whistle-like noise, which is a note of alarm and anger, and may be heard when one is at a distance of about fifty yards from the animal. After we had made figures from those specimens, we examined their mouths, but did not find any pouches. . . .

. . . These Marmots sleep during the greater part of the day, stealing from their burrows early in the morning and towards evening. They climb trees or bushes awkwardly, and when they have found a comfortable situation in the sunshine, either on the branch of a tree, or on a bush, will remain there for hours. They clean their faces with the fore-feet, whilst sitting up on their hind-legs, like a squirrel, and frequently lick their fur in the manner of a cat, leaving the coat smoothed down by the tongue. The body of the Wood–Chuck is extremely flabby after being killed its flesh is, however, tolerably good, although a little strong, and is frequently purchased by the humbler classes of people, who cook it like a roasting pig. Occasionally, and especially in autumn, it is exceedingly fat.

This species becomes torpid about the time the leaves have fallen from the trees in the autumn and the frosty air gives notice of the approach of winter, and remains burrowed in the earth until the grass has sprung up and the genial warmth of spring invites it to come forth.

We once observed one sunning itself at the mouth of its burrow, on the 23d of October, in the State of New-York; and in the same State, saw one killed by a dog on the first of March, when the winter's snow was yet lying in patches on the ground. . . .

May we here be allowed to detain you, kind reader, for a few moments, whilst we reflect on this, one among thousands of instances of the all-wise dispensations of the Creator? Could any of the smaller species of quadrupeds, incapable, as many of them are, of migrating like the swift-winged inhabitants of the air to the sunny climes of the South, and equally unable to find any thing to subsist on among the dreary wastes of snow in the frost-bound lands of the North during winter, have a greater boon at the hands of Nature than this power of escaping the rigours and cold blasts of that season, and resting securely, in a sleep of insensibility, free from all cravings of hunger and all danger of perishing with cold, till the warm sun of spring once more calls them into life and activity? The Wood–Chuck and several other species of quadrupeds, whose organization in this respect differs so widely from general rules, may be said to have no winter in their year, but enjoy the delightful weather of spring, summer, and autumn, without caring for the approach of that season during which other animals often suffer from both cold and hunger. . . .

In the month of May, or sometimes in June, the female brings forth her young, generally four or five in number. We have however on two occasions, counted seven, and on another eight, young in a litter. In about three weeks, they may be seen playing around the mouth of the burrow, where sitting on their hind-feet in the manner of the Kangaroo, they closely watch every intruder, retreating hastily into the hole at the first notes of alarm sounded by the mother. . . .

When the young are a few months old they prepare for a separation, and dig a number of holes in the vicinity of their early domicile, some of which are only a few feet deep and are never occupied. . . .

WOODCHUCK

Marmota monax monax (Linnaeus)

The woodchuck is one animal that has profited by the coming of the white man. With the conversion of forests to fields and pastures, the species has increased and spread enormously.

Each woodchuck digs its own burrow (sometimes 45 feet long) and carries the earth out in its mouth. Several branches may lead to sleeping rooms — some with a nest, some without. The bedding of dry grass and leaves is changed whenever it gets damp. Toilet rooms that open off corridors are cleaned out from time to time. All need for housekeeping is suspended from November to February. The woodchuck plugs up its hibernating room so that it will not be disturbed by winter guests in the corridor, and goes to sleep. Its breathing becomes very slow, and the body temperature drops to 38° F. Eating nothing, the animal loses from one-third to one-half of its heavy autumn weight.

During mating season in March and April, the males seek out several females in succession. Gestation requires 21 or 22 days. The young at birth are blind, naked, about four inches long and weigh one to 1½ ounces. The eyes open at about four weeks but the young do not venture outside until they are two or three weeks older. By midsummer, they leave the home den to establish their individual ranges 75 to 100 feet in diameter. A few 'chucks are capable of mating when 11 or 12 months old but the majority must wait for another year. The life span is probably five or six years.

Fox, dog, black bear and man are the most deadly enemies, but ticks, fleas, warbles and intestinal worms may make the woodchuck and other marmots miserable.

Woodchucks are heavy eaters, consuming as much as 1½ pounds daily. They feed on grasses, other herbs, farmers' crops and fruits. Although they sometimes do considerable damage in gardens, hayfields and orchards, woodchucks provide shelters for other wildlife. They also benefit the fields by moving large quantities of subsoil (715 pounds was weighed at one burrow), mixing and aerating it.

The name may be a corruption of "woodchook," which is supposedly derived from the Cree *"otcheck."* Another common name, "groundhog," comes of course from the animal's squat form and waddling gait.

Woodchucks are 16 to 26 inches long, including the 4- to 7-inch tail, and weigh 5 to 10 pounds, to an exceptional 14 pounds. The range extends from Nova Scotia and central Alabama northwest to northern Idaho, British Columbia and east central Alaska. An isolated race occurs on the coast of Labrador.

ARCTOMYS FLAVIVENTER, BACH.
YELLOW BELLIED MARMOT.

The specimen from which our description of this Marmot was drawn up, was found by us among the skins sent to England by DRUMMOND and DOUGLAS /David Douglass, Scottish botanist/, procured by those gentlemen in our northwestern territories, and placed in the museum of the Zoological Society of London. Since we described it, the skin has been stuffed and set up.

Not a line was written in regard to its habits or the place where it was killed; its form and claws, however, indicate that like the other species of Marmot found in America, it is a burrowing animal, and feeds on seeds, roots, and grasses. We may also presume it has four or five young at a birth.

YELLOW-BELLIED MARMOT

Marmota flaviventris flaviventris (Audubon and Bachman)

The yellow-bellied (sometimes called yellow-footed) marmot, with its yellowish belly and brownish-yellow feet, is also known as a rockchuck, for it is seldom seen away from talus (rock) slopes. Even loose heaps of rocks which have resulted from clearing farm land have been known to harbor this marmot. A boulder which towers above the area is especially attractive as a lookout. This species seems to be more watchful than its two closest relatives, the woodchuck and the hoary marmot. (Or there are more dedicated sentinels!) Well-worn trails connect the lookouts with burrows and feeding places.

Since this species is much more sociable than the woodchuck, small colonies may gather on a single slope. Their chirps, barks and calls are lively. Each adult animal has its own den. Attempts by naturalists to excavate and map the tunnels generally have failed because of the exceedingly stony sites. Only the most determined bears and persevering badgers succeed in digging out the occupants.

Yellow-bellied marmots mate on emerging from hibernation in March. The young, which may number three to eight but average five, are born about a month later. They can leave the den briefly when they are about four weeks old

Coyotes and golden eagles are known to kill juvenile marmots. A marten which encroached on a colony in Colorado was chased off by one of the adults.

The diet is similar to that of the woodchuck, but obviously with a smaller proportion of grass and clover. While the upper limit of the range is over 10,000 feet, these marmots also live in low valleys. This sometimes brings them into conflict with agriculture, for their large size and stomach capacity make serious inroads on forage, grain and other crops. They have an especial liking for alfalfa which makes them a target for irate farmers, as well as sportsmen in the off-season for big game. Marmots that survive hunting by telescope-equipped rifles become shy and elusive, even to the extent of feeding by night. Occasionally the marmots which are shot are used for food.

Yellow-bellied marmots measure 19 to 28 inches in total length, including the tail which is 5¼ to 8¾ inches long. They weigh 4 to 12 and occasionally up to 17 pounds. The species occurs from northern New Mexico and the Black Hills of South Dakota west to the Sierra Nevada and to the Cascade mountain systems of California and southern British Columbia.

ARCTOMYS LEWISII, AUD. & BACH.

LEWIS' MARMOT.

From the form of this animal we may readily be convinced that it possesses the characteristics of the true Marmots. These animals are destitute of cheek-pouches; they burrow in the earth; live on grasses and grains; seldom climb trees, and when driven to them by a dog do not mount high, but cling to the bark, and descend as soon as the danger is over. As far as we have been able to ascertain, all the spermophiles or burrowing /ground/ squirrels are gregarious, and live in communities usually numbering several hundreds, and often thousands. On the contrary, the Marmots, although the young remain with the mother until autumn, are found to live solitarily, or at most in single pairs. It was not our good fortune ever to have met with this species in a living state, hence we regret that we are unable to offer anything in regard to its peculiar habits. . . .

We have no doubt this species, like the other Marmots, has an extensive geographical range, but coming from so distant a part of our country as Oregon, which has been so little explored by naturalists, we are obliged to make use of the vague term "shores of the Columbia river" as its habitat.

We have not felt at liberty to quote any authorities or add any synonymes for this species, inasmuch as we cannot find that any author has referred to it. . . .

YELLOW-BELLIED MARMOT

Marmota flaviventris [*flaviventris* (Audubon and Bachman)?]

The specimen which Audubon and Bachman named "Lewis' Marmot" is still preserved in the British Museum. From the description in the original *Quadrupeds* (vol. 3, p. 32, not quoted here) as well as the painting which J. W. Audubon made from the specimen, the animal appears to be a yellow-bellied marmot. Because it is probable that the museum skin was obtained from the region of the fur trading center at the mouth of the Columbia River rather than far up-river, I have tentatively placed "Lewis' Marmot" under the subspecies *flaviventris* — the typical yellow-bellied.

Audubon and Bachman were the first naturalists to recognize the distinctiveness of the yellow-bellied marmots. Their *Quadrupeds of North America* was the earliest scientific book to describe all three groups of North American marmots — the eastern woodchucks, the western yellow-bellied, and the hoary marmots.

ARCTOMYS PRUINOSUS, PENNANT.
HOARY MARMOT – THE WHISTLER.

This Marmot was described by /Thomas/ PENNANT /noted British zoologist/, from a skin preserved in the Leverian Museum, which was for many years the only specimen in any known collection. It appears to have afterwards become a question whether there was such an animal, or whether it might not prove to be the Maryland Marmot /woodchuck/, the original specimen, above mentioned, having been lost. . . . Dr. RICHARDSON quotes PENNANT's description, and states that he did not himself obtain a specimen; but "if correct" in considering it as the same as the Whistler of HARMON, "we may soon hope to know more of it, for the traders who annually cross the Rocky Mountains from Hudson's Bay to the Columbia and New Caledonia are well acquainted with it.". . . .The Doctor then gives the following account of it, and appears to have been quite correct in supposing it identical with the animal referred to by HARMON: "The Whistler inhabits the Rocky Mountains from latitude 45° to 62°, and probably farther both ways: it is not found in the lower parts of the country. It burrows in sandy soil, generally on the sides of grassy hills, and may be frequently seen cutting hay in the autumn, but whether for the purpose of laying it up for food, or merely for lining its burrows, I did not learn. While a party of them are thus occupied, they have a sentinel on the lookout upon an eminence, who gives the alarm on the approach of an enemy, by a shrill whistle, which may be heard at a great distance. The signal of alarm is repeated from one to another as far as their habitations extend. According to Mr. HARMON, they feed on roots and herbs, produce two young at a time, and sit upon their hind-feet when they give their young suck. They do not come abroad in the winter."

"The Indians take the Whistler in traps set at the mouths of their holes, consider their flesh as delicious food, and, by sewing a number of their skins together, make good blankets."

Our drawing of this Marmot was made from the specimen now in the museum of the Zoological Society of London, which is, we believe, the only one, even at this day, to be found in Europe, with the exception of a "hunter's skin" (i.e., one without skull, teeth, or legs), which was presented to the British Museum by Dr. RICHARDSON, and was probably the one he refers to in the extract we have given above from the Fauna Boreali Americana. The specimen in the Zoological Museum is well preserved, the animal, which was alive when presented to the Society by B. KING Esq., having died in the Menagerie (Zoological Gardens) in Regent's Park.

The living animal, when we observed it, seemed to be dull and sleepy. Its cage was strewed with grass and herbs, on which it had been feeding.

HOARY MARMOT

Marmota caligata okanagana (King)

The white tips of its black coat give a "hoary" look to this animal and account for its name. It is the largest and loudest of the three marmots (woodchuck, yellow-bellied and hoary). Its strident whistle of alarm can be heard perhaps a mile away.

Although adults live singly, hoary marmots are more social than their relatives to the extent that they den in larger communities. The clamor of their shrill alarms undoubtedly has considerable survival value against carnivorous mammals and the golden eagle. Because their dens are nearly always in broken rocky slopes and ledges, these marmots are relatively safe from powerful digging enemies such as grizzlies and black bears.

Hoary marmots emerge from hibernation early in spring, often while their above-timberline habitat is still covered by several feet of snow. The young, up to five in number, are born in April or May, or early June in the far north. Like all their relatives, these marmots are usually active above ground only in sunny, or at least warm, weather. They eat many kinds of herbaceous plants, after going some distance

from dens to forage. Their food is preferred green and fresh-cut. Only grass is gathered, dried and taken into the nest chamber for bedding; little is ever eaten. The animals go into hibernation in early fall usually before the advent of chilly weather. They have not eaten for about two weeks and their intestines are empty. Each one rolls itself into a ball, folds its forepaws over its face and goes to sleep for seven or eight months of the year.

The scientific name, "caligata," means "boots" and refers to the blackish-brown feet. Because of the handsome coloration, dense underfur and tough, durable skin, the pelts have been used frequently by Eskimos of northern Alaska for parkas, sleeping bags and robes. Great numbers of a very similar marmot in northern Europe and Asia are trapped for the commercial trade.

The hoary marmot is 25 to 32 inches long, including the 7- to 10-inch tail, and weighs 5 to 15 pounds or more. The range extends from western Montana, northern Idaho and southern Washington north through British Columbia and the Yukon to Alaska.

65

SPERMOPHILUS TOWNSENDII, BACH.

AMERICAN SOUSLIK.

In a letter addressed to us by the late Mr. TOWNSEND he states that this handsome Spermophile /ground squirrel/, in summer inhabits the prairies near the Wallawalla /Walla Walla River, southeastern Washington/, where it is rather common; it becomes excessively fat, and is eaten by the Indians. It disappears in August and re-appears early in spring in a very emaciated state. We have heard from other sources that it lives in small families, like the Spermophiles, generally burrowing in holes, and that it is seen either sitting on the side of them or with the head partially protruded, but disappears in its underground retreat, on the approach of man or any other animal.

/Editor's comment: Figure 2 shows an Oregon Meadow Mouse, now called creeping vole (Microtus oregoni oregoni *(Bachman))*. *It resembles a small grayish or brownish meadow vole (p. 163) and spends much of its life underground. Audubon and Bachman's Texan Meadow Mouse, Figure 3, is now a subspecies of the hispid cotton rat* (Sigmodon hispidus texianus *(Audubon and Bachman)) (p. 157)./*

Fig. 3

Fig. 2

TOWNSEND'S GROUND SQUIRREL

Citellus townsendii townsendii (Bachman)

The 25 species of American ground squirrels spend most of their lives underground. Generally they are earth-colored, but some are reddish or blackish; they may be striped, spotted, dappled, or of solid color. All have cheek pockets and many resemble chipmunks but, unlike the latter, they never have stripes on their cheeks. A few ground squirrels look much like tree squirrels; however, they den in the ground or among rocks, usually forage on the ground, and if startled among low branches, they dash to the ground instead of up the tree for safety. Ground squirrels generally hibernate; tree squirrels never do. Most of the western two-thirds of the continent from the Arctic Coast to central Mexico is occupied by ground squirrels. Like other rodents, they may carry tularemia, bubonic plague and Rocky Mountain spotted fever. To their credit, they aerate quantities of soil and destroy many weeds and harmful insects.

* * * *

Although Townsend's ground squirrels live close to each other, often in large colonies, they appear to be quite anti-social. Each adult has two burrows: a short one in the feeding area for emergencies, and a much more extensive resident tunnel 50 or more feet long and as much as six feet below ground. Although most of the colonies are on sagebrush flats, diggings often extend onto rocky, juniper-covered ridges.

The nest of fine grass or shredded bark is in a one-foot spherical cavity at the end of a spur tunnel. Here the seven to 10 (even as many as 15) young are born in March or April, after a gestation of about 24 days. While the mother is foraging, adult males of their own species may raid the nest and eat the small squirrels. In mid-June, when two-thirds grown, the young disperse.

Food consists of herbs (especially grass), grasshoppers, cicadas and many other insects. Occasionally the squirrels climb into low shrubs. Their voices are faint, insect-like trills and clear chirps similar to the notes of the horned lark.

Beginning as early as July, Townsend's ground squirrels spend nearly or all of the next eight months underground in aestivation and hibernation. During the years when spring foods dry up early, the animals may not put on enough fat to last through the winter. In these cases, the squirrels may stay up longer or come out after their summer sleep and forage before going into hibernation. Otherwise they sleep right through the eight months. When another spring arrives, the emerging males still have a little abdominal fat to get them through the mating season. The females are lean but rarely ever are actually "emaciated" as described by Townsend (opposite page).

Adults are 8 to 10½ inches long, including the 1¼- to 3-inch tail, and weigh 6 to 9 ounces. The species occurs from southern Washington and Idaho to southern Nevada and western Utah. Townsend's ground squirrel is *not* spotted; J. W. Audubon may have painted the closely related Washington ground squirrel.

SPERMOPHILUS RICHARDSONII, SABINE.

RICHARDSON'S SPERMOPHILE.

We possess no personal knowledge of this species, never having met with it in a living state. The specimens from which our figures and descriptions were made, were obtained by Mr. TOWNSEND, and we are indebted to the excellent work of RICHARDSON for the following account of its habits: "This animal inhabits sandy prairies, and is not found in thickly wooded parts. It is one of the animals known to the residents of the fur countries by the name of Ground-squirrel, and to Canadian voyagers by that of Siffleur. It has considerable resemblance to the squirrels, but is less active, and has less sprightliness and elegance in its attitudes.

"It can scarcely be said to live in villages, though there are sometimes three and four of its burrows on a sandy hummock or other favourable spot. The burrows generally fork or branch off near the surface, and descend obliquely downwards to a considerable depth; some few of them have more than one entrance. The earth scraped out, in forming them, is thrown up in a small mound at the mouth of the hole, and on it the animal seats itself on its hind-legs, to overlook the short grass, and reconnoitre before it ventures to make an excursion. In the spring, there are seldom more than two, and most frequently only one individual seen at a time at the mouth of a hole; and, although I have captured many of them at that season, by pouring water into their burrows, and compelling them to come out, I have never obtained more than one from the same hole, unless when a stranger has been chased into a burrow already occupied by another. There are many little well-worn pathways diverging from each burrow, and some of these roads are observed, in the spring, to lead directly to the neighbouring holes, being most probably formed by the males going in quest of a mate. They place no sentinels, and there appears to be no concert between the Tawny /Yellow-bellied/ Marmots residing in the neighbourhood, every individual looking out for himself. They never quit their holes in the winter; and I believe they pass the greater part of that season in a torpid state. The ground not being thawed when I was at Carlton House /Saskatchewan/, I had not an opportunity of ascertaining how their sleeping apartments were constructed, nor whether they lay up stores of food or not. About the end of the first week of April, or as soon as a considerable portion of the ground is bare of snow, they come forth, and when caught on their little excursions, their cheek-pouches generally contain the tender buds of the *Anemone Nuttalliana* /now *A. patens multifida,* the windflower or pasque flower/, which is very abundant, and the earliest plant on the plains. They are fat when they first appear, and their fur is in good condition; but the males immediately go in quest of the females, and in the course of a fortnight they become lean and the hair begins to fall off. They run pretty quick, but clumsily, and their tails at the same time move up and down with a jerking motion. They dive into their burrows on the approach of danger, but soon venture out again if they hear no noise, and may be easily shot with bow and arrow, or even knocked down with a stick, by any one who will take the trouble to lie quietly on the grass near their burrow for a few minutes. Their curiosity is so great that they are sure to come out to look around.

"As far as I could ascertain, they feed entirely on vegetable matter, eating in the spring the young buds and tender sprouts of herbaceous plants, and in the autumn the seeds of grasses and leguminous plants.

"Their cry when in danger, or when angry, so nearly resembles that of *Arctomys* /now *Citellus/ Parryi* /see following account/, that I am unable to express the difference in letters.

"Several species of falcon that frequent the plains of the Saskatchewan, prey much on these marmots /ground squirrels/; but their principal enemy is the American badger, which, by enlarging their burrows, pursues them to their inmost retreats. Considerable parties of Indians have also been known to subsist for a time on them when large game is scarce, and their flesh is palatable when they are fat."

RICHARDSON'S GROUND SQUIRREL

Citellus richardsonii richardsonii (Sabine)

Richardson's account (see opposite page) of the ground squirrel which bears his name is remarkable. During the hundred years that have passed since then, naturalists have added little more than details.

If alarmed while foraging, the Richardson's ground squirrel stands bolt upright on its "heels," with front feet hanging loosely on the chest, and gives a short, shrill whistle. This habit of standing up straight is responsible for the common name of "picket pin" — which, for the same reason, is shared with several other ground squirrels. When an enemy attempts to approach, the Richardson's squirrel rushes to the entrance of its burrow where it stops and lifts its head high for a last confirming look. Then it dives below with a spasmodic switching of the tail and usually a final upward flip. Another colloquial name, therefore, is "flickertail."

Richardson's ground squirrels live in colonies which may have up to 50 animals in one acre. They prefer sandy or gravelly ridges on open prairie, and flats near streams and lakes. Their burrows, which are sometimes as long as 50 feet, extend three to six feet below the surface of the ground. A single cavity from six to nine inches in diameter contains the grass nest.

The single annual litter numbers two to 11 young, the average being seven or eight. They are born after a gestation period of 28 to 32 days, and appear above ground as early as April 20, and as late as June 1. They remain active until September or even later, although most of their elders become dormant in July. Depending upon the snow melt, hibernation ends in February or March.

This species needs little drinking water. It eats many herbaceous plants, grasses being the favorite food. Seeds, insects and their larvae, including grasshoppers, are also taken. Damage to grain crops may be extensive along the margins of fields adjacent to this ground squirrel's colonies. As many as 240 grains of wheat have been taken from the cheek pouches of a single animal, and two quarts of wheat have been measured in the autumn storage bin of a burrow.

The range of the species — western Minnesota and southwestern Manitoba to central Alberta and south to Colorado (with an isolated race in northwestern Nevada) — covers a considerable portion of the continental granary. Richardson's ground squirrels measure 11 to 12¼ inches long, including the 2½- to 3½-inch tail, and weigh 11 to 18 ounces.

SPERMOPHILUS PARRYI, RICHARDSON.

PARRY'S MARMOT SQUIRREL.

The only account we have of this handsome spermophile is that given by its talented discoverer /John Richardson/, who says of it,—

"It is found generally in stony districts, but seems to delight chiefly in sandy hillocks amongst rocks, where burrows, inhabited by different individuals, may be often observed crowded together. One of the society is generally observed sitting erect on the summit of the hillocks, whilst the others are feeding in the neighbourhood. Upon the approach of danger, he gives the alarm, and they instantly betake themselves to their holes, remaining chattering, however, at the entrance until the advance of the enemy obliges them to retire to the bottom. When their retreat is cut off, they become much terrified, and seeking shelter in the first crevice that offers, they not unfrequently succeed only in hiding the head and fore-part of the body, whilst the projecting tail is, as usual with them when under the influence of terror, spread out flat on the rock. Their cry in this season of distress strongly resembles the loud alarm of the Hudson's Bay squirrel /red squirrel/, and is not very unlike the sound of a watchman's rattle. The Esquimaux name of this animal, *Seek–Seek,* is an attempt to express this sound. According to /Samuel/ HEARNE, they are easily tamed, and are very cleanly and playful in a domestic state. They never come abroad during the winter. Their food appears to be entirely vegetable; their pouches being generally observed to be filled, according to the season, with tender shoots of herbaceous plants, berries of the Alpine arbutus, and of other trailing shrubs, or the seeds of bents, grasses, and leguminous plants. They produce about seven young at a time."

Captain Ross /Arctic explorer, 1818–1851/ mentions that some of the dresses of the Esquimaux at Repulse Bay, were made of the skins of this species; these people also informed him that it was very abundant in that inhospitable region.

ARCTIC GROUND SQUIRREL

Citellus undulctus parryii (Richardson)

When cornered by an enemy, this ground squirrel stands up on its hind legs, hisses, squeaks, claws and bites. The Eskimos say that not even a fox can kill this little fighter if its back is protected.

The Arctic ground squirrel lives in the bleak northland which is green less than three months of the year. Yet the animal is abundant (at least in favorable years) over more than a million square miles.

In late April or May, although their world is still deep in snow and ice, the squirrels emerge from hibernation. Until green foliage appears in June, they live on such dead and frozen vegetation as they can dig out of the snow, and on food stored in their burrows.

During May, while searching for successive mates, the males lose up to one-quarter of their already diminished weight. The young are born after a gestation period of 25 days. Blind and naked, the six or seven (sometimes 10) can wriggle and make noises. Apparently due to the short time for foraging in the North, the young (1/3 to ½ ounce) are born larger and develop faster than many of their relatives. At the age of one month, they are nearly three-quarters as large as their mother. To attain nearly adult weight, the young are active until September or early October. Older Arctic squirrels, however, have already regained the weight

lost during the previous hibernation and mating seasons, and they become dormant in August.

Over much of their range, Arctic ground squirrels are restricted to low knolls and ridges where the permanent frost line is well below the surface. Every squirrel has an intricate burrow system that may contain up to 70 feet of tunnels, 3½ feet down, within a 14-foot square.

Each burrow has three to six or even more openings. Additional burrows within 300 yards of the home den are three to six feet long and serve as refuges in emergency. The animal may still forage as much as half a mile from the main den. A frightened squirrel always tries to run back to home territory instead of taking to the first available crevice.

Despite round-the-clock sunlight during June and July, the Arctic ground squirrel stays below ground from six P.M. to four A.M. Its "keek-keek!" changes to a harsh scolding chatter or a bird-like chirp, depending on the circumstances. With little fear of man, it is easily trapped. The animals are an important source of food and clothing for the Eskimos and Indians who "live off the land" within the squirrels' range from Hudson Bay west through the Yukon and Alaska to the Bering Sea.

An adult Arctic ground squirrel is 13 to 20 inches long, including the 3- to 6-inch tail, and weighs 1 to 2 pounds.

71

SPERMOPHILUS TRIDECEMLINEATUS, MITCHELL.

LEOPARD SPERMOPHILE.

. . . .The little animal which is here presented to you is /eminently beautiful/. In the distribution of the tints that compose its gaudy dress, in the regularity of its lines and spots, and in the soft blendings of its various shades of colour, we have evidence that even species whose habitations are under ground, may present to the eye as rich and beautiful a vesture as is found in the garb of a majority of the lively songsters of the woods.

In the warm days of spring the traveller on our Western prairies is often diverted from the contemplation of larger animals, to watch the movements of this lively little species. He withdraws his attention for a moment from the bellowing buffalo herd that is scampering over the prairies, to fix his eyes on a lively little creature of exquisite beauty seated on a diminutive mound at the mouth of its burrow, which seems by its chirrupings and scoldings to warn away the intruder on its peaceful domains. . . .

There is a great similarity in the habits of the various spermophili that compose the interesting group to which the present species belongs.

They live principally on the open prairies, make their burrows in the earth, and feed on roots and seeds of various kinds, which they carry in their pouches to their dark retreats under ground.

The holes of this species, according to RICHARDSON, run nearly perpendicularly, and are so straight, that they will admit a stick to be inserted to the depth of four or five feet. He supposes that owing to the depth of their burrows, which the sun does not penetrate very early in spring, they do not make their appearance as early as some others, especially *S. Richardsonii* /Richardson's ground squirrel/.

As soon as they feel the warmth of spring they come forth and go in quest of their mates; at this period they seem fearless of danger, and are easily captured by the beasts and birds of prey that frequent the plains. The males are said to be very pugnacious at this season.

This is believed to be the most active and lively of all our known species of marmot-squirrels /ground squirrels/; we recently observed one in New York that played in a wheel in the manner of the squirrel. We saw in Charleston a pair in a cage, that were brought from Missouri by an officer of the army. . . . They would come to the bars of the cage and take a nut from the hand, but would then make a hasty retreat to a little box in the corner of their domicile. On our placing a handful of filberts in front of the cage, they at first came out and carried off one by one to their store-house; but after we had retired so as not to be observed, they filled their pouches by the aid of their paws, and seemed to prefer this mode of transporting their provisions. As we were desirous of taking measurements and descriptions, we endeavoured to hold one in the hand by the aid of a glove, but it struggled so lustily and used its teeth so savagely that we were compelled to let it go.

This species frequently takes up its residence near the fields and gardens of the settlers; and in the neighbourhood of Fort Union /eastern Montana/ and other places, was represented as particularly destructive to the gardens.

We /J. J. Audubon/ found the Leopard–Spermophile quite abundant near Fort Union, on the Upper Missouri. Their burrows were made in a sandy gravelly soil; they were never deep or inclined downwards, but ran horizontally within about a foot of the surface of the earth. . . .

RICHARDSON states that "the males fight when they meet, and in their contests their tails are often mutilated." All the specimens, however, that we obtained, were perfect and in good order.

The Leopard–Spermophile has two more teats than are found in the majority of the species of this genus, and hence it may be expected to produce an additional number of young. RICHARDSON informs us that ten young were taken from a female killed at Carlton House /Saskatchewan/. This was on the 17th May, and we from hence presume that they produce their young soon after this period.

THIRTEEN-LINED GROUND SQUIRREL

Citellus tridecemlineatus tridecemlineatus (Mitchill)

The dramatic name "leopard" of Audubon's time applied to color and pattern. When this little ground squirrel is frightened and cannot reach its burrow, it "freezes" flat on the ground so that the tawny body with spots and stripes blends completely with the earth and grass patterns.

Often called the "striped gopher," this ground squirrel goes into deeper hibernation than most mammals. Beginning in July for some adults, and as late as November for the juveniles, the animals roll up into balls, become stiff, and their body temperature drops to only one or two degrees above that of the surrounding air. Their respiration (100 to 200 breaths a minute when active) is reduced to one breath in five minutes.

By the time they emerge between mid-March and mid-April, the animals have lost one-third to one-half of their autumn weight. Twenty-seven or 28 days after a very brief courtship-mating procedure, the litter is born. The eyes of the four to 14 young (average eight to 10) open at 25 days and they begin to take solid food. The mother will still risk her life trying to drive off hungry snakes and road runners. Ten days after the young first appear above ground, they start to disperse. The larger litters break up first and males go farther than females in the search for new homes. Even

when settled down, the males will continue to roam over 12 acres; females are satisfied with three.

Perhaps smarter than many of its relatives, the 13-lined ground squirrel pushes the dirt out of its tunnel on top of its head, or with paws, and sprinkles it around the opening. No tell-tale mounds call attention to the entrances. The animal builds short tunnels only three to six feet long in forage areas for emergency refuges. The long home tunnel drops almost perpendicularly (rarely to four feet) and then turns horizontally for about 20 feet with numerous side passages. When the den is not drained by a long enough downward shaft, successive litters of young are drowned. The entrance to the den is plugged at night and during their hibernation.

Fifty percent or more of this ground squirrel's diet is protein — insects, birds' eggs, nestlings and occasional mice. Living on the border of dry, open fields where vegetation is short and sparse, the animal seldom climbs even a low tree.

A relatively small ground squirrel, the 13-lined species is 7 to 12 inches long, including the 2½- to 5-inch tail, and weighs 5½ to 9 ounces. The range extends from central Ohio and central Alberta south to the Gulf coast of Texas and eastern Arizona.

SPERMOPHILUS SPILOSOMA, BENNET.

CALIFORNIAN MARMOT SQUIRREL.

This Mexican Spermophile /ground squirrel/ has all the activity and sprightliness of the squirrel family, and in its movements greatly reminds one of the little ground-squirrel (*Tamias Lysteri*) /i.e. eastern chipmunk, *T. striatus*/ of the middle and northern States. It feeds standing on its hind feet and holding its food in the fore paws like a common squirrel, and is remarkable for the flexibility of its back and neck, which it twists sideways with a cunning expression of face while observing the looker on. When caught alive this pretty species makes a pet of no common attractions, having beautiful eyes and being very handsomely marked, while its disposition soon becomes affectionate, and it retains its gay and frolicsome habits. It will eat corn and various kinds of seeds, and is fond of bits of potatoe, apple, or any kind of fruit, as well as bread, pastry, cakes, &c.: grasses and clover it will also eat readily, and in fact it takes any kind of vegetable food. Even in the hottest summer weather this animal is fond of making a nest of tow and bits of carpet, and will sleep covered up by these warm materials as comfortably as if the temperature was at freezing point outside instead of 85°.

For some time we have had a fine living animal of this species in a cage, and he has been a source of great amusement to the little folks, who are fond of feeding him and pleased to see his antics. When threatened he shows fight, and approaches the bars of his cage gritting or chattering with his teeth like a little fury, and sometimes uttering a sharp squeak of defiance; but when offered any good thing to eat he at once resumes his usual playful manner, and will take it from the hand of any one. In eating corn this little animal picks out the soft part and leaves the shell and more compact portion of the grain untouched.

At times he will coil himself up, lying on one side, almost entirely concealed by the tow and shredded carpet; if then disturbed, he looks up out of one eye without changing his position, and will sometimes almost bear to be poked with a stick before moving. Like the human race he occasionally shows symptoms of laziness or fatigue, by yawning and stretching. When first placed in his cage he manifested some desire to get out, and attempted to gnaw the wires: he would now and then turn himself upside down, and with his fore paws holding on to the wires above his head bite vigorously at the horizontal wires for half a minute at a time, before changing this apparently uncomfortable position. This Spermophile is not in the habit of eating a very great deal at a time, but seems to prefer feeding at intervals, even when plenty of food lies within his reach, retiring to his snug nest and sleeping for a while after eating a sufficient portion. When thus sleeping we sometimes found him lying on his back, with his fore paws almost joined, held close by his nose, while his hind legs were slightly turned to one side so as to give his body the appearance of complete relaxation. . . .

MEXICAN GROUND SQUIRREL

Citellus mexicanus mexicanus (Erxleben)

This was one of the first American ground squirrels to be recognized as a species; it was named and described in 1777 by the German zoologist, Johann Erxleben.

The Mexican ground squirrel lives in the hot, sandy, southwestern desert among mesquite, acacia, creosote bush and other warmth-loving shrubs. It makes its burrow at the base of a bush or in a clump of cactus, digging straight down for a foot and then proceeding at an angle. The species does not hibernate, at least over the warmer portions of the range, but stays underground for considerable periods during the colder weather. At such times it keeps its burrow entrance plugged with earth.

The animal is shy and silent but if alarmed it may give a short, trilling whistle which descends slightly in pitch.

Mexican ground squirrels eat vegetable matter and insects in about the same proportion. The food is varied but mesquite and acacia beans are favorites. One squirrel of this species was caught in the act of attacking a young cottontail about one-fourth its size. The squirrel had cut off a forefoot and inflicted wounds in the neck and shoulder. Presumably it would have killed the rabbit had it not been shot.

Mexican ground squirrels sometimes do considerable damage near the margins of small farms by digging up planted and germinating seeds and by eating ripening grain. In at least partial compensation, they destroy harmful insects.

Adults measure 11 to 15 inches in total length, including the tail which is 4½ to 6¾ inches. The species occurs in western Texas and southwestern New Mexico, thence to southern Tamaulipas and central Coahuila; also across central Mexico from Jalisco east to Puebla. (Continued)

SPERMOPHILUS MEXICANUS LICHT.

MEXICAN MARMOT - SQUIRREL.

In our first edition (folio plates), we gave figures of the *young* of this species as *S. spilo-soma* of BENNETT, but having since ascertained that his specimen was only the young of *S. Mexicanus*, a species which had been previouly published, we have not set down *S. spilosoma* as a synonyme of the latter, and have placed the figures of both old and young on the same plate.

MEXICAN GROUND SQUIRREL

Citellus mexicanus mexicanus (Erxleben)

John Woodhouse Audubon inadvertantly made two paintings of this species for the imperial folio edition of *The Viviparous Quadrupeds of North America.* The first (Plate 109), showed two small ground squirrels which were declared to be "Californian Marmot-Squirrels." The second painting (Plate 124) contained but a single animal which was considerably larger in size, and which was labeled "Mexican Marmot-Squirrel."

After the large folios had been issued, Bachman (presumably) learned that the so-called "Californian Marmot-Squirrels" were actually young animals about half grown, and while they were within the size range of *adult* Californian squirrels, they were not as heavily spotted. It was then determined that they too were "Mexican Marmot-Squirrels."

Since all three animals belonged to the same species, Plate 124 (above) was dropped and the three figures were brought together in a single plate (original 109) for the smaller

published (octavo) edition of *The Qudarupeds,* and "correctly" titled Mexican Marmot-Squirrels *(Spermophilus mexicanus* Lichtenstein).

Alas, one more error had to be corrected, Lichtenstein was NOT the discoverer, as his description in a serial work, published between 1827 to 1834, had indicated. Later research eventually proved that the account of Lichtenstein had been antedated many years by another German scientist, Johann Erxleben, who in 1777 had described the skin of a spotted squirrel from Mexico as *"Sciurus mexicanus."*

When the great group of sciurid rodents was broken up early in the 20th century, the name of Erxleben as discoverer was attached to the new scientific name of the Mexican ground squirrel *(Citellus mexicanus).*

The evolution of the scientific name of this animal is an excellent example of the trials and tribulations of scientists in nomenclature!

SPERMOPHILUS FRANKLINII, SABINE.

FRANKLINS MARMOT SQUIRREL.

We possess but little information of the habits of several of the Spermophili /ground squirrels/ of America. None of the species are found in the settled portions of our country, where opportunities are afforded the naturalist to observe and note down their habits; every one has undoubtedly an interesting history attached to its life, which yet remains to be collected and written. RICHARDSON observes of this species, that it lives in burrows in the sandy soil amongst the little thickets of brushwood that skirt the plains. That it is about three weeks later in its appearance in the spring than the *Arctomys Richardsonii /Citellus richardsonii,* Richardson's ground squirrel/, probably from the snow lying longer on the shady places it inhabits, than on the open plains frequented by the latter. It runs on the ground with considerable rapidity, but has not been seen to ascend trees. It has a louder and harsher voice than the *A. Richardsonii,* more resembling that of *Sciurus Hudsonius /Tamiasciurus hudsonicus,* red squirrel/ when terrified. Its food consists principally of the seeds of liguminous plants, which it can procure in considerable quantity as soon as the snow melts and exposes the crop of the preceding year. Mr. TOWNSEND, who observed it in Oregon, does not refer particularly to any habit differing from the above.

FRANKLIN'S GROUND SQUIRREL

Citellus franklinii (Sabine)

When not alarmed, the whistle of Franklin's ground squirrel is exceptionally clear and musical. The males do most of the vocalizing; the female's call is less frequent, but equally clear. This characteristic leads to another common name: "whistling ground squirrel." Occasionally it is called the "gray gopher."

This animal probably spends more than 90 percent of its life underground. Gregarious, five to 15 of these squirrels may use three to 10 widely spaced burrows in small colonies. The tunnel system has several chambers opening off each main corridor for defecating rooms.

Hibernation starts in October, sometimes with several animals in one den, and ends in April. Males emerge a week ahead. As soon as the females appear, mating begins and lasts through much of May. They are chased by the males over the ground, under bushes, up trees, and down into dens. Rivalry causes a great deal of fighting among the males. They bite each other's rump until almost every male has a bare spot or a cut on its back near the base of its tail

The annual litter of four to 11 (usually seven) arrives in May or June. Weaned when about five weeks old, they are on their own a little later. Extremely curious, like many of its relatives, Franklin's ground squirrels will dash down a hole when startled but pop back up immediately or appear in another entrance to see what is going on. They need drinking water more than some other ground squirrels, and can swim if necessary.

About one-third of their diet is animal life — mice, young hares, rabbits, toads, frogs, insects and sometimes birds' eggs and nestlings. Populations of this ground squirrel fluctuate violently with peaks of abundance every four to six years. At such times serious damage may be done to gardens, green crops, poultry and possibly nesting waterfowl. As with most rodents, extensive killing by man may sometimes only result in increased production by surviving females. It is better, if possible, to depend on predators and the inevitable epidemic of disease to reduce abnormal numbers.

Franklin's ground squirrels measure 14 to 16½ inches, including the 4½- to 6¼-inch tail. The normal weight is 14 to 16 ounces, which may jump to 24 ounces just before hibernation. These ground squirrels live mostly in aspen groves and among scattered trees on the borders of streams and marshes — never in forests or on open prairies where cover is scarce or less than a foot high. The species' range is from western Indiana and Kansas northwest to Saskatchewan. It does not extend to Oregon. (See opposite page.)

SPERMOPHILUS MACROURUS, BENNETT.
LARGE-TAILED SPERMOPHILE.

/The rock squirrel/ is an active and sprightly fellow, readily ascending trees on occasion, and feeding on nuts as well as seeds, roots, and grasses.

This species is in some districts rather numerous, and when in the rainy season some of the low grounds are submerged, takes to the trees, and sometimes curious fights occur between it and the wood-peckers. Five or six of the latter will on observing the Spermophile, unite against him, and cutting about in the air, peck at him as they dart swiftly around the persecuted animal, which is lucky if a hollow into which he can retreat be near, and frequently indeed the wood-peckers' holes are entered by him, but the angry and noisy birds still keep up their cries and fly with fury at the hole, and although they can no longer peck the animal they keep him in a state of siege for a considerable time.

The origin of this animosity may be the fact of the Spermophile (as well as many kinds of squirrels) sometimes turning out the wood-peckers from their nests, an injury which unites them against the wrong-doer. By what process the birds are influenced to attack when the animal is not in their nests, nor even on a tree upon which they have built (or dug, we should say), we know not, but that the birds comprehend that union is strength is quite evident, and the Spermophile knows it too, for he always instantly tries to escape and conceal himself as soon as the vociferous cries of the first bird that observes him are heard, and before its neighbours called thereby to the fight can reach the spot.

We have not been able to ascertain how many young this Spermophile produces at a birth, nor at what season they are brought forth. It is seen on the plains and in localities where no trees grow, in which places it burrows or runs into holes in the rocks. . . .

ROCK SQUIRREL

Citellus variegatus variegatus (Erxleben)

One of the largest of the ground squirrels, this species derives its common name from its affinity for rock. Almost any rock will do; the animal has even been found on warm lava. An individual may venture into a peach orchard for the fruit or onto an open field for grain, but invariably the loot is carried off in the cheek pouches and back to the safety of the den in a cliff crevice or talus slope.

The typical habitat is the widely spaced oak-juniper woodland in a canyon of the southwestern mountains. It extends upward through the pine forest and occasionally to or even above timberline.

The rock squirrel's call is a loud, sometimes quavering whistle. If alarmed, a short, sharp blast is followed by a brief, lower-pitched trill as the animal ducks into the den or a temporary hiding place among the rocks. It has not been learned whether the species aestivates or hibernates, but at higher elevations where snow accumulates, it is likely that the squirrels sleep away the coldest months. In warmer canyon bottoms, individuals have been seen abroad at various times throughout the winter. Little is known of the reproductive habits except that litters contain five to seven young and some females may rear two broods annually.

The diet is predominantly vegetable matter — in spring, roots and tubers, blossoms of woody shrubs and cactus, and cactus pulp; later, berries and seeds of a great variety of plants from juniper and currant to cacti of many kinds. Piñon nuts, walnuts and acorns are staples and these are frequently gathered in the treetops. In fall, much of this food is stored, not only in the burrow but in pockets here and there under rocks and logs and in rock slides. Grasshoppers, crickets and other insects as well as birds' eggs and nestlings are eaten but these make up a relatively small part of the fare as compared with that of most other ground squirrels. Locally, the rock squirrel makes enemies by raiding gardens and orchards.

Adults are 13 to 21 inches long, including the 7- to 10½-inch tail. Males weigh 20 to 26 ounces, females average about 2 ounces more. The range extends from central Nevada, northern Utah and northern Colorado to Puebla in south central Mexico. Like the Mexican ground squirrel, this species was first identified in 1777 by the German zoologist, Johann Erxleben.

SPERMOPHILUS DOUGLASSII. RICHARDSON.

DOUGLASSE'S SPERMOPHILE.

We regret to state, that with the habits of this species we are wholly unacquainted. Mr. TOWNSEND, who kindly loaned us four specimens, from which we made our drawing and prepared our description, did not furnish us with any account of them.

Of *Spermophilus /Citellus/ Beecheyi,* which we have supposed might be found identical with this species, Dr. RICHARDSON states that, "Mr. COLLIE, surgeon of his majesty's ship Blossom, informs me that this kind of Spermophile burrows in great numbers in the sandy declivities and dry plains in the neighbourhood of San Francisco and Monterey, in California, close to the houses. They frequently stand upon their hind-legs when looking round about them. In running they carry the tail generally straight out, but when passing over any little inequality, it is raised as if to prevent its being soiled. In rainy weather, and when the fields are wet and dirty, they come but little above ground. They take the alarm when any one passes within twenty or thirty yards of them, and run off at full speed till they can reach the mouth of their hole, where they stop a little and then enter it; they soon come out again, but with caution, and if not molested, will proceed to their usual occupation of playing or feeding. *Artemesias /sages/* and other vegetable matters were found in their stomachs."

CALIFORNIA GROUND SQUIRREL

Citellus beecheyi douglasii (Richardson)

These small animals do great damage to grain, forage, fruit and nut crops. Large sums of money have been spent in California and Oregon trying to destroy them.

Natural predators — coyote, gray fox, badger, rattlesnake and red-tailed hawk — eliminate many young when they first appear above ground in May and June. Disease and weather (extremes of temperature and humidity) also help to check the population. But the California ground squirrel is hardy. Although parasitized by tapeworms, protozoans, roundworms, ticks, fleas and mites, it not only survives but increases. It is accused, along with many other wild creatures, of carrying bubonic plague (on its fleas) to humans. Actually this is very rare.

The California ground squirrel lives in dense colonies and its burrows have been occupied by successive tenants for years. Although individually anti-social, several animals may at times occupy the same burrow which is three to six inches in diameter and five to 200 feet long. In these cases, each squirrel may have its own entrance. Out of force of habit, when scared, it will dash for that opening rather than stop in the first hole that it sees. (Of course it might waste time in being ejected by an inhospitable owner.)

Mating occurs from the last of January to mid-March. A pair may remain together as long as two weeks. The squirrel's nest, in an oval chamber eight to 10 inches across, is made of finely shredded grass and rootlets. Here the annual litter is born between late February and mid-April, or as late as July at high altitudes, after a gestation period of 25 to 30 days. By fall the young appear to be as large as their mother.

Ground squirrels fold back their ears in rage. They wrinkle their noses to sniff each other, their watching-posts, human footprints and anything else that needs investigating. Varied emotions are expressed by faint, low chirps, an explosive growl, a very loud, high-pitched short bark or by the chattering of teeth.

Most California ground squirrels both aestivate and hibernate; a few are active the year round. They put on fat before aestivating but depend more on storing food before hibernating. (Sometimes they bring their cached supplies above ground and eat while sunning themselves.) Adults become dormant before the juveniles; males both retire into and come out of hibernation earlier.

Adults of this species are 16 to 20 inches long, including the 5½- to 8-inch tail, and weigh 1 to 2 pounds, or occasionally more. Except for a major extension into western Nevada, the range is limited to the Pacific Slope between southern Washington and northern Baja California.

SPERMOPHILUS ANNULATUS, AUD. & BACH.

ANNULATED MARMOT SQUIRREL.

We possess no knowledge of the habits of this species, but presume from its form, that it possesses the burrowing propensities of the genus. All the *Spermophili* /ground squirrels/ avoid thickly wooded countries, and are either found in rocky localities, or burrowing in the prairies.

The specimen we have. . . . was obtained on the Western Prairies, we believe on the east of the Mississippi river; the locality was not particularly stated. It was politely presented to us by Professor SPENCER F. BAIRD, of Carlisle, Pennsylvania, a young Naturalist of eminent attainments.

RING-TAILED GROUND SQUIRREL

Citellus annulatus annulatus (Audubon and Bachman)

This ground squirrel was named by Audubon and Bachman in 1842, on the basis of a specimen which was purchased from a dealer by a 15-year-old amateur naturalist, Spencer F. Baird of Carlisle, Pennsylvania. Baird sent it to Audubon as a token of his admiration. Struck by the contrasting blackish bands on the pink, buff and black tail, and regarding the animal as a link between the marmots and the tree squirrels, they gave it the all-inclusive name of "annulated marmot squirrel."

Without any indication of their specimen's geographic origin, they assumed it to have come from "the western prairies." Fifteen years later Baird, who was now Secretary of the Smithsonian Institution and one of the world's foremost zoologists, had come to the conclusion that his specimen was an African tree squirrel. It was not until 1877 that the question was settled when a second specimen, undoubtedly a ground squirrel, was taken in western Mexico.

The ring-tailed ground squirrel is found only in the tropics. It lives in colonies on sandy flats and rocky hillsides. It digs its burrow among rocks, in a clump of cactus, at the base of a mesquite or acacia, or under a mass of fallen palm frends.

Although gregarious, it tends to be a furtive, silent animal. Creeping noiselessly through undergrowth, it may freeze in a crouch when an intruder appears. Its very dark, spotted coat will probably not be detected among the shadows. At other times, however, the squirrel's curiosity may overcome fear and it will approach, stretch upright, bracing itself with hind legs and tail, and take a long look.

When not trying to conceal itself, the ring-tailed squirrel is sprightly and more agile than most of its relatives. It climbs readily and often into low trees but, if surprised while seed-gathering, it rushes lightly down the far side of the trunk to hide in its burrow or under dense brush. When it gives an alarm, the call is a series of short, shrill chirps, quickly repeated. It eats cactus "leaves" and a variety of fruits and nuts, including mesquite beans, cactus seeds, wild figs, and the nuts of the oil palm and moho.

Ring-tailed ground squirrels are 15½ to 19 inches long, including the 7½- to 9½-inch tail. They are restricted to an area not more than 35 miles wide and extending 200 miles along the Pacific Coast of Mexico from the state of Nayarit to western Guerrero.

SPERMOPHILUS LATERALIS, SAY

SAY'S MARMOT SQUIRREL.

This beautiful inhabitant of the wooded valleys of the Rocky Mountains was not seen by us /John J. Audubon/ on our journey up the Missouri river, although it is probably found within the district of country we traversed. We are therefore unable to give any personal information in regard to its habits, and we find but little in the works of others.

Mr. DRUMMOND obtained several specimens on the Rocky Mountains as far north as latitude 57°, and observed that it burrowed in the ground.

Mr. SAY did not give any account of its habits, and probably the specimen he described was brought into camp by the hunters attached to the expedition, without his ever having seen the animal alive.

All the Spermophiles /ground squirrels/ that we have seen are lively, brisk, and playful, resembling the common ground-squirrels *(Tamias Lysteri)* /*T. striatus*, the eastern chipmunk/ in their general habits.

The Mexican women make pets of some of the species inhabiting that country, and they become very fond of their mistresses, running over their shoulders, and sometimes nestling in their bosoms, or the pockets of their gowns.

GOLDEN-MANTLED GROUND SQUIRREL

Citellus lateralis lateralis (Say)

The reddish-brown ("golden") mantle and striped coat are kept clean and glossy by rolling in the dust and combing with teeth and paws. Surprisingly, this animal is said to be less clean and tidy in its burrow sanitation.

Although generally silent, golden-mantled squirrels occasionally give a bird-like, high-pitched chirp which may be followed by a musical trill. When fighting, they have a throaty growl and, if frightened, they squeal.

The ground squirrel digs a shallow burrow, usually only six to 12 inches below ground, but up to 100 feet long. Occupied by one adult, it is relatively simple with two or three entrances on separate spurs, several turn-arounds, nest chambers and food storage pockets. Hibernation may last up to seven months in the north and at high altitudes, but there are several interruptions, especially near the beginning and end. Once out in the world again, they sun themselves for hours at a time.

Litters averaging five, with extremes of two to eight, arrive in June and July or even into August. The young venture from the den when they are about three weeks old and one-third grown. If alarmed, the mother will push them down the burrow or into a crevice with her forepaws. When they go into hibernation about a month later than the adults, they appear to be full size. They, and especially their elders, get very fat under the skin and around the kidneys before becoming dormant.

If it were not for their burrows, these squirrels would be popular on our front lawns. In the Colorado mountains, dandelions make up more than 80 percent of their summer diet! This is also true of the least chipmunk which shares the same habitat. There is no competition, for the chipmunk eats the dandelion flowers and seeds, while the ground squirrel prefers the stems. When not gobbling dandelions, the ground squirrel eats numerous insects, a great assortment of seeds of trees, shrubs, vines and herbs, and any mushrooms that happen to be around.

Adults total 9 to 12½ inches in length, of which the tail constitutes 2½ to 4½ inches, and weigh 6 to 10 ounces. They are found among rocks and fallen logs in open forests, from foothills at 5,000 feet or less up to timberline at 13,000 feet. The range of the species extends from British Columbia to New Mexico and west to southwestern Oregon.

SPERMOPHILUS LUDOVICIANUS, ORD.

PRAIRIE DOG – PRAIRIE MARMOT SQUIRREL.

The general impression of those persons who have never seen the "Prairie Dog" called by the French Canadians *"petit chien,"* would be far from correct in respect to this little animal, should they incline to consider it as a small "dog." It was probably only owing to the sort of yelp, chip, chip, chip, uttered by these marmots, that they were called Prairie *Dogs,* for they do not resemble the genus *Canis* much more than does a common gray squirrel!

This noisy *spermophile,* or marmot, is found in numbers, sometimes hundreds of families together, living in burrows on the prairies; and their galleries are so extensive as to render riding among them quite unsafe in many places. Their habitations are generally called "dog-towns," or villages, by the Indians and trappers, and are described as being intersected by streets (pathways) for their accommodation, and a degree of neatness and cleanliness is preserved. These villages, or communities, are, however, sometimes infested with rattle-snakes and other reptiles, which feed upon the marmots. The burrowing owl, *(Surnia /now Speot-yto/ cunicularia,)* is also found among them, and probably devours a great number of the defenceless animals.

The first of these villages observed by our party, when we were ascending the Missouri river in 1843, was near the "Great bend" of that stream /probably above the present site of Kansas City/. . . .

. . . .Occasionally these marmots stood quite erect, and watched our movements, and then leaped into the air, all the time keeping an eye on us. We found that by lying down within twenty or thirty steps of their holes, and remaining silent, the animals re-appeared in fifteen or twenty minutes. Now and then one of them, after coming out of its hole, issued a long and somewhat whistling note, perhaps a call, or invitation to his neighbours, as several came out in a few moments. . . . They are, as we think more in the habit of feeding by night than in the day time. . . .

Lewis and Clark give a very good description of the Prairie Dog . . . They poured five barrels of water into one of their holes without filling it, but dislodged and caught the owner. They further say that after digging down another of the holes for six feet, they found on running a pole into it that they had not yet dug half-way to the bottom; they discovered two frogs in the hole, and near it killed a dark rattlesnake, which had swallowed one of the Prairie Dogs. . . .

For an amusing account of a large village of these marmots, we extract the following from KENDALL's Narrative of the Texan Santa Fé Expedition . . . "We had proceeded but a short distance, after reaching this beautiful prairie, before we came upon the outskirts of the commonwealth, a few scattering dogs were seen scampering in, their short, sharp yelps giving a general alarm to the whole community. The first brief cry of danger from the outskirts was soon taken up in the centre of the city, and now nothing was to heard or seen in any direction but a barking, dashing, and scampering of the mercurial and excitable denizens of the place, each to his burrow. . . .

. . . .One of them had perched himself upon the pile of earth in front of his hole, sitting up and exposing a fair mark, while a companion's head was seen poking out of the entrance, too timid, perhaps, to trust himself farther. A well-directed ball from my rifle carried away the entire top of the former's head, and knocked him some two or three feet from his post perfectly dead. While reloading, the other boldly came out, seized his companion by one of his legs, and before we could reach the hole had drawn him completely out of sight. There was a touch of feeling in the little incident, a something human, which raised the animals in my estimation, and ever after I did not attempt to kill one of them, except when driven by extreme hunger."

. . . ."They are a wild, frolicsome, madcap set of fellows when undisturbed, uneasy and ever on the move, and appear to take especial delight in chattering away the time, and visiting from hole to hole to gossip and talk over each other's affairs — at least, so their actions would indicate. When they find a good location for a village, and there is no water in the immediate vicinity, old hunters say, they dig a well to supply the wants of the community. . . ."

BLACK-TAILED PRAIRIE DOG

Cynomys ludovicianus ludovicianus (Ord)

Waddling gait, tail-wagging and barking explain the name of this animal — which is *not* a dog. At the beginning of the nineteenth century, one of the dog towns had a population of over a million "dogs." Another town in Texas was 250 miles long and 150 miles wide. Wholesale poisoning drastically reduced numbers and range.

Prairie dogs are social. They hurry back and forth to their neighbors and kiss any friend they meet. They cooperate in defending boundaries, repelling intruders, grooming each other and sometimes help to dig a burrow or repair a mound.

Each dog town is divided into wards, the boundaries being determined by topographical features or vegetation growth. Each ward consists of several (or numerous) coteries which may have two to 35 residents. An "average" coterie includes four females, two males and the young of the last two years. No member of any coterie is permitted to enter the domain of any other coterie. Boundaries are jealously guarded by all. The dominant male takes over authority. Whenever an outcry announces a border dispute or a trespasser, he hustles over to the scene to settle the matter.

Four or five inches in diameter, the prairie dog's burrow may go down as much as 16 feet before leveling off or turn-ing slightly upward for about 15 feet further to a grass-lined nest chamber and a toilet on separate branches. A "listening post" and turn-around station is located about three feet below the entrance. Here the owner pops in during an alarm and waits to decide when it is safe to come out again.

Around the entrance is a circular mound of earth as much as three feet high and 10 feet across. This prevents surface water from running into the home and provides a lookout.

How does the animal drink when there is no water for months at a time? Like many other rodents, its stomach converts starches into water.

While above ground, the prairie dog spends 57 percent of its time eating. It prefers fleshy roots and large seeds of plants which ranchers call "weeds." Prairie dogs, like ground squir-rels and jack rabbits, increase and spread only where land has been over-grazed. Contrary to Audubon's surmise, it does not feed at night. Since it does not like cold, rain or snow, it is much more active in summer than in winter.

Adults are 14½ to 16½ inches long, including the 3- to 4½-inch tail, and weigh 1 1/3 to 2¼ pounds. In the origi-nal range — Montana to western Texas and New Mexico — vast areas have been depopulated by poisoning campaigns.

SCIURUS CAROLINENSIS. GMELIN.

CAROLINA GREY SQUIRREL.

This species differs as much in its habits from the Northern Gray Squirrel as it does in form and colour. /See opposite page./ From an intimate acquaintance with the habits of the latter, we are particularly impressed with the peculiarities of the present species. Its bark has not the depth of tone of that of the Northern species, and is more shrill and querulous. Instead of mounting high on the tree when alarmed, which the latter always does, the *Sc. Carolinensis* generally plays round the trunk, and on the side opposite to the observer at a height of some twenty or thirty feet, often concealing itself beneath the Spanish moss *(Tillandsia Usneoides)* which hangs about the tree. . . .

It is, however, capable of climbing to the extremity of the branches and leaping from tree to tree with great agility, but is less wild than the Northern species, and is almost as easily approached as the chickaree, *(Sc. Hudsonius.) /Tamiasciurus hudsonicus/* One who is desirous of obtaining a specimen, has only to take a seat for half an hour in any of the swamps of Carolina and he will be surprised at the immense number of these squirrels that may be seen running along the logs or leaping among the surrounding trees. . . .

The Carolina Gray Squirrel is sometimes seen on high grounds among the oak and hickory trees, although its usual haunts are low swampy places or trees overhanging streams or growing near the margin of some river. In deep cypress swamps covered in many places with several feet of water during the whole year, it takes up its constant residence, moving among the entwined branches of the dense forest with great facility. Its hole in such situations may sometimes be found in the trunk of a decayed cypress. On the large tupelo trees, *(Nyssa aquatica,)* which are found in the swamps, many nests of this species, composed principally of Spanish moss and leaves, are every where to be seen. In these nests, or in some woodpecker's hole, they produce their young. These are five or six in number, and are brought forth in March; it is well ascertained also that the female litters a second time in the season, probably about mid-summer.

This species has one peculiarity which we have not observed in any other. It is in some degree nocturnal, or at least crepuscular, in its habits. In riding along by-paths through the woods, long after sunset, we are often startled by the barking of this little Squirrel, as it scratches among the leaves, or leaps from tree to tree, scattering over the earth the seeds of the maple, &c., which are shaken off from the uppermost branches as it passes over them. . . .

We have observed the Carolina Gray Squirrel on several occasions by moonlight, as actively engaged as the Flying Squirrel usually is in the evening; and this propensity to prolong its search after food or its playful gambols until the light of day is succeeded by the moon's pale gleams, causes it frequently to fall a prey to the Virginian /great horned/ owl, or the barred owl; which last especially is very abundant in the swamps of Carolina, where, gliding on noiseless pinions between the leafy branches, it seizes the luckless Squirrel ere it is aware of its danger, or can make the slightest attempt to escape. The gray fox and the wild cat often surprise this and other species by stratagem or stealth. We have beheld the prowling lynx concealed in a heap of brushwood near an old log, or near the foot of a tree frequented by the Squirrel he hopes to capture. For hours together will he lie thus in ambush, and should the unsuspicious creature pass within a few feet of him, he pounces on it with a sudden spring, and rarely fails to secure it.

Several species of snakes, the rattle-snake, *(Crotalus durassus /C. horridus/,)* black snake, *(Coluber constrictor,)* and the chicken snake, *(Coluber /now Elaphe/ quadrivittatus,)* for instance, have been found on being killed, to have a Squirrel in their stomach; and the fact that Squirrels, birds, &c., although possessing great activity and agility, constitute a portion of the food of these reptiles, being well established, the manner in which the sluggish serpent catches animals so far exceeding him in speed, and some of them endowed with the power of rising from the earth and skimming away with a few flaps of their wings, has been the subject of much speculation. Some persons have attributed a mysterious power, more especially to the rattle-snake and black snake — we mean the power of *fascinating,* or as it is commonly called, *charming.* . . .

SCIURUS MIGRATORIUS, BACH.

MIGRATORY SQUIRREL.

This appears to be the most active and sprightly species of Squirrel existing in our Atlantic States. It sallies forth with the sun, and is industriously engaged in search of food for four or five hours in the morning, scratching among leaves, running over fallen logs, ascending trees, or playfully skipping from bough to bough, often making almost incredible leaps from the higher branches of one tree to another. In the middle of the day it retires for a few hours to its nest, resuming its active labours and amusements in the afternoon, and continuing them without intermission till long after the setting of the sun . . .

In addition to the usual enemies of this species in the Northern States, such as the weasel, fox, lynx, &c., the red-tailed hawk seems to regard it as his natural and lawful prey. It is amusing to see the skill and dexterity exercised by the hawk in the attack, and by the squirrel in attempting to escape. When the hawk is unaccompanied by his mate, he finds it no easy matter to secure the little animal; unless the latter be pounced upon whilst upon the ground, he is enabled by dodging and twisting round a branch to evade the attacks of the hawk for an hour or more, and frequently worries him into a reluctant retreat.

But the red-tails learn by experience that they are most certain of this prey when hunting in couples. The male is frequently accompanied by his mate, especially in the breeding season, and in this case the Squirrel is soon captured. The hawks course rapidly in opposite directions above and below the branch; the attention of the Squirrel is thus divided and distracted, and before he is aware of it the talons of one of the hawks are in his back, and with a shriek of triumph the rapacious birds bear him off . . .

This species of squirrel has occasionally excited the wonder of the populace by its wandering habits and its singular and long migrations. Like the lemming (*Lemmus Norvegicus* /now *L. lemmus*/) of the Eastern continent /Europe/, it is stimulated either by scarcity of food, or by some other inexplicable instinct, to leave its native haunts, and seek for adventures or for food in some (to it) unexplored portion of our land.

. . . .Mountains, cleared fields, the narrow bays of some of our lakes, or our broad rivers, present no unconquerable impediments. Onward they come, devouring on their way every thing that is suited to their taste, laying waste the corn and wheat-fields of the farmer; and as their numbers are thinned by the gun, the dog, and the club, others fall in and fill up the ranks, till they occasion infinite mischief, and call forth more than empty threats of vengeance. It is often inquired, how these little creatures, that on common occasions have such an instinctive dread of water, are enabled to cross broad and rapid rivers, like the Ohio and Hudson for instance. It has been asserted by authors, and is believed by many, that they carry to the shore a suitable piece of bark, and seizing the opportunity of a favourable breeze, seat themselves upon this substitute for a boat, hoist their broad tails as a sail, and float safely to the opposite shore. This together with many other traits of intelligence ascribed to this species, we suspect to be apocryphal. That they do migrate at irregular, and occasionally at distant periods, is a fact sufficiently established; but in the only two instances in which we had opportunities of witnessing the migrations of these Squirrels, it appeared to us, that they were not only unskilful sailors but clumsy swimmers. One of these occasions, (as far as our recollection serves us), was in the autumn of 1808 or 1809; troops of Squirrels suddenly and unexpectedly made their appearance in the neighbourhood; among them were varieties not previously seen in those parts; some were broadly striped with yellow on the sides, and a few had a black stripe on each side, bordered with yellow or brown, resembling the stripes on the sides of the Hudson's Bay Squirrel, (*S. Hudsonius* /*Tamiasciurus hudsonicus,* the red squirrel/.) They swam the Hudson in various places between Waterford and Saratoga; those which we observed crossing the river were swimming deep and awkwardly, their bodies and tails wholly submerged; several that had been drowned were carried downwards by the stream; and those which were so fortunate as to reach the opposite bank were so wet and fatigued, that the boys stationed there with clubs found no difficulty in securing them alive or in killing them. . . .

EASTERN GRAY SQUIRREL

Sciurus carolinensis pennsylvanicus Ord

Sometimes gray squirrels are out all day; you may see one resting on a tree limb with its tail hanging down, swinging idly back and forth. Occasionally one will forage in full moonlight. Usually, however, they spend the late morning and noon hours in the nest, coming out in mid-afternoon and almost invariably retiring an hour or so before sunset. Generally active all winter, they subsist on the food they have stored in the ground. They may sleep soundly through periods of stormy weather.

Home is a natural cavity which may be enlarged by biting away projections, high in a tree. Bulky twig-and-leaf nests, tightly woven to be nearly waterproof, are often constructed among the branches. Several adult squirrels may occupy a single den or nest, but as a rule they are solitary. Acorns and hickory nuts are the major food through much of the year; buds, tender twigs, seeds, insects and possibly a nestling bird or two are eaten in spring and summer. The squirrel usually forages quietly on the ground or in the trees but, if alarmed, it repeats a harsh, gutteral "bark," flipping its tail with each "qua - ak." (Continued)

SCIURUS NIGER, LIN.

BLACK SQUIRREL.

An opportunity was afforded us, many years since, of observing the habits of this species, in the northern part of the State of New-York. A seat under the shadow of a rock near a stream of water, was for several successive summers our favourite resort for retirement and reading. In the immediate vicinity were several large trees, in which were a number of holes, from which at almost every hour of the day were seen issuing this species of Black Squirrel. There seemed to be a dozen of them; they were all of the same glossy black colour, and although the Northern gray squirrel and its black variety were not rare in that neighbourhood, during a period of five or six years we never discovered any other than the present species in that locality; and after the lapse of twenty years, a specimen (from which our description was in part drawn up) was procured in that identical spot, and sent to us.

This species possesses all the sprightliness of the Northern gray squirrel, evidently preferring valleys and swamps to drier and more elevated situations. We observed that one of their favourite trees, to which they retreated on hearing the slightest noise, was a large white-pine *(Pinus strobus)* in the immediate vicinity. We were surprised at sometimes seeing a red squirrel, *(Sciurus /now Tamiasciurus/ Hudsonius,)* which had also given a preference to this tree, pursuing a Black Squirrel, threatening and scolding it vociferously, till the latter was obliged to make its retreat. When the Squirrels approached the stream, which ran within a few feet of our seat, they often stopped to drink, when, instead of lapping the water like the dog and cat, they protruded their mouths a considerable distance into the stream, and drank greedily; they would afterwards sit upright, supported by the tarsus, and with tail erect, busy themselves for a quarter of an hour in wiping their faces with their paws, the latter being also occasionally dipped in the water. Their barking and other habits did not seem to differ from those of the northern gray squirrel.

/Editor's Comment: Although Bachman recognized a black "variety" of the (north) eastern gray squirrel (see following account), he apparently felt that the black squirrel that nested around his "favorite resort" in New York State was distinctly different. Subsequently, however, it was determined to be merely a black color phase which may be common or even abundant in local areas. Bachman's "glossy black" animals were apparently purely melanistic, but often this phenomenon is only partial and abundant black hairs give merely a blackish cast to the normal gray coat. Both black and gray adults interbreed freely and young of both color phases may occur in the same litter./

EASTERN GRAY SQUIRREL

Sciurus carolinensis carolinensis Gmelin

The marked color variations in the gray squirrels and fox squirrels and their tendency toward melanism and albinism led to great confusion in names during much of the eighteenth and nineteenth centuries. Bachman's four "species" of eastern gray squirrels have since been reduced to one, three "species" of western grays to one, and six "species" of fox squirrels to one. These three resulting valid species as well as five others in the United States are grouped in the genus *Sciurus*. This Latin term for squirrels was derived from two Greek words which meant "the animal that sits

in the shadow of its tail." The coat moults twice a year; the tail only once.

Gray squirrels are 17 to 20 inches long, of which the bushy tail accounts for 8½ to 9½ inches, and weigh 14 to 25 ounces. The species occurs in hardwood forests between the Atlantic Coast and the Great Plains, from Maine and Manitoba to southern Florida, the Gulf Coast and central Texas. Audubon and Bachman's Carolina squirrel (above) occupies much of the southern half of this area.

Information on habits continues on following pages.

Fig. 3

Fig. 1

EASTERN GRAY SQUIRREL

Sciurus carolinensis pennsylvanicus Ord

Fighting among males and the pursuit of females over the ground and through the tree tops mark the winter and early summer mating seasons. Young females breed in their second summer, then twice a year.

Gestation requires about 44 days and the litter contains one to five (usually three or four) young, each weighing about one-half ounce. The mother leaves, or the young disperse, about two months after the birth, but late summer litters usually remain with the female over winter. Juveniles are adult size by autumn. Normal life expectancy is five years.

As a rule, gray squirrels forage within 200 yards of home, hopping short distances, then walking with rolling gait while sniffing here and there. The senses of sight, hearing, touch and smell are well developed; the last is used to find food and to recover nuts which are buried individually for weeks or months at an earlier time.

The great migrations described by Bachman and others have occurred in recent years only on a very small scale if at all. Overpopulation and/or shortage of food may have caused the movements.

SCIURUS FERUGINIVENTRIS, AUD. AND BACH.

RED-BELLIED SQUIRREL.

We are unfortunately without any information or account of the habits of this singularly marked and bright coloured Squirrel. We have represented three of them in our plate in different attitudes on a branch of mulberry.

Several specimens, differing a little in colour, which differences we have represented in our plate, were received from California; the precise locality was not given.

This species should perhaps be compared with the dusky squirrel (*S. nigrescens*) of BENNET, to which it bears some resemblance. From the description, however, which we made of the original specimen of *S. nigrescens,* deposited in the museum of the London Zoological Society, we have little hesitation in pronouncing this a distinct species. /See page 98./...

RED-BELLIED SQUIRREL

Sciurus aureogaster aureogaster F. Cuvier

The specimens of the red-bellied squirrel that Audubon and Bachman described as a new species were incorrectly labeled. Instead of being from California, they had been collected somewhere in eastern Mexico. More unfortunately, the "new species" was not new, but had been described in 1829, by the French zoologist, Georges Frederic Cuvier. He, also, believed that his type specimen had originated in California, but the location has since been restricted on the basis of the best evidence available, to Altamira, Tamaulipas.

Not realizing that melanism is very common in the species, Dr. Bachman was misled by the variation of color into naming two additional "species." His specimens later proved to be only dark color phases of the red-bellied squirrel. One, the "dusky squirrel," is discussed and pictured in the following account. The second, published jointly by Audubon and Bachman under the name "weasel-like squirrel," was not pictured in the *Quadrupeds* and accordingly is not given a place in the present book. (Continued)

SCIURUS NIGRESCENS, BENNETT.

DUSKY SQUIRREL.

The existence in North America of an unusual number of species of squirrels has been made known to our subscribers in the course of this publication. There are many closely allied, and many very beautiful species among them; all are graceful and agile, and possess very similar habits.

The great number of these nut-eating animals in North America would be a proof (were any such wanting) that nature has been more bountiful to our country in distributing nut-bearing trees over the whole extent of our continent than to other parts of the globe, and this in connexion with the fact that so great a proportion of wood-land cannot be found in any other part of the world of similar extent, marks America as intended for a very dense population hereafter. In Europe there is only one well determined species of squirrel known, at present at least, although at some remote period there may have been more. /See below./

In regard to the peculiar habits of the Dusky Squirrel, we have nothing to say. It is one of the species which, being shot or procured by collectors of objects of natural history, and sent to Europe, have there been described by naturalists who, having the advantages of museums which contain specimens from every part of the globe, and the largest libraries in the world also to which they can refer, may sometimes discover new species with much less difficulty, but also less certainty, than the student of nature must encounter while seeking for knowledge in the woods.

But the naturalist who learns from books only, and describes from dried skins, is at best liable to mistakes. We have in fact always found that where young animals, or accidental varieties, have been described as new species, this has been the result of study in the musum or cabinet, not in the fields.

This species, of which, so far as we know, only one specimen exists in any museum or collection, is stated to have been procured in California. We have not received any positive accounts of its occurrence there, but have no doubt it will be found, and its habits, as well as locality, determined ere long. /See opposite page./

/Editor's Comment: Dr. Bachman wrote in glowing terms (above) of the bountiful manner in which nature had endowed North America with habitats favoring squirrels as compared with her niggardliness in Europe. While the latter has only two species (Persian squirrel of the Caucasus and the red squirrel), scientists have listed two dozen species in America north of Panama. Most of them are restricted to the tropics and outside the geographic scope of the Quadrupeds. A few of these species may be doubtful, but the number of valid kinds of tree squirrels in North America is still large./

RED-BELLIED SQUIRREL

Sciurus aureogaster aureogaster F. Cuvier

This usually colorful Mexican squirrel (dark phase above) lives in a wide variety of tropical habitats. It is found chiefly below 4,000 feet elevation in dense, steamy jungle, but it may occur in open pine woodland as high as 8,000 feet. In the lowland it eats mango fruit, green figs, plums, tamarind pods and chico zapote. It also raids farmers' fields for corn. Most of its life is spent in trees; it seldom comes down except to look for ground foods. In Tamaulipas, country people refer to it as "ardilla pinta" (golden squirrel) or "ardilla colorada" (red squirrel). Hunters seek it in early morning and late afternoon when it is most active.

Little is known about reproduction except that mating is in January. A female, killed early in March for a museum specimen, was found to have two fully developed embryos.

Nearly 20 percent larger than the eastern gray squirrel, the red-bellied squirrel is 18 to 23 inches long, including the 9- to 11-inch bushy tail. The known range is from southern Tamaulipas southeastward to Chiapas (perhaps including northern Guatemala) and within 150 miles from the Gulf Coast of Mexico. Only the northern tip of this region is north of the Tropic of Cancer and within the area covered by the *Quadrupeds*.

99

SCIURUS COLLIÆI, RICH.

COLLIES SQUIRREL

Our figures of this Squirrel were made from the specimen presented to the Zoological Society of London by Captain /Frederick William/ BEECHEY /British explorer who made a voyage to the west coast of North America, 1825–1828/; the original from which the species was described and named by our friend Dr. RICHARDSON.

All the information we have as to the habits of this animal is contained in the above-mentioned appendix (p. 8): "Mr. COLLIE observed this Squirrel, in considerable numbers, sporting on trees at San Blas in California (?), where its vernacular name signifies 'Little Fox–Squirrel.' It feeds on fruits of various kinds. Although unwilling to incur the risk of adding to the number of synonymes with which the history of this large genus is already overburdened, I do not feel justified in referring it to any of the species admitted into recent systematic works; and I have therefore described it as new, naming it in compliment to the able and indefatigable naturalist who procured the specimen."

This species was given by RICHARDSON, as appears by the above quotation, as existing at San Blas, California; this place, however, if we have not mistaken the locality, is in the district of Xalisco in Mexico, and within the tropics; it is doubtful, therefore, whether the species will be found to inhabit any portion of California. J. W. AUDUBON did not observe it in his travels through Upper California.

COLLIE'S SQUIRREL

Sciurus colliaei colliaei Richardson

This dark squirrel with the black tail frosted by white is a little larger than the eastern gray squirrel. It was included in Audubon's *Quadrupeds* by error. At the time that the naturalist Collie made observations in western Mexico, California was a part of the country and its southern limits were nebulous. We now know that the coastal village of San Blas where Collie watched the squirrels "sporting on trees" is in the state of Nayarit, almost a thousand miles south of California. However, zoologists have recently de-termined that the range of this squirrel does actually extend 280 miles above Audubon and Bachman's southernmost limit, the Tropic of Cancer.

Collie's squirrel occupies a relatively small territory. It inhabits the scrubby, subtropical thorn forest on the Pacific coastal plain and in deep canyons at the western base of the Sierra Madre Occidental. Seldom is it found more than 2,500 feet above sea level. Adults measure 19½ to 21½ inches long, of which the tail is 10½ to 11 inches.

SCIURUS LEPORINUS, AUD &BACH.
HARE SQUIRREL.

This species, which is one of our most beautifully furred Squirrels, is especially remarkable for its splendid tail, with its broad white border. We know nothing of its habits, as it was brought from California, without any other information than that of its locality.

We have represented two of these Squirrels in our plate, on a branch of hickory, with a bunch of nearly ripe nuts attached.

/Editor's Comment: Audubon and Bachman described their "hare squirrel" in 1841. Their specimen, which came from "northern California," proved to be abnormally brownish in color. Seven years later, Titian Ramsay Peale, the mammalogist-ornithologist of the U.S. Exploring Expedition of 1838–42, published the description of a "California grey squirrel, Sciurus fossor." The latter was included in the Quadrupeds along with a statement on habits which is quoted below. It was demonstrated later that Audubon and Bachman's "hare squirrel" and Peale's "California grey squirrel" were synonymous, and that both had been antedated by George Ord's publication in 1818 of Sciurus griseus, which we now call the western gray squirrel./

This beautiful squirrel has been often killed by Mr. J. E. CLEMENTS, in the pine woods of California, near Murphy's "diggings." It is exceedingly swift on the ground, and will not readily take to a tree, or, if it does, ascends only a few feet, and then jumping down to the ground runs off with its tail held up but curved downwards towards the tip like that of a fox when in flight.

By the aid of a fast cur dog, it may, however, be put up a tree. In this case it hides if a hole offers in which to conceal itself; and unlike some others of its genus, seldom leaps from one tree to another over the higher boughs in the endeavour to make its escape.

It appears to make its nest generally in the decayed part of an oak tree, and in the desire to reach its secure retreat, is doubtless led to attempt to run to this tree on the ground, rather than by ascending the nearest trunk and jumping from branch to branch.

A large part of its food consists of nuts, which are stuck in hollows or holes bored in the pine trees by a species of woodpecker called by the Californians "Sapsuckers." /the Acorn woodpecker, Melanerpes/ These nuts are placed in holes in the bark, which are only so deep as to admit the nuts (which are placed small end foremost in them), leaving the large end visible and about flush with the bark — they thus present the appearance of pins or pegs of wood stuck into the trees, and are very curious objects to the eye of the stranger.

The California grey squirrel is a roving animal. One may sometimes see from one to a dozen in a morning's hunt in the pines, and again not meet any. They very seldom leave the pines, but are occasionally seen in the dry season following the beds of the then almost empty water courses, which afford them, in common with other animals and birds, water and such roots and grasses as they cannot find on the uplands at that period of the year.

They bark somewhat in the same tones as the grey squirrel of the Atlantic States, but immediately cease when they perceive they are observed by man. Sometimes they seem to be excited to the utterance of their cries by the whistling of the California partridges, which, near the hills, approach the edges of the pine woods.

Most of those shot by Mr. CLEMENTS were killed when running on the ground.

WESTERN GRAY SQUIRREL

Sciurus griseus griseus Ord

A little larger than its eastern relative, the western gray squirrel has a narrower tail, dusky feet, and forages more on the ground. Although the two species are otherwise quite similar, they do not hybridize; this is proof that they belong to different species.

The western gray squirrel inhabits lowland oak forest and mountain pine belt from sea level to nearly 8,000 feet. In summer it is inclined to wander and, despite the statement on the opposite page, it may travel far through the treetops. In the years that food is scarce, the animals migrate.

Living in a relatively mild climate, the western gray squirrel is active throughout the winter except during storms and, for this reason, stores little food. It uses a tree-trunk den or a leaf nest in either of which the three to five young are born in late winter or early spring. The diet consists of acorns and pine seeds with samplings of buds and flowers of coniferous trees, fungi, and occasional birds' eggs and nestlings.

The species is 20½ to 23 inches long, including the 10½- to 11½-inch tail, and weighs 26 to 32 ounces. It occurs from southern California to Puget Sound, east to Nevada.

103

SCUIRUS CINEREUS. LINN. GMEL.

CAT SQUIRREL

This Squirrel has many habits in common with other species, residing in the hollows of trees, building in summer its nest of leaves in some convenient fork of a tree, and subsisting on the same kinds of food. It is, however, the most inactive of all our known species; it climbs a tree, not with the lightness and agility of the northern gray squirrel, but with the slowness and apparent reluctance of the little striped squirrel /eastern chipmunk/, *(Tamias Lysteri /T. striatus/.)* After ascending, it does not immediately mount to the top as is the case with other species, but clings to the body of the tree on the side opposite to you, or tries to conceal itself behind the first convenient branch. We have seldom observed it leaping from bough to bough.

When it is induced, in search of food to proceed to the extremity of a branch, it moves cautiously and heavily, and generally returns the same way. On the ground it runs clumsily and makes slower progress than the gray squirrel. It is usually fat, especially in autumn, and the flesh is said to be preferable to that of any of our other species of squirrel. The Cat-Squirrel does not appear to be migratory in its habits. The same pair, if undisturbed, may be found in a particular vicinity for a number of years in succession, and the sexes seem paired for life.

WILLIAM BAIRD, Esq., of Carlisle, Pennsylvania, says of this species — "The Fox-Squirrel, as this species is called with us, will never, unless almost in the very jaws of a dog, ascend any other tree than that which contains its nest, differing very greatly in this respect from our gray squirrel."

The nest, which we have only seen on two occasions, was constructed of sticks and leaves, in the crotch of a tree about twenty feet from the ground, and in both cases the pair had a safer retreat in a hollow of the same tree above.

This species is said to have young but once a year. We have no positive evidence to the contrary, but suspect that it will hereafter be discovered that it produces a second litter in the summer, or toward autumn.

On taking some of them from the nest, we found on one occasion three, and on another four, young. These nests were placed in the hollows of oak trees.

The Cat-Squirrel is rather a rare species, but is not very uncommon in the oak and hickory woods of Pennsylvania; we have seen it near Easton and York; it is found occasionally in Maryland and Virginia, and is met with on Long Island and in some other portions of the State of New-York, but in the northern parts of that State is exceedingly rare, as we /John Bachman/ only saw two pair during fifteen years' close observation. At certain seasons we have found these squirrels tolerably abundant in the markets of the city of New-York, and have ascertained that persons who had them for sale were aware of their superior value, as we were frequently charged 37½ cents for one, whilst the common gray squirrel could easily be purchased for 12½ cents. . . .

FOX SQUIRREL

Sciurus niger niger Linnaeus

The "cat squirrel" (above and opposite) and five others are described in *Quadrupeds* as different species. Four of these had been discovered by the authors. (One, the "Large Louisiana Black Squirrel," was not painted for the imperial folio and is not included in the present book.) After much study and the modern use of the trinomial system of classification, these six "species" are now considered three races of one species — the fox squirrel. The up-dated account accompanying this and following plates is therefore under one title.

Variations of color (see above and next plate), size and even skull characteristics are more extreme in fox squirrels than in most species of North American mammals. In fact, differences between some of the fox squirrel races (subspecies), are wider than those between numerous species. These variations and surprising points of similarity of some individuals to other species, such as the gray squirrel, have bewildered many zoologists in addition to Audubon and Bachman. (Continued)

SCIURUS CAPISTRATUS, BOSC.

FOX SQUIRREL.

. . .The Fox Squirrel, instead of preferring rich low lands, thickly clothed with timber, as is the case with the Carolina Grey Squirrel, is seldom seen in such situations; but prefers elevated pine ridges, where the trees are not crowded near each other, and where there is an occasional oak and hickory interspersed. It is also frequently found in the vicinity of rich valleys, to which it resorts for nuts, acorns and chinquepins, *(castanea pumila,)* which such soils produce. In some aged and partially decayed oak, this Squirrel finds a safe retreat for itself and mate . . . The tree selected is in all cases hollow, and the Squirrel only gnaws through the outer shell in order to find a residence, which requires but little labour and skill to render it secure and comfortable. At other times, it takes possession of the deserted hole of the ivory-billed woodpecker, *(Picus /Campephilus/ principalis).)* The summer duck *(Anas /Aix/ sponsa /*the wood duck/*)* too, is frequently a competitor for the same residence; contests for possession occasionally take place between these three species, and we have generally observed, that the tenant that has already deposited its eggs or young in such situations is seldom ejected. The male and female summer duck unite in chasing and beating with their wings any Squirrel that may approach their nests, nor are they idle with their bills and tongues, but continue biting, hissing and clapping their wings until the intruder is expelled. . . .

In the vicinity of the permanent residence of the Fox Squirrel, several nests, composed of sticks, leaves and mosses, are usually seen on the pine trees. These are seldom placed on the summits, but in the forks, and more frequently where several branches unite and afford a secure basis for them. These nests may be called their summer home, for they seem to be occupied only in fine weather, and are deserted during wintry and stormy seasons.

In December and January, the season of sexual intercourse, the male chases the female for hours together on the same tree, running up one side and descending on the other, making at the same time a low gutteral noise, that scarcely bears any resemblance to the barking which they utter on other occasions. The young are produced from the beginning of March, and sometimes earlier, to April. The nests containing them, which we have had opportunities of examining, were always in hollow trees. They receive the nourishment of the mother for four or five weeks, when they are left to shift for themselves, but continue to reside in the vicinity of, and even to occupy the same nests with, their parents till autumn. It has been asserted by several planters of Carolina, that this species has two broods during the season. . . .

Most other species of this genus when alarmed in the woods immediately betake themselves to the first convenient tree that presents itself, — not so with the Fox Squirrel. When he is aware of being discovered whilst on the ground, he pushes directly for a hollow tree, which is often a quarter of a mile distant, and it requires a good dog, a man on horseback, or a very swift runner, to induce him to alter his course, or compel him to ascend any other tree. When he is silently seated on a tree and imagines himself unperceived by the person approaching him, he suddenly spreads himself flatly on the limb, and gently moving to the opposite side, often by this stratagem escapes detection. When, however, he is on a small tree, and is made aware of being observed, he utters a few querulous barking notes, and immediately leaps to the ground, and hastens to a more secure retreat. If overtaken by a dog, he defends himself with great spirit . . .

He is very tenacious of life, and an ordinary shot gun, although it may wound him repeatedly, will seldom bring him down from the tops of the high pines to which he retreats when pursued, and in such situations the rifle is the only certain enemy he has to dread.

This Squirrel is seldom seen out of its retreat early in the morning and evening, as is the habit of other species. He seems to be a late riser, and usually makes his appearance at 10 or 11 o'clock, and retires to his domicile long before evening. He does not appear to indulge so frequently in the barking propensities of the genus as the other and smaller species. This note, when heard, is not very loud, but hoarse and gutteral. He is easily domesticated, and is occasionally seen in cages . . .

FOX SQUIRREL

Sciurus niger niger Linnaeus

More tame than the gray, the brightly colored fox squirrel can usually be distinguished by its larger size, heavier body, noticeably squarish head and reddish tinge. In the southeast, *grayish* fox squirrels are common but they can still be recognized by their whitish noses (which gray squirrels lack). Albino fox squirrels are rare; black (melanistic) animals occur frequently in the southeast and some other localities. (The type specimen was melanistic according to the scientific name, *niger*.)

Although Audubon and Bachman believed that fox squirrels ("cat squirrels") mate for life, later naturalists have found no evidence of monogamy. Although they are tolerant of neighbors, and several may den together to keep warm during severe cold spells, each adult squirrel lives by itself and mating is only a transitory episode.

This occurs in mid-winter (January to February) and the young (one to six, usually three or four) are born about 45 days later. They are blind, naked and may weigh one-half ounce. The mother covers them with nest materials while she forages. Shortly after their eyes open at five weeks, the young venture from the nest to climb hesitantly through the branches and later to explore on the ground. Weaned at about 10 weeks, they remain with the mother until they are three months old. They breed at 10 or 11 months. Yearling females have only one litter, but thereafter mate twice a year — the second time in spring or early summer. A late-born litter may stay with the mother for the first winter. During squirrel "population explosions," young adults may migrate five or 10 miles, up to an extreme of 40, to find new food territory. When necessary they can swim as much as two miles if the water is not rough.

In comparison with its relatives, the fox squirrel walks, climbs and even waves its tail rather slowly and deliberately. When foraging on the ground, it hops along sedately sniffing here and there. If frightened, however, it can make long leaps up to 12 miles an hour.

In the trees it climbs up and down but without the grace and agility of the gray squirrel. Sometimes it loses its footing and falls, perhaps 40 feet, to the ground. Apparently it can brake itself for it usually lands right side up and runs off without injury. Today, this race is commonly called the "eastern fox squirrel." (Continued)

107

SCIURUS RUBRICAUDATUS. AUD: & BACH:

RED-TAILED SQUIRREL.

We have obtained no information in regard to the habits of this species, but have no doubt it possesses all the sprightliness and activity of other squirrels, particularly the Northern gray and cat squirrels, as well as the great tailed squirrel, to which in form and size it is allied /and actually synonymous/.

The specimen from which our drawing was made, was procured in the State of Illinois. This squirrel is also found in the barrens of Kentucky: we possess a skin sent to us by our good friend Dr. CROGHAN, procured we believe near the celebrated Mammoth cave, of which he is proprietor.

Mr. CABOT, of Boston, likewise has one, as well as we can recollect, in his collection. We /J. J. Audubon/ sought in vain while on our journey in the wilds of the Upper Missouri country, for this species, which apparently does not extend its range west of the well-wooded districts lying to the east of the great prairies. It will probably be found abundant in Indiana, although it has been hitherto most frequently observed in Illinois. Of its northern and southern limits, we know nothing, and it may have a much more extended distribution than is at present supposed.

FOX SQUIRREL

Sciurus niger rufiventer E. Geoffroy-Saint-Hilaire

This fox squirrel was originally named for its red belly (*rufiventer,* above). Audubon and Bachman belatedly called it red-tailed (*rubicaudatus,* opposite page). Today the common name for this subspecies is western fox squirrel.

All fox squirrels prefer to live in open, old-growth forests on dry ridges but may have to settle for second-growth. A tree cavity is the favorite home, especially in cold weather. If too cramped, the squirrel enlarges it to six inches across by 15 inches deep, with a three-inch entrance. Too-large cavities are filled in with leaves.

One or more roughly globular leaf nests are built in the individual home range of 10 or more acres, usually close to plentiful food supplies where a hollow tree is not available. These are perched in large treetops sometimes 40 feet above ground. One nest is frequently exchanged for another when too many fleas and fecal pellets accumulate. (The fox squirrel grooms itself carefully but may be careless in the nest.) A winter nest requires a dozen or more hours of leaf-gathering and weaving. It can be used six months or, with repairs, up to two or three years. (Continued)

109

SCIURUS SAYI, AUD. & BACH.

SAY'S SQUIRREL.

The habits of this Squirrel are not very different from those of the Cat Squirrel, to which it is most nearly allied. It does not run for so great a distance on the ground before taking a tree as the southern Fox Squirrel, nor does it leap quite as actively from tree to tree as the northern Gray Squirrel, *(S. migratorius /carolinensis/,)* but appears to possess more activity, and agility than the Cat Squirrel. /The latter proved to be the same as the southern race of the fox squirrel./

The forests on the rich bottom lands of the Wabash, the Illinois, and the Missouri rivers are ornamented with the stately pecan-tree *(Carya olivaeformis /illinoensis/),* on the nuts of which these squirrels luxuriate; they also resort to the hickory and oak trees, in the vicinity of their residence, as well as to the hazel bushes, on the fruits of which they feed

They are becoming troublesome in the corn-fields of the farmer, who has commenced planting his crops in the remote but rapidly improving states and territories west of the Ohio.

The flesh is represented by all travellers as delicate, and is said to be equal in flavour to that of any of the species.

FOX SQUIRREL

Sciurus niger rufiventer E. Geoffroy-Saint-Hilaire

Nearly all of the fox squirrels' food comes from trees. In spring the animals often gnaw holes in maple and elm trees to lick the sap and eat the tender cambium. Buds and twigs are also relished. Many wild fruits such as Osage orange are enjoyed and, after summer rains, the mushrooms offer gustatory fillips. The year-round staples are nuts and other seeds — mainly acorns, hickory nuts, walnuts and hazelnuts. Squirrels have been seen drinking from puddles but the majority of their water requirements are apparently satisfied by succulent plants.

Throughout the winter, squirrels live on the nuts and acorns which they have buried or cached individually here and there in the ground during the previous autumn. They find and recover these small stores, sometimes through a foot or more of snow, by their acute sense of smell. There seems to be little or no resentment between individuals when fox squirrels dig up and eat nuts that their neighbors have buried on adjacent territory. There is a minimum of social competition between the fox and gray squirrels where both live on the same range.

Numerous fox squirrels fall victim to speeding automobiles, but relatively few are taken by predators such as rough-legged and red-tailed hawks, the barred and great horned owls. When fox squirrels sprawl out on tree limbs to enjoy the midday sun, they are usually close enough to a den or nest to take refuge in a few seconds. Then their alarms are sounded from the entrance. One to three high-pitched, explosive barks, "kwah, kwah," followed by a series of lower-toned, short and rapid sounds, "kwuh, kwuh, kwuh," etc. Even if you can't see the squirrel, you may be able to tell whether it is fox or gray — the bark of the fox squirrel is more guttural.

The greatest scourge of the fox squirrel is scabies formed by mange. Open sores and ears stuck down to the head may be the first indications. All or part of the hair on its body falls out, leaving it nude or nearly so. The animal is emaciated and in cold weather suffers from the cold and may die of exposure. In one minor epizootic, some of the diseased squirrels recovered. Barring illness and predation, and given the ease and comfort of captivity, the fox squirrel may survive 15 years; the average squirrel in the wild lives to be only four or five years old. (Continued)

SCIURUS SUB-AURATUS, AUD: & BACH:

ORANGE-BELLIED SQUIRREL.

During the winter season the city of New-Orleans is thronged by natives of almost every land, and the Levee (which is an embankment extending along the margin of the river) presents a scene so unlike anything American, that as we walk along its smooth surface we may imagine ourselves in some twenty different countries, as our eyes fall upon many a strange costume, whose wearer has come from afar, and is, like ourselves, perchance, intent on seeing the curiosities of this Salmagundi city. Here a Spanish gentleman from Cuba, or a Mexican, next a pirate or thief, perhaps, from the same countries; all Europe is here represented, and the languages of many parts of the world can be heard whilst walking even half a mile; the descendants of Africa are here metamorphosed into French folks, and the gay bandanna that turbans the heads of the coloured women, is always adjusted with good taste, and is their favourite head-dress.

But the most interesting figures are the few straggling Choctaw and Chickasaw Indians, who bring a variety of game to the markets, and in their blankets, red flannel leggings, moccasins and bead finery, form a sort of dirty picturesque feature in the motley scene, and generally attract the artist's eye: many of these Indians have well formed legs and bodies, and their half-covered shoulders display a strength and symmetry indicating almost a perfect development of the manly form — their sinews and muscles being as large as is compatible with activity and grace. Whilst conversing with one of these remnants of a once numerous race, it was our /J. J. Audubon's/ good fortune to see for the first time the singular and beautiful little Orange-bellied Squirrel which the Indian hunter had brought with him along with other animals for sale, having procured it in the recesses of the forest on the borders of an extensive swamp.

Rarely indeed does the Orange-bellied Squirrel leave its solitary haunts and quit the cypress or sweet-gum shades, except to feed upon pecan-nuts, berries, persimmons, or other delicacies growing in the uplands; and it does not hoard up the small acorn from the swamp-oak until late in the autumn, knowing that the mild winters of Louisiana are seldom cold enough to prevent it from catching an unlucky beetle from time to time during the middle of the day, or interfere with searches for food among the dry leaves and decaying vegetable substances in the woods. Besides, early in the year the red-maple buds will afford a treat to which this little squirrel turns with as much eagerness as the horse that has been kept all winter upon hay and corn, dashes into a fine field of grass in the month of May.

The hole inhabited by the present species is generally in some tall tree growing in the swamp, and perhaps sixty or one hundred yards from the dry land, and the animal passes to it from tree to tree, or along some fallen monarch of the woods, over the shallow water, keeping his large eye bent upon the surrounding lands in fear of some enemy; and, in faith, he runs no little risk, for should the red-shouldered hawk, or the sharped-shinned, dart upon him, he is an easy prey; or, on a warm day, a snake, called the "water moccasin," curled up in his way, might swallow him, "tail and all." But good fun it must be to see the sportsman following in pursuit, splashing and floundering through the water, sometimes half-leg deep, and at others only up to the ankles, but stumbling occasionally, and making the "water fly;" so that when he *has* a chance to pull trigger, he is certain to snap *both barrels!*

Of the breeding of this species we know nothing, nor can we say more of its habits, which are yet to be farther investigated.

/Editor's Comment: Bachman's "Orange-bellied Squirrel" is a small fox squirrel which is restricted to the lower Mississippi Valley. Another specimen was obtained in Louisiana in 1839 by J. W. Audubon. Being a melanistic (black) animal, Bachman assumed that it represented a different species and he named it Sciurus auduboni in honor of the collector. Years later John W. Audubon painted it with the "weasel-like squirrel" in a "bonus" plate for the Quadrupeds (not reproduced in the present volume). Sad to relate, Audubon's squirrel was found to be merely a synonym for sub-auratus, which his father had seen on the Levee at New Orleans and painted, before his death, in Plate 58./

FOX SQUIRREL

Sciurus niger subauratus Bachman

These "orange-bellied" squirrels (above and opposite), like the rest of the fox squirrels, give great pleasure to many people. Unfortunately, fox squirrels sometimes girdle trees, raid crops, chew insulation from electric wiring, gnaw holes into homes and scamper noisily in attics.

On the other hand, fox squirrels are tree planters. Some of the nuts which they store singly here and there are not recovered and eaten. If viable, these nuts sprout and take their place in the forest succession, eventually to provide food and shelter for future generations of squirrels as well as valuable timber for man.

When hunted, they habitually conceal themselves by using the tree trunk or a large limb as a shield. An adult animal provides about a pound of delicious meat; millions are harvested every year. Total length of the fox squirrel is 18 to 28 inches, including the 8- to 13-inch tail; weight, 1½ to 3 pounds. The range: eastern half of the United States exclusive of New England and New York.

SCIURUS LONGIPILIS, AUD & BACH.

LONG HAIRED SQUIRREL.

We have been unable to obtain any information in regard to the habits of this species. Its form, however, indicates that it is a climber, like all the species of the genus, living in forests, feeding on nuts and seeds. Its long woolly coat proves its adaptation to cold regions.

Our specimens were procured from the northern and mountainous portions of California.

The difficulty in finding characters by which the various species of this genus can be distinguished, is very great. There is, however, no variety of any other species of squirrel that can be compared with that here described. Its black head and legs, brown back and belly, its broad ears and long woolly hair, are markings by which it may be easily distinguished from all others.

SQUIRREL

Sciurus (species?)

A description of the Wooly Squirrel, *Sciurus lanigerus,* was published by Audubon and Bachman in 1841. Later, when Audubon painted a picture of the two specimens of this animal for the first volume of *Quadrupeds,* the name was changed to "Long-haired Squirrel, *S. longipilis.*" Nine years later the 1854 edition restored the names of 1841.

This is the "Case of the Missing Squirrel!" Measurements of Audubon and Bachman's two specimens and the locality where they were collected agree closely with those of the western gray squirrel. Unfortunately the "wooly and much longer hair," as well as its color, does not match that of the gray squirrel or of any other large tree squirrel in western North America.

Audubon may have taken "artistic license" when he painted the belly of one of the squirrels a bright rufous (above). In the text it is described as "brown." Except for too vivid color, the picture agrees rather closely with the Douglas squirrel (following pages). However, the animals on which the description is based were considerably larger.

It is concluded that the "Wooly Squirrel" is unidentifiable.

SCIURUS FREMONTII, TOWNSEND.

FREMONT'S SQUIRREL.

We possess no information in regard to this animal farther than that it was obtained on the Rocky Mountains.

It no doubt, like all the other small species of Squirrels which are closely allied with it (*Richardsonii, Hudsonius, lanuginosus,* &c.), feeds on the seeds of pines, and other coniferae. /The three "species," with *fremonti,* are now ranked as subspecies of the red squirrel./

All these squirrels /chipmunks/ inhabit elevated regions of country, and in addition to their habit of climbing, have burrows in the ground, wherein they make their dormitories, and dwell in winter; whilst in summer they select the hollow of a tree, in which they construct their nests.

Their note is peculiar, like *chicharee chicharee* repeated in quick succession, and differing from the *qua qua quah* note of the larger squirrels.

By their habit of burrowing or living in holes in the ground, these small squirrels make an approach to the genus *Tamias,* or ground squirrels.

RED SQUIRREL

Tamiasciurus hudsonicus fremonti (Audubon and Bachman)

North American red squirrels, often called "chickarees" and "pine squirrels," are spunky, active and colorful. Excepting flying squirrels, they are the smallest of the tree squirrels. They are also among the most expert aerialists in the mammal world. It is easy for them to leap eight to 10 feet from tree to tree and to hang by the claws of their hind feet to reach tempting fruit below. Most travel is through the trees. When foraging on the ground, they bound gracefully rather than trotting or running. They seldom walk.

Their favorite habitat is coniferous or mixed woodland, but hardwoods are acceptable.

Although they do not hibernate, red squirrels may "hole up" for several days during severe storms. Most daily activity is concentrated in the two hours after sunrise and before sunset. This species is non-migratory but individuals may move if food becomes short or their nests are disturbed. A red squirrel may swim for several miles. Its head and tail are held up high and dry. (Continued)

117

SCIURUS HUDSONIUS, PENNANT.

HUDSON'S BAY SQUIRREL CHICKAREE RED SQUIRREL

. . .The Chickaree, or Hudson's Bay Squirrel /red squirrel/, is the most common species of this numerous genus around New-York and throughout the Eastern States. It is a graceful, lively animal, and were you to walk with us through the woods in the neighbourhood of our great commercial metropolis, where boys and sportsmen (?) for years past have been hunting in every direction, and killing all the game left in the vicinity; where woodcocks are shot before the first of July, and quails (Virginian partridges) when they are half-grown, in defiance of the laws for their preservation, you would be glad to find the comparative silence which now reigns amid the trees, interrupted by the sprightly querulous cry of the Chickaree, and would pause with us to look at him as he runs along the rocky surface of the ground, or nimbly ascends some tree; for in these woods, once no doubt abounding in both beasts and birds, it is now a hard task to start anything larger than a robin, or a *High-hole* /flicker/, (*Picus /Colaptes/ auratus.*) The Hudon's Bay Squirrel is fearless and heedless, to a great degree, of the presence of man; we have had one occasionally pass through our yard, sometimes ascending an oak or a chesnut, and proceeding leisurely through our small woody lawn. These little animals are generally found singly, although it is not uncommon for many to occupy the same piece of wood-land, if of any extent. In their quick graceful motions from branch to branch, they almost remind one of a bird, and they are always neat and cleanly in their coats, industrious, and well provided for the cold of winter.

In parts of the country, the Chickaree is fond of approaching the farmer's store-houses of grain, or other products of the fields, and occasionally it ventures even so far as to make a nest for itself in some of his outbuildings, and is not dislodged from such snug quarters without undergoing a good deal of persecution.

One of these Squirrels made its nest between the beams and the rafters of a house of the kind we have just spoken of, and finding the skin of a peacock in the loft, appropriated the feathers to compose its nest, and although it was destroyed several times, to test the perseverance of the animal, it persisted in re-constructing it. The Chickaree obtained this name from its noisy chattering note, and like most other Squirrels, is fond of repeating its cries at frequent intervals. Many of the inhabitants of our Eastern States refuse to eat Squirrels of any kind, from some prejudice or other; but we can assure our readers that the flesh of this species, and many others, is both tender and well-flavoured . . .

The habits of this little Squirrel are, in several particulars, peculiar; whilst the larger Gray Squirrels derive their sustenance from buds and nuts, chiefly inhabit warm or temperate climates, and are constitutionally fitted to subsist during winter on a small quantity of food, the Chickaree exhibits the greatest sprightliness and activity amidst the snows and frosts of our Northern regions, and consequently is obliged, during the winter season, to consume as great a quantity of food as at any other. Nature has, therefore, instructed it to make provision in the season of abundance for the long winter that is approaching; and the quantity of nuts and seeds it often lays up in its store-house, is almost incredible. On one occasion we were present when a bushel and a half of shell-barks /shag-bark hickory/ (*Carya alba* /now *C. ovata*/), and chesnuts, were taken from a hollow tree occupied by a single pair of these industrious creatures; although generally the quantity of provision laid up by them is considerably less. The Chickaree has too much foresight to trust to a single hoard, and it often has several, in different localities among the neighbouring trees, or in burrows dug deep in the earth. Occasionally these stores are found under leaves, beneath logs, or in brush-heaps; at other times they are deposited in holes in the ground . . .

. . . This species can both swim and dive. We once observed some lads shaking a Red-Squirrel from a sapling that grew on the edge of a mill-pond. It fell into the water and swam to the opposite shore, performing the operation of swimming moderately well, and reminding us by its movements of the meadow-mouse, when similarly occupied. It was "headed" by its untiring persecutors on the opposite shore, where on being pelted with sticks, we noticed it diving two or three times, not in the graceful curving manner of the mink, or musk-rat, but with short and ineffectual plunges of a foot or two at a time. . . .

RED SQUIRREL

Tamiasciurus hudsonicus hudsonicus (Erxleben)

The red squirrel can be a silent observer or a noisy watchman that alerts the woodland. It stamps its feet and switches its body and tail with every call. The chattering alarm of "cher--r--r--r" starts at a high pitch and then descends as it slows. This may be prolonged for five or six seconds and carry for a quarter of a mile. A more routine call, "kak-kak-kak," is repeated at intervals of a minute or less. During mating season the squirrel spends less time exclaiming, chattering and scolding.

Home is a tree cavity or weather-tight leaf nest perhaps 60 feet high. Temporary, loosely woven nests are for casual use. Burrows are dug in the ground mostly for storage except in the far north where trees are dwarfed. Fecal pellets are dropped carelessly but not in the nest. During the winter, tunnels are made through the snow to reach food. A barred owl has been seen to swoop down into an entrance, disappearing right up to its tailfeathers, and yank out the unwary builder. (Continued)

SCIURUS LANIGUNOSUS, BACH.

DOWNY SQUIRREL.

This downy and beautifully furred squirrel exists in the north-western portions of our continent. The specimen from which our drawing was made, is the only one which we have seen, and was brought from near Sitka, by Mr. J. K. TOWNSEND, who kindly placed it in our hands, in order that we might describe it. As the animal was presented to Mr. TOWNSEND by an officer attached to the Hudson's Bay Company, and was not observed by him, he could give us no account of its habits. We think, however, that from its close approximation to that group of squirrels of which the Hudson's Bay, or chickaree squirrel, is the type, and with which we are familiar, we can form a pretty correct judgment in regard to its general characteristics, and we will venture to say that it is less agile and less expert in climbing than the chickaree; it no doubt burrows in the earth in winter like the latter species, and as its tail is more like that of a spermophile /ground squirrel/ than the tail of a /tree/ squirrel, although the rest of its specific characters are those of the true /or tree/ squirrels, we are disposed to consider it a closely connecting link between these two genera, and it very probably, according to circumstances, adopts the mode of life commonly observed in each.

/Editor's Comment: The specimen which formed the basis for Dr. Bachman's new "species," the downy squirrel, came not from Sitka, Alaska, but from a now-defunct trading post, Fort McLoughlin, on Campbell Island (near Vancouver Island), British Columbia. Townsend apparently had been misinformed regarding the locality where the animal was killed. It proved to be, not a "connecting link," but a true red squirrel./

RED SQUIRREL

Tamiasciurus hudsonicus lanuginosus (Bachman)

Normally solitary, most red squirrels mate briefly and promiscuously in February and March. After 38 days, the one to seven young (usually four or five) are born pink-skinned and blind, weighing about ¼ ounce. White hair on the belly and black on the back appears in 10 days and three days later reddish hair on the head. Eyes open in 27 days and the youngsters begin to climb about, even before being weaned at the age of five weeks. If they climb too far or dangerously, the mother grabs them with her teeth and hoists them to safety. Adults play with their young and with each other. Soon after the juveniles begin eating solids, they drive the mother out of the crowded nest, or she leaves of her own volition. South of Canada, many females have a second brood between July and September — some of those in the south may have three. The population is cyclic with peaks at five- to 10-year intervals. A red squirrel in the wild would be elderly at eight years of age; most die before they are four years old. (Continued)

SCIURUS RICHARDSONII. BACH.

RICHARDSON'S COLUMBIAN SQUIRREL.

The only knowledge we have obtained of the habits of this species, is contained in a note from Mr. TOWNSEND, who obtained the specimen from which the above description was taken. He remarks: "It is evidently a distinct species. Its habits are very different from the *Sciurus Hudsonius* /presumably the eastern form of the red squirrel/. It frequents the pine trees in the high ranges of the Rocky Mountains west of the Great Chain, feeding upon the seeds contained in the cones. These seeds are large and white, and contain a good deal of nutriment. The Indians eat a great quantity of them, and esteem them good.

"The note of this squirrel is a loud jarring chatter, very different from the noise of *Sciurus Hudsonius*. It is not at all shy, frequently coming down to the foot of the tree to reconnoitre the passenger, and scolding at him vociferously. It is, I think, a scarce species."

LEWIS and CLARK speak of the "Brown Squirrel" as inhabiting the banks of the Columbia river. Our specimen is labelled, Rocky Mountains, Aug. 12, 1834. From Mr. TOWNSEND'S account, it exists on the Mountains a little west of the highest ridge. It will be found no doubt to have an extensive range along those elevated regions.

In the Russian possessions to the Northward, it is replaced by the Downy Squirrel, *(Sc. lanuginosus,)* /see preceeding account/ and in the South, near the Californian Mountains, within the Territories of the United States, by another small species.

The first account we have of this species is from LEWIS and CLARK, who deposited a specimen in the Philadelphia Museum, where it still exists. We have compared this specimen with that brought by Mr. TOWNSEND, and find them identical. The description by LEWIS and CLARK (vol. iii., p. 37) is very creditable to the close observation and accuracy of those early explorers of the untrodden snows of the Rocky Mountains and the valleys beyond, to Oregon.

"The small brown Squirrel," they say, "is a beautiful little animal, about the size and form of the red squirrel *(Sc. Hudsonius)* of the Atlantic States and Western lakes. . . . This animal subsists chiefly on the seeds of various species of pine and is always found in the pine country.". . . .

/Editor's Comment: Townsend collected the squirrel, which became the type for Dr. Bachman's new species, near the head of Big Lost River in south central Idaho. It was a young animal only about two-thirds grown, a fact which helped to lead both Townsend and Bachman to believe it was a distinct species. Evidently, the specimen which was obtained earlier by Lewis and Clark was also an immature (and therefore small) squirrel./

RED SQUIRREL

Tamiasciurus hudsonicus richardsoni (Bachman)

The red squirrel stores much more than it can eat. Middens of buried pine cones and discarded shuckings may be up to 35 feet long by 10 feet wide and three feet deep. Additional small stores are hidden in many places on its 200-yard territory. Bones are gnawed and sap is sucked from the cuts that the squirrel makes in branches. (Icicles from dripping sap are licked eagerly.) Eaten on the spot are seeds, nuts, tree flowers, buds, bark, lichens, berries, snails, carrion and sometimes birds' eggs and nestlings. After finishing meals, the red squirrel licks its paws and washes its face repeatedly.

The species measures 11½ to 14 inches, including the tail which is 4 to 5¾ inches. Weight is 5 to 11 ounces. It occurs from the limit of tree growth inside the Arctic Circle south (in the mountains) to northern South Carolina and southern New Mexico. Although the pelt is small it is durable, and in northern Alaska and Canada red squirrels are trapped and sold for fur.

123

SCIURUS DOUGLASSII, GRAY.

DOUGLASS SQUIRREL

Our specimens of Douglass' Squirrel were procured by Mr. TOWNSEND. He remarks in his notes: — "This is a very plentiful species, inhabits the pine trees along the shores of the Columbia River, and like our common Carolina /gray/ squirrel lays in a great quantity of food for consumption during the winter months. This food consists of the cones of the pine, with a few acorns. Late in autumn it may be seen very busy in the tops of the trees, throwing down its winter stock; after which, assisted by its mate, it gathers in and stows away its store, in readiness for its long incarceration."

/Editor's Comment: Bachman intended to name his new species in honor of his friend and collector of the specimens, J. K. Townsend. Before publication of his paper, however, Bachman learned that nearly two years previously, in 1836, John Edward Gray of the British Museum had named a similar specimen after its collector, the young Scottish botanist David Douglass, who obtained it near the mouth of the Columbia River. Because Gray had not given even a brief description of the animal, his name was not binding according to the rules of science. However, Bachman adopted the name, "Douglass Squirrel," and published it over his previously prepared description. Thus Bachman's name is attached to the scientific designation as the "discoverer" of the species. Douglass' name has since been Anglicized by dropping the final letter./

DOUGLAS' SQUIRREL

Tamiasciurus douglasii douglasii (Bachman)

In the humid, dim and often foggy forests of the Pacific Slope, Douglas' squirrel has evolved. Belonging to the same genus as the red squirrel, it is also called "pine squirrel" and "chickaree." Although very similar in size, color, habits and disposition, it can be recognized by the color of its underparts. Those of the red squirrel are whitish; those of Douglas' are rusty. Even when the two species occupy the same territory, as in north-central Washington and southwestern British Columbia, there is no intergradation.

Douglas' squirrels live in tree cavities and in nests woven from twigs, conifer needles and shredded bark. The spring litter, containing usually four but occasionally up to seven young, is born early in June. Some females produce a second brood in September.

In spring Douglas' squirrel is shy and almost silent. By fall its mood has changed; it is unwary to the point of boldness, and it becomes very voluble. Similar to the red squirrel's churring, the most frequent sounds of Douglas' species are softer and less distinct. It also barks in several tones; the danger signal is a loud, explosive "pe-ee!" (Continued)

SCIURUS MOLLIPILOSUS, AUD. AND BACH.

SOFT-HAIRED SQUIRREL.

This species was procured in Upper California, near the Pacific ocean, and we are obliged to confess ourselves entirely unacquainted with its habits. From its form, however, we have no doubt of its having more the manners of the Carolina gray-squirrel than those of the chickaree /or red squirrel/. We may suppose that it lives on trees, and never burrows in the ground, as the chickaree sometimes does.

DOUGLAS' SQUIRREL

Tamiasciurus douglasii mollipilosus (Audubon and Bachman)

This squirrel cuts quantities of pine cones (each with a single bite) and then drops them to the ground. One squirrel was seen to clip off 537 green sequoia cones in 30 minutes with only one rest of a little over a minute. When tired of cutting, the chickaree gathers the cones and buries them nearby in moist soil, sometimes even in water, to keep them from drying out, opening and losing the seeds before the lean winter arrives.

Even when biting off the stickiest stems of cones, the pine squirrel usually avoids getting pitch on its face. Other seeds (firs, spruces and maples), hazelnuts, berries of dogwood, salal, huckleberry and Oregon grape and mushrooms supplement its diet. Potential enemies are the marten, fisher, coyote, fox and weasels.

Douglas' squirrels are 11 to 14 inches long, including the 4- to 6-inch tail, and weigh 7 to 8 ounces. They occur from west-central British Columbia to San Francisco Bay, and inland south past Lake Tahoe in the Sierra Nevada.

PTEROMYS VOLUCELLA, GMEL.
COMMON FLYING SQUIRREL.

... We recollect a locality not many miles from Philadelphia, where, in order to study the habits of this interesting species, we occasionally strayed into a meadow containing here and there immense oak and beech trees. One afternoon we took our seat on a log in the vicinity to watch their lively motions. . . . for some time not a Flying-Squirrel made its appearance. Suddenly, however, one emerged from its hole and ran up to the top of a tree; another soon followed, and ere long dozens came forth, and commenced their graceful flights from some upper branch to a lower bough. At times one would be seen darting from the topmost branches of a tall oak, and with wide-extended membranes and outspread tail gliding diagonally through the air, till it reached the foot of a tree about fifty yards off, when at the moment we expected to see it strike the earth, it suddenly turned upwards and alighted on the body of the tree. It would then run to the top and once more precipitate itself from the upper branches, and sail back again to the tree it had just left. Crowds of these little creatures joined in these sportive gambols; there could not have been less than two hundred. Scores of them would leave each tree at the same moment, and cross each other, gliding like spirits through the air, seeming to have no other object in view than to indulge a playful propensity. We watched and mused till the last shadows of day had disappeared. . . .

During the day this species avoids the light, its large eyes like those of the owl cannot encounter the glare of the sun; hence it appears to be a dull and uninteresting pet, crawling into your sleeve or pocket, and seeking any dark place of concealment. But twilight and darkness are its season for activity and pleasure. . . .

This is a harmless and very gentle species, becoming tolerably tame in a few hours. After a few days it will take up its residence in some crevice in the chamber, or under the eaves of the house, and it or its progeny may be seen in the vicinity years afterwards. On one occasion we took from a hollow tree four young with their dam; she seemed quite willing to remain with them, and was conveyed home in the crown of a hat. We had no cage immediately at hand, and placed them in a drawer in our library, leaving a narrow space open to enable them to breathe; next morning we ascertained that the parent had escaped through the crevice, and as the window was open, we presumed that she had abandoned her young rather than be subject to confinement in such a narrow and uncomfortable prison. We made efforts for several days to preserve the young alive by feeding them on milk; they appeared indifferent about eating, and yet seemed to thrive and were in good order. A few evenings afterwards we were surprised and delighted to see the mother glide through the window and enter the still open drawer; in a moment she was nestled with her young. She had not forsaken them, but visited them nightly and preserved them alive by her attentions. We now placed the young in a box near the window, which was left partly open. In a short time she had gained more confidence and remained with them during the whole day. They became very gentle, and they and their descendants continued to reside on the premises for several years. . . .

Although the diet of this species generally consists of nuts and seeds of various kinds, together with the buds of trees in winter, yet we have known many instances in which it manifested a strong desire for animal food. On several occasions we found it caught in box-traps set for the ermine /long-tailed weasel/, which had been baited only with meat. The bait, (usually a blue jay,) was frequently wholly consumed by the little prisoner. In a room in which several Flying-Squirrels had been suffered to go at large, we one evening left a pine grosbeak, (*Corythus /Pinicola/ enucleator,*) a rare specimen, which we intended to preserve on the following morning. On searching for it however next day it was missing; we discovered its feet and feathers at last in the box of the Flying-Squirrels, they having consumed the whole body.

This species has from three to six young at a time. We have been assured by several persons that they produce young but once a year in the Northern and Middle States. In Carolina, however, we think they have two litters in a season, as we have on several occasions seen young in May and in September. . . .

SOUTHERN FLYING SQUIRREL

Glaucomys volans volans (Linnaeus)

The velvet-furred flying squirrel is the smallest, most carnivorous, and only nocturnal tree squirrel. It is not a flyer — but a glider. Spreading out its four feet and "wing" membranes, it leaps from the treetops at an angle of 30 to 50 degrees. By turning its flattened tail and varying the slack of the membranes, it steers, stabilizes and regulates speed. Swooping diagonally over a horizontal distance of 150 feet, it suddenly turns upward and lands with a thud on the lower trunk of another tree.

Southern flying squirrels live in hardwood forests. Besides tree dens, and rarely a nest in a ground burrow, they build leaf nests. Sometimes they sleep and eat hanging upside down by their claws. Sleeping nests are always kept clean; old nests are apparently used for feeding stations and latrines. In most details, the life history is similar to that of the northern species as related in following accounts.

Southern flying squirrels are 8½ to 10¼ inches long, including the 3¼- to 4¾-inch tail, and weigh 2 to 4 ounces. Range: southern Ontario to the Gulf Coast; also in Mexico.

PTEROMYS ALPINUS, RICH.

ROCKY MOUNTAIN FLYING SQUIRREL.

We found this interesting Flying-Squirrel in abundance at Quebec, and many of them were offered for sale in the markets of that city during our sojourn there. It appears indeed to take the place of the common small Flying-Squirrel of the United States (*P. volucella* /*Glaucomys volans,* the southern flying squirrel/) in Lower Canada, where we did not observe the latter east of Montreal.

We heard that one of these pretty animals was caught alive by a soldier who saw it on the plains of Abraham, and ran it down.

A brood of young of this species, along with the mother was kept in confinement by an acquaintance of ours, for about four months, and the little ones, five in number, were suckled in the following manner: the younglings stood on the ground floor of the cage, whilst the mother hung her body downwards, and secured herself from falling by clinging to the perch immediately above her head by her fore-feet. This was observed every day, and some days as frequently as eight or ten times.

This brood was procured as follows: a piece of partially cleared wood having been set on fire, the labourers saw the Flying-Squirrel start from a hollow stump with a young one in her mouth, and watched the place where she deposited it, in another stump at a little distance. The mother returned to her nest, and took away another and another in succession, until all were removed, when the wood-cutters went to the abode now occupied by the affectionate animal, and caught *her* already *singed* by the fire, and her five young unscathed.

After some time a pair of the young were given away to a friend. The three remaining ones, as well as the mother, were killed in the following manner:

The cage containing them was hung near the window, and one night during the darkness, a /brown or Norway/ rat, or rats (*mus decumanus* /now *Rattus norvegicus*/), caught hold of the three young through the bars, and ate off all their flesh, leaving the skins almost entire, and the heads remaining inside the bars. The mother had had her thigh broken and her flesh eaten from the bone, and yet this good parent was so affectionately attached to her brood that when she was found in this pitiable condition in the morning, she was clinging to her offspring, and trying to nurse them as if they had still been alive.

This species is said to bear a considerable resemblance to the European Flying-Squirrel. It was first described by FORSTER, who not having distinguished it from the European animal, PENNANT stands as its discoverer.

We /J. J. Audubon/ did not observe any of these Flying-Squirrels on the borders of the Yellow Stone or Upper Missouri, and have no further information as to their habits. . . .

We have learned little of the habits of this animal. DRUMMOND, who obtained it on the Rocky Mountains, states that it lives in pine forests, seldom venturing from its retreats except during the night.

From its heavy structure, and the shortness of the bony process that supports the flying membrane, we are led to infer that it is less capable of supporting itself in sailing from one tree to another, than the other species of this genus.

Fig. 1

Fig. 2

NORTHERN FLYING SQUIRREL

Glaucomys sabrinus sabrinus (Shaw)

Larger than the southern species, the northern flying squirrel has proportionately bigger eyes and ears. It lives in old-growth mixed coniferous and deciduous woods. Preferring moist forest, it scampers over mossy logs or leaps from tree to tree. Northern flying squirrels are found rarely in hardwoods, the habitat of the southern species, but where the ranges of the two species overlap *sabrinus* can be distinguished by larger size and slate-colored base of the white fur on the abdomen.

The winter home is nearly always a tree cavity but oc-

casionally the loft or corner of a vacant cabin is used. In summer, the squirrel builds nests of twigs and strips of bark against the trunks of spruce or other conifers from five to 35 feet above the ground. About 12 inches in diameter, the nest has one or sometimes two entrances and is lined with soft shredded bark, lichens or other soft material.

Less vocal than its southern cousin, the northern flying squirrel communicates with a series of faint, low-pitched chirps. If frightened, it gives a loud penetrating shriek or squeal. (Continued)

PTEROMYS ORIGONENSIS, BACHMAN.

OREGON FLYING SQUIRREL.

The habits of this handsome Flying Squirrel, we regret to say, are almost unknown to us; but from its general appearance, it is undoubtedly as active and volatile as our common little species; and much do we regret that we have never seen it launch itself into the air, and sail from the highest branch of one of the enormous pines of the valley of the Columbia river, to some other tall and magnificent tree. Indeed, much should we like to know the many works of the Creator that yet remain to be discovered, examined, figured, and described, in the vast mountain-valleys and forests beyond the highest peaks of the great Rocky Chain.

We hope, however, to obtain a good deal of information through various sources ere the conclusion of this work, from the remote portions of our Continent that have not yet been well explored by naturalists, and we shall then perhaps be able to say something more in regard to the subject of this article, of which we can now only add, that Mr. TOWNSEND remarks, that it inhabits the pine woods of the Columbia /River/, near the sea, and has the habits of *P. volucella* /*Glaucomys volans,* the southern flying squirrel/.

NORTHERN FLYING SQUIRREL

Glaucomys sabrinus oregonensis (Bachman)

Northern flying squirrels have only one mating season a year — March to mid-May. The usually three young are born in May or June and nurse one or two months. If danger threatens, the mother repeatedly leaps or glides with offspring in mouth until all are saved. Two weeks after weaning, the young are nearly full grown and on their own.

Flying squirrels are rather gregarious and up to 50 have been known to snuggle together in a single den during cold weather. They live on nuts, seeds, berries, buds and mushrooms, and are fond of meat, fresh or decayed.

If handled gently, a flying squirrel will seldom bite, even when first caught. A delightful pet, its only shortcoming in captivity is its night schedule — an inconvenience for most human observers!

About two inches longer than the southern form, northern squirrels weigh 3 to 6½ ounces. They live from the northern limit of sizeable trees to the southern Appalachians and the Sierra Nevada.

PSEUDOSTOMA BOREALIS, RICH. MSS.
THE CAMAS RAT.

The Camas Rat /northern pocket gopher/ derives its name, according to RICHARDSON, from its fondness for the bulbous root of the quamash or camas plant *(Scilla esculenta* /now *Camassia scilloides,* the camass/).

Like all the pouched Rats /pocket gophers/ of America, it feeds upon nuts, roots, seeds, and grasses, and makes burrows, extending long distances, but not very far beneath the surface of the ground, throwing up mole-hills in places as it comes to the surface. These animals are generally found to be in a certain degree gregarious, or at least a good many of them inhabiting the same locality, and more or less associated together; and are said to be very common on the plains of the Multnomah river.

Mr. DOUGLAS informed Sir JOHN RICHARDSON that they may be easily snared in the summer.

We believe that some of the Indians of those parts of Oregon in which this burrowing Rat exists eat them, but have no information concerning the peculiarities they exhibit, the number of young they produce at a time, or the depredations they commit on the fields and gardens of the settlers. . . .

NORTHERN POCKET GOPHER

Thomomys talpoides clusius Coues

The pocket gopher occurs only in North America. A fur-lined pocket with outside opening extends from each side of its lower jaw down to the shoulders. With first one forepaw and then the other, or with both at one time, the animal stuffs food and bedding into these carryalls to take to food storage rooms or nest chamber. Having arrived, the animal empties the load by squeezing forward with both paws. These pouches can be turned inside out and have a special stretching muscle to pull them back into place.

The pocket gopher spends most of its life underground searching for food. Day and night, summer and winter, it keeps on extending its tunnel system. Powerful forelegs have huge feet with long, sharp digging claws that fold back under the soles when the gopher is walking. Paired sets of yellow incisors are set well ahead of the cheek teeth. The lips close back of the incisors so that when the teeth are used as chipping tools in hard earth or rocky soil, or for shearing roots, the animal doesn't get dirt in its mouth. Little deters its progress — not even electric and telephone cables. This may result in short-circuited railroad signal systems and home power systems, and cause the utility companies to incur considerable expense.

The gopher's eyes are small with tightly fitting lids to keep out most loose dirt. Ears are small and valved for the same reason. The short hind legs with small curved claws are strong but function in tunneling only by pushing forward, or kicking dirt backward. The scantily haired tail is a tactile organ for feeling the way when the gopher runs backward (as often and fast as forward) in the dark, narrow tunnel.

Finally, the loose skin is covered with soft glossy hair to which damp soil does not adhere. There is no underfur.

The gopher shakes off dirt and cleans its claws with its teeth before settling down to rest or a stored meal. The incisor teeth of all rodents and rabbits are rootless and continue to grow outward as long as the animal lives. Those of the pocket gopher apparently grow twice as fast as most. The upper buck teeth grow about nine inches every year, and the lower ones 14 inches.

After a brief spring mating, the pocket gopher resumes its solitary existence. High-mountain litters have been found to contain four or five young while those at lower elevations, in the northern part of the range, average seven. Accordingly, lowland females have six or seven pairs of teats while those at high altitudes usually have only four. Blind, hairless, toothless and pocketless, the young grow rapidly; most of them are nearly adult size by early autumn and breed when one year old.

* * * *

The three "species" described first by Richardson and included in the original *Quadrupeds* under the names "Camas Rat" (above plate and opposite page), "Columbia Pouched Rat" (p. 136, 137) and "Mole-shaped Pouched Rat" (p. 138, 139) have since been determined to be merely subspecies of the northern pocket gopher.

The range of the species extends from the Dakotas to Puget Sound and from central Saskatchewan to northern New Mexico. The animal's length is 6½ to 10 inches, including the tail of 1½ to 3 inches.

GEOMYS DOUGLASSII, RICHARDSON

COLUMBIA POUCHED RAT.

This species of Sand-Rat /pocket gopher/ was first obtained by Mr. DAVID DOUGLAS, near the mouth of the Columbia river, since which, specimens have been sent to England by various collectors. According to Mr. DOUGLAS, the animal, "when in the act of empyting its pouches, sits on its hams like a Marmot or Squirrel, and squeezes its sacs against the breast with the chin and fore-paws."

"These little Sand-Rats are numerous in the neighbourhood of Fort Vancouver, where they inhabit the declivities of low hills, and burrow in the sandy soil. They feed on acorns, nuts *(Corylus rostrata /C. californica,* hazel/), and grasses, and commit great havoc in the potato-fields adjoining to the fort, not only by eating the potatoes on the spot, but by carrying off large quantities of them in their pouches." — *Fauna Boreali Americana,* p. 201.

NORTHERN POCKET GOPHER

Thomomys talpoides douglasii (Richardson)

Living from tropical lowlands to cold, high mountain "tundra," pocket gophers have become diversified by adaptation to their soil environments. For example, the gophers whose coats matched their background most closely were less noticeable to predators. After thousands of generations of survival of the fittest, gophers' coats now range from black (on volcanic soils) to pale cream (on desert sands).

Since gophers are often restricted by natural barriers to local areas such as mountain meadows, individual populations have developed a degree of uniqueness which would be impossible for wide ranging mammals like deer and wolves. As a result, some 300 kinds (subspecies) of pocket gophers have been named. There is little or no overlap of any of these various kinds, probably partly because pocket gophers are normally solitary and notoriously ferocious toward each other.

Coat colors, length of claws and other physical characteristics may differ somewhat, but habits do not. When tunneling, earth is scraped off with the forefeet, kicked under the belly and to the rear. When a load has accumulated, the animal turns a half somersault to reverse its direction. Holding the pile to its chest with the forearms, it pushes the dirt to a lateral tunnel and out to the surface. After heaping a mound as high as it can, the gopher backs down into the tunnel and plugs the exit solidly from within.

A gopher's mound is roughly fan-shaped with the plugged opening at one side, while a mole hill, having been formed from a vertical rather than a lateral shaft, is circular and the peak of the cone is nearly over the opening. The main shaft of the gopher's burrow is from six inches to three feet deep and does not raise a ridge on the surface. One gopher may drive several hundred feet of tunnel within its one- or two-acre territory.

In undeveloped areas, gophers perform valuable work by mixing the soil and adding much humus to lower layers. In farming areas, however, they bore through irrigation structures and, by eating the roots, cause destruction in planted fields and orchards.

* * * *

The "Columbia Pouched Rat" (above plate and opposite page) is now classified as a subspecies of the northern pocket gopher. A medium sized pocket gopher, it occurs in an area only five by seven miles in extent, on either side of the Columbia River at Vancouver, Washington, where the original specimen was obtained by Richardson, probably in 1825.

PSEUDOSTOMA TALPOIDES, RICH.

MOLE SHAPED POUCHED RAT.

Very little is known of the habits of this peculiar sand-rat /pocket gopher/. The manners, however, of all the species of the genus *Pseudostoma* /now *Thomomys* and other genera/ are probably very similar: they live principally under ground, and leave their galleries, holes, or burrows, pretty much as we of the genus *Homo* quit our houses, for the purpose of procuring the necessaries of life, or for pleasure, although they do find a portion of their food while making the excavations which serve them as places in which to shelter themselves and bring forth their young. They are generally nocturnal, and in the day time prefer coming abroad during cloudy weather.

They never make their appearance, nor do they work in their galleries or burrows during the winter in our northern latitudes, unless it be far beneath the hard frozen ground, which would not permit them to make new roads.

RICHARDSON says that as soon as the snow disappears in the spring, and whilst the ground is as yet only partially thawed, little heaps of earth newly thrown up attest the activity of this animal.

The specimen from which our figures were made was presented to the Zoological Society /of London/ by Mr. LEADBEATER /a London fur dealer/, who obtained it from Hudson's Bay. It also served Dr. RICHARDSON for his description: he was inclined to identify it with a small animal inhabiting the banks of the Saskatchewan, which throws up little mounds in the form of mole hills, but generally rather larger; he, however, could not procure any specimens.

As an evidence that this animal never feeds upon worms, he mentions the fact that none exist in high northern latitudes. A gentleman who had for forty years superintended the cultivation of considerable pieces of ground on the banks of the Saskatchewan, informed him that during the whole of that period he never saw an earthworm turned up. All the species of *Pseudostoma,* as far as our knowledge goes, feed on bulbs, roots, and grasses.

The pouches serve as sacks, in which after filling them with food they carry it to their nests in their subterranean retreats, where they deposit considerable quantities, which evidently serve them as supplies throughout the winter.

We are under the impression that none of the species of this genus become perfectly dormant in winter, as we have observed in Georgia a few fresh hillocks thrown up by the Southern pouched-rat /southeastern pocket gopher, *Geomys pinetus*/ after each warm day in that season.

NORTHERN POCKET GOPHER

Thomomys talpoides talpoides (Richardson)

Guided by smell, the pocket gopher burrows for underground parts of succulent plants. Sometimes, however, the leaves and stems above ground become too tempting. These can be reached only by venturing into a little-known and dangerous world.

After tunneling to the surface, the gopher sticks its head out cautiously. If all seems well, it quickly cuts off the nearest plant, hastily backs down into the burrow and immediately plugs the opening. Some species are even more wary; they merely stretch out as far as they can reach, keeping their hind feet still in the entrance. Short legs and poor eyesight make gophers easy prey above ground. Except when a male is searching for a mate, a juvenile is looking for territory of its own, or a gopher in a snow tunnel far from home suddenly finds the roof melted away, it never goes farther than 30 inches from the safety of its burrow opening.

Hawks, owls and foxes are watching to snatch the unwary; badgers dig the gophers out of their tunnels; weasels and snakes go in after them. For this reason, pocket gophers keep all of their entrances plugged. A "smart" gopher not only pushes a mound up against the doorway, but blocks the entire side tunnel.

The gopher's food may be eaten at once or stored in side chambers off the lower tunnel. Much of these supplies spoil and are then sealed off with earth plugs. Defecating as well as old nesting rooms are closed and new ones excavated from time to time. Numerous insects and arthropods live in the nest, the runways and at least a few on the animal.

No pocket gopher takes time out to hibernate. In the north, in higher altitudes, the animal may tunnel through the snow looking for food and drier ground. In this way it may cross a river that it would never try to swim. Many an explorer never finds its way back again. It builds a spherical nest with inedible food remnants (no insects or arthropods up here) about the size of the one underground. Large piles of droppings accumulate conveniently nearby, and holes in the snow tunnel are plugged with dried grass. If the summer home has been a good one, and the gopher is merely ambitious, it keeps a corridor open between the snow burrow and underground where it has access to stored food. Gophers that are satisfied with their residences continue to dig underground throughout the winter. They may pack excavations into old unused extensions or into snow tunnels. When the snow melts, the network of "ropes" of earth remain, attesting that work has continued below. Unlike most other animals, gophers tend to weigh more when the winter is over than at other seasons.

* * * *

The "Mole-shaped Pouched Rat" (above plate and opposite page) is now named the typical subspecies of the northern pocket gopher. It occurs from central Montana and Alberta east to Manitoba. No species of pocket gopher lives within 300 miles of Hudson Bay, so the statement on the opposite page concerning the origin of the Zoological Society's specimen probably refers to the territory of the Hudson's Bay Company; i.e., western Canada.

PSEUDOSTOMA BURSARIUS, SHAW.

CANADA POUCHED RAT.

During a visit which we /John J. Audubon/ made to the Upper Missouri in the spring and summer of 1843, we had many opportunities of studying the habits of this species. In the neighbourhood of St. Louis, at the hospitable residence of the late PIERRE CHOUTEAU, Esq. /fur trader, Indian agent and founder, with Manuel Lisa and others, of the St. Louis Missouri Fur Company/, we procured several of them alive. In that section of country they are called "Muloes." /from the French *mulots* — field mice/

They are considered by the gardeners in that vicinity as great plagues, devouring every tap-root vegetable, or grass, within their reach, and perforating the earth in every direction, not only at night, but oftentimes during the day.

Having observed some freshly thrown up mounds in Mr. CHOUTEAU's garden, several servants were called, and set to work to dig out the animals, if practicable, alive; and we soon dug up several galleries worked by the Muloes, in different directions. One of the main galleries was about a foot beneath the surface of the ground, except where it passed under the walks, in which places it was sunk rather lower. We turned up this entire gallery, which led across a large garden-bed and two walks, into another bed, where we discovered that several fine plants had been killed by these animals eating off their roots just beneath the surface of the ground. The burrow ended near these plants under a large rose-bush. We then dug out another principal burrow, but its terminus was amongst the roots of a large peach-tree, some of the bark of which had been eaten off by these animals. We could not capture any of them at this time, owing to the ramifications of their galleries having escaped our notice whilst following the main burrows. On carefully examining the ground, we discovered that several galleries existed that appeared to run entirely out of the garden into the open fields and woods beyond, so that we were obliged to give up the chase. . . .

The commonly received opinion is, that these rats fill their pouches with the earth from their burrows, and empty them at the entrance. This is, however, quite an erroneous idea. Of about a dozen, which were shot dead in the very act of rising out of their mounds and burrows, none had any earth in their sacs; but the fore-feet, teeth, nose, and the anterior and upper portion of their heads, were found covered with adherent earth. On the contrary, most of them had their pouches filled with either blades of grass or roots of different trees; and we think of these pouches, that their being hairy within, rather corroborates the idea that they are only used to convey food to their burrows. This species appears to raise up the earth very much in the manner of the common shrew-mole.

When running, the tails of these animals drag on the ground, and they hobble along at times with their long front claws bent underneath their feet as it were, backwards, and never by leaps. They can travel almost as fast backwards as forwards. When turned on their backs they have great difficulty in regaining their natural position, and kick about in the air for a minute or two with their legs and claws extended, before they can turn over. They can bite severely, as their incisors by their size and sharpness plainly indicate; and they do not hesitate to attack their enemies or assailants with open mouth, squealing when in a rage like the common Norway or wharf rat, *(Mus decumanus* /now *Rattus norvegicus/.)* When they fight among themselves they make great use of their snouts, somewhat in the manner of hogs. They cannot travel faster when above ground than a man walks; they feed frequently whilst seated on their rump, using their fore-feet and long claws somewhat in the manner of squirrels. When sleeping they place their heads beneath the shoulder on the breast, and look like a round ball or a lump of earth. . . .

We kept four of these animals alive for several weeks, and they never during that time drank any thing, although we offered them both water and milk. We fed them on cabbages, potatoes, carrots, &c., of which they ate a larger quantity than we supposed them capable of consuming. They tried constantly to make their escape, by gnawing at the floor of the apartment. They slept on any of the clothing about the room which would keep them warm; and these mischievous pets cut the lining of our hunting coat, so that we were obliged to have it repaired and patched. . . .

140

PLAINS POCKET GOPHER

Geomys bursarius bursarius (Shaw)

This pocket gopher, as well as the Southeastern species (shown on page 5), are in a separate genus from the preceding *Thomomys* because of differences (grooves) in the teeth.

In general appearance and mode of life, the two genera are very similar. Like other pocket gophers, the plains species has reversible, fur-lined cheek pockets and powerful claws. Thick fluid from lachrymal glands wash out the tiny eyes when dirt manages to penetrate the tightly closed lids. Its lower incisors grow 14 inches each year. During its brief matings, it has been known to purr. At other times, it hisses in anger and sometimes cries out in pain.

The plains pocket gopher lives in treeless areas of the prairie-plains states, preferring deep soil. One animal may dig and keep in use as much as 500 feet of burrows, 90 percent of which are within a foot of the surface. The remainder may go to an extreme depth of six feet. Spring flooding probably drowns many of the rodents in their tunnels. Even if they could get above ground, they would die because, unlike most mammals, they cannot swim far.

Some digging continues below frost line throughout the winter. At this season, unlike the western species (*Thomomys*), the plains pocket gopher does not shove earth to the surface; instead it moves the soil into some of its upper galleries. In summer, the familiar fan-shaped mounds result from burrowing, although there is little work done during extremely hot weather. Even so, an average pocket gopher in Kansas is estimated to bring up and dump on the surface each year 52 cubic feet — 2¼ tons — of soil!

Males in the spring mating season may have to wander overground in search of mates. Otherwise, all pocket gophers are acutely uncomfortable in the open. This gopher usually only leans out of its burrow to grab a bite of food. If it emerges completely, like its relatives it will cut a stalk and whisk back into the tunnel in seconds.

After a gestation of about 28 days, the litter of three to five (with extremes of one to six) young is born in March, April or May. In the far south, females may produce two litters annually. At birth the young are pink and wrinkled, about two inches long and weigh one-fifth ounce. At five to six weeks, the eyes, ears and cheek pouches open and the lips begin to close at will behind the incisors. Even before fully grown, the juveniles will disperse to dig separate tunnel systems of their own. They are sexually mature at nine months and may live longer than seven years.

The plains pocket gopher measures 8 to 14 inches long, including the 2- to 4-inch tail, and weighs 5 to 18 ounces. It is found between the Mississippi River and the Rockies, from Canada to the Gulf Coast of Texas.

DIPODOMYS PHILLIPSII, GRAY,

POUCHED JERBOA MOUSE

The pretty colours and the liveliness of this little kangaroo-like animal, together with its fine eyes and its simplicity in venturing near man, of whom it does not seem afraid, would no doubt make it a favourite pet in confinement. It is able to exist in very arid and almost barren situations, where there is scarcely a blade of anything green except the gigantic and fantastic cacti that grow in Sonora and various other parts of Western Mexico and California. As JOHN W. AUDUBON and his party travelled through these countries the *Dipodomys Phillippsii* was sometimes almost trampled on by the mules, and was so tame that they could have caught the animal by the hand without difficulty.

This species hop about, kangaroo fashion, and jump pretty far at a leap. When the men encamped towards evening, they sometimes came smelling and moving about the legs of the mules, as if old friends. One was observed by J. W. AUDUBON just before sunset; its beautiful large eyes seemed as if they might be dimmed by the bright rays which fell upon them as it emerged from a hole under a large boulder, but it frisked gaily about, and several times approached him so nearly, as he sat on a stone, that he could have seized it with his hands without any trouble, and without rising from his hard seat.

After a while, as the party had to take up the line of march again, he with some difficulty frightened it, when with a bound or two it reached its hole and disappeared underneath the large stone, but almost immediately came out again; and so great was its curiosity that as the party left the spot it seemed half inclined to follow them.

These animals appear to prefer the sides of stony hills which afford them secure places to hide in, and they can easily convey their food in their cheek-pouches to their nests.

The young when half grown exhibit the markings of the adults to a great extent. This species is crepuscular if not nocturnal, and was generally seen towards dusk, and occasionally in such barren deserts that it was difficult to imagine what it could get to feed on. A dead one was picked up one day while the party were traversing a portion of the great Colorado desert, where nothing could grow but clumps of cacti of different species, and not a drop of water could be found. The only living creatures appeared to be lizards of several kinds, and one or two snakes: the party felt surprised as they toiled on over the sun-baked clay, and still harder gravel, to find the little animal in such a locality.

/Editor's Comment: Bachman's scientific description and J. W. Audubon's painting of Phillips kangaroo rat were based on a specimen in the British Museum. The animals, however, that Audubon saw on his trip to California, by way of the Rio Grande valley and Arizona, and described above cannot have been of this species for the Phillips kangaroo rat is confined to east central Mexico (eastern Vera Cruz to near Mexico City and south to northern Oaxaca).

Judging from Audubon's account and location, the kangaroo rats that he saw were probably Merriam kangaroo rats. This slightly smaller species is friendly and curious with man, as Audubon described; Phillips and most other kangaroo rats are very wild and probably impossible to catch in the hand by firelight or with aid of a flashlight.

Since Audubon and Bachman's time, 20 species and more than 50 races of kangaroo rats have been identified. They are all similar in form, color and habits. Since little is known about the habits of the Phillips kangaroo rat, a general account of the genus is given on the opposite page./

PHILLIPS' KANGAROO RAT

Dipodomys phillipsii phillipsii Gray

Neither a rat nor a kangaroo, this nocturnal animal hops and leaps along on its big hind feet, holding its small forearms in front of its chest. One leap may take it eight feet. The long tail is used for a balance when traveling and a prop when standing. The creature's only defense against predators is to dodge in and out of reach at the rate of 12 miles an hour. The coat blends with the desert, but panting breath and quivering vibrissae may give the fugitive away. Because of owls, coyotes, badgers, weasels, foxes and snakes, the kangaroo rat seldom forages more than 30 feet from its home burrow or escape den. Experienced adults come out only when the moon is dark, but the young are less cautious. Big luminous eyes see well on the darkest of nights; hearing and scent are excellent. Even inside their home burrows, however, they are not safe from digging carnivores.

A vegetarian, except for some insects, the kangaroo rat stuffs seeds, grass for food and bedding into fur-lined cheek pockets and then empties them in its burrow by squeezing both cheeks forward. Thirteen pounds of grass seed (different kinds piled separately) were found in one tunnel; an estimated 680,000 pieces of grass in another.

When fighting one of its own kind, the kangaroo rat seldom bites. Standing up on hind legs, it may spar with its forepaws. More often each combatant kicks furiously first with one hind foot and then another, like fighting cocks. When especially angered, one may hop on its opponent's back and give a terrific beating.

The kangaroo rat seldom cries out but when friend or foe approaches its home, it thumps loudly in the burrow. Since its kidneys are four times as efficient as those of a human being, much less liquid is needed to carry off body wastes. Like many other animals living in dry climates, kangaroo rats metabolize starch into water and use dew and moisture in succulent forbs and grasses. Oil from the gland on the back is well distributed by constant grooming. The surplus is wiped off by rolling in dust bowls maintained for that purpose.

Home is a complex tunnel on two to four levels with large nest chamber and numerous wall pockets and rooms for food storage. Sometimes there are drains below the main living area and nest. At the entrance, excavated dirt from remodeling and repairs, discarded food and trash form a conspicuous mound that may rise four feet high and extend 15 feet across. (A few of the smaller species do not make mounds.) Two to 12 entrances, large enough for the animal to enter when standing up, may be in these piles. Most openings are left open for emergency use.

They usually breed in March and April, those on warm deserts during most other months. The number of young varies from one to six, usually about three. The mother licks and fondles the newborn with her forepaws. If necessary to shift the litter, she grabs them one at a time by the back with her teeth, supporting them with her forearms.

The friendly Merriam kangaroo rats store some food in surface pockets but not in their burrows. Instead they habitually steal from the pantries of larger members of their race. If caught, they get a sound drubbing and maybe death.

Kangaroo rats measure from about 9½ to 14 inches long (50 to 60 percent of this length is tail) and weigh ½ to over 6 ounces. They live on the plains of western North America from Alberta and Saskatchewan to Oaxaca, Mexico.

CASTOR FIBER AMERICANUS, LINN.

AMERICAN BEAVER.

The sagacity and instinct of the Beaver have from time immemorial been the subject of admiration and wonder. The early writers on both continents have represented it as a rational, intelligent, and moral being, requiring but the faculty of speech to raise it almost to an equality, in some respects with our own species. . . . romantic stories have so fastened themselves on the mind of childhood, and have been so generally made a part of our education, that we now are almost led to regret that three-fourths of the old accounts of this extraordinary animal are fabulous; and that with the exception of its very peculiar mode of constructing its domicile, the Beaver is, in point of intelligence and cunning, greatly exceeded by the fox, and is but a few grades higher in the scale of sagacity than the common musk-rat. . . .

Beavers prefer small clear-water rivers, and creeks, and likewise resort to large springs. They, however, at times, frequent great rivers and lakes. The trappers believe that they can have notice of the approach of winter weather, and of its probable severity, by observing the preparations made by the Beavers to meet its rigours; as these animals always cut their wood in good season, and if this be done early, winter is at hand.

The Beaver dams, where the animal is at all abundant, are built across the streams to their very head waters. Usually these dams are formed of mud, mosses, small stones, and branches of trees cut about three feet in length and from seven to twelve inches round. The bark of the trees in all cases being taken off for winter provender, before the sticks are carried away to make up the dam. . . .

In constructing the dams, the sticks, mud and moss are matted and interlaced together in the firmest and most compact manner; so much so that even men cannot destroy them without a great deal of labour. . . .

. . . .In cutting down trees they are not always so fortunate as to have them fall into the water, or even towards it, as the trunks of trees cut down by these animals are observed lying in various positions; although as most trees on the margin of a stream or river lean somewhat towards the water, or have their largest branches extended over it, many of those cut down by the Beavers naturally fall in that direction. . . .

It is stated by some authors that the Beaver feeds on fish. We doubt whether he possesses this habit, as we on several occasions placed fish before those we saw in captivity, and although they were not very choice in their food, and devoured any kind of vegetable, and even bread, they in every case suffered fish to remain untouched in their cages.

The food of this species, in a state of nature, consists of the bark of several kinds of trees and shrubs, and of bulbous and other roots. It is particularly fond of the bark of the birch, *(Betula,)* the cotton-wood, *(Populus,)* and of several species of willow, *(Salix;)* it feeds also with avidity on the roots of some aquatic plants, especially on those of the *Nuphair /Nuphar/ luteum.* In summer, when it sometimes wanders to a distance from the water, it eats berries, leaves, and various kinds of herbage.

The young are born in the months of April and May; those produced in the latter month are the most valuable, as they grow rapidly and become strong and large, not being checked in their growth, which is often the case with those that are born earlier in the season. Some females have been taken in July, with young, but such an event is of rare occurrence. The eyes of the young Beaver are open at birth. The dam at times brings forth as many as seven at a litter, but from two to five is the more usual number. The young remain with the mother for at least a year, and not unfrequently two years, and when they are in a place of security, where an abundance of food is to be procured, ten or twelve Beavers dwell together.

About a month after their birth, the young first follow the mother, and accompany her in the water; they continue to suckle some time longer, although if caught at that tender age, they can be raised without any difficulty, by feeding them with tender branches of willows and other trees. Many Beavers from one to two months old are caught in traps set for old ones. The gravid female keeps aloof from the male until after the young have begun to follow her about. She resides in a separate lodge till the month of August, when the whole family once more dwell together.

BEAVER

Castor canadensis carolinensis Rhoads

The beaver's dense, oiled fur and automatically valved ears and nostrils are waterproof. Small eyes see well under water. Using the flat, scaly tail as a rudder, the rear paddle feet can drive at the rate of two miles an hour. With oversize lungs, it can stay under water 10 to 12 minutes, swimming as much as one-half mile. Double-edged claws on two inner toes of each webbed hind foot are used for combing surface water off the hair and distributing oil.

Most beavers live in a lodge built in shallow water near shore or on an island. One giant lodge was 16 feet high and 40 feet across. The single room in an average lodge is four or five feet across and two to three feet high. Individual nests are around the walls. Two or three exit tunnels lead down from openings in the chamber floor to water deep enough to be free of ice in winter. The pond made by the beavers' dam acts as a moat protecting the lodge, as a waterway for travel, and ice-free (deep) storage for winter food.

Beavers often dig canals in order to tow branches and logs to the pond, instead of dragging them laboriously overland where predators may lie in ambush. Beavers rarely venture more than 500 feet from water. An animal needs only three minutes to cut down a five-inch willow.

When streams are large or very swift, or wherever water levels fluctuate widely, the beaver digs a bank burrow instead of building a pond lodge. This tunnel, with entrance usually under water, is 12 to 18 inches in diameter and up to 50 feet long. It ends above normal high water in a den about three feet across and 1½ to two feet high.

Beavers tend to be monogamous — especially the females. Following the late winter breeding, the annual litter of one to eight (average three or four) young arrive in April to June. The male, which left the lodge just before the birth, returns when the kits are weaned at about five weeks of age. When one year old, the juveniles weigh 20 to 30 pounds but they remain at home until sexually mature, shortly before the arrival of the third litter. Thus a family consists of parents, yearlings, and young of the year.

Adults are 34 to 54 inches long, including the 9- to 18-inch tail. Ordinarily they weigh 30 to 60 pounds, but up to 97 pounds has been recorded. The range is transcontinental, from the tree line south to northeastern Mexico — excepting most of Florida and the lower Great Basin. Following near-extermination by the fur trade, beavers have been restored to most of the continental United States.

MUS RIPARIUS, AUD.&BACH

BANK RAT.

The Rice Meadow-Mouse /Marsh Rice Rat/, as its name implies, is found in particular localities in the banks of the rice-fields of Carolina and Georgia. It burrows in the dykes or dams a few inches above the line of the usual rise of the water. Its burrow is seldom much beyond a foot in depth. It has a compact nest at the extremity, where it produces its young in April. They are usually four or five. In spring this Mouse is in the habit of sitting on the dams near the water, and is so immoveable, and so much resembles the colour of the surrounding earth, that it is seldom noticed until it moves off to its retreat in the banks. We have observed it scratching up the rice when newly planted and before it had been over-flowed by the water. When the rice is in its milky state this animal commences feeding on it, and continues during the autumn and winter, gleaning the fields of the scattered grains. We have also seen its burrows in old banks on deserted rice-fields, and observed that it had been feeding on the large seeds of the Gama grass *(Tripsicum /i.e., Tripsacum/ dactyloides)*, and on those of the wild rye *(Elymus Virginicus)*. A singular part of the history of the Rice Mouse is the fact that in the extensive salt-marshes along the borders of Ashley and Cooper rivers, this species is frequently found a quarter of a mile from the dry ground. Its nest is suspended on a bunch of interlaced marsh grass. In this situation we observed one with five young. At certain seasons this little animal feeds on the seeds of the marsh grass *(Spartina glabra /now S. alterniflora/)*. When these fail it sometimes retires to the shore for food, but has no disrelish to the small crustacea and mollusks that remain on the mud at the subsiding of the tide.

This species swims rapidly, and dives in the manner of the European water-rat /or water vole/ *(Arvicola amphibia)*, or of our *Arvicola Pennsylvanica /Microtus pennsylvanicus*, the meadow vole or mouse/. In an attempt at capturing some alive, they swam so actively, and dived so far from us, that the majority escaped. Those we kept in captivity produced young in May and September; they were fed on grains of various kinds, but always gave the preference to small pieces of meat.

/Editor's Comment: Townsend's Arvicola, now Townsend's vole (Microtus townsendii townsendii (Bachman)), *shown on the plate as Figure 1, resembles a large, dark meadow vole (see p. 163); it lives in low, damp places in western Oregon and Washington. The Sharp-nosed Arvicola, Figure 2, is actually a meadow vole./*

Fig. 3

Fig. 1

Fig. 2

MARSH RICE RAT

Oryzomys palustris palustris (Harlan)

Being nocturnal, rice rats are seldom seen although they are the most abundant animal in many areas of their range. Apparently overcrowding leads to neurotic behavior, for the animals are notoriously quarrelsome at such times. Their normally soft squeals become shrill and sharp, and the animals sometimes kill and eat one of their own kind. In their favor, rice rats are very clean and spend much time moistening their paws and washing their faces and bodies from the soles of their feet to the ends of their tails.

Diving well, they swim long distances underwater if alarmed. They may dig short, shallow tunnels in banks and occasionally locate their nest there. More often it is on the surface under a tangle of brush or weeds, if dry; otherwise it is tied above to tall vegetation like cattails. The spherical nest is woven of dry, shredded plants. Here the one to seven (usually three to five) young are born after a gestation of 25 days. Blind, sparsely haired, and weighing only about one-eighth ounce, they grow rapidly. Soon weaned and driven out by the mother, they are capable of breeding at six to eight weeks of age and attain adult stature at four months. They continue to get heavier, however, until they are a year old — if they live that long. Most wild rats do not.

Cold winters are often hard on rice rats. During these periods they may become more communal. Three, four and even five adults sometimes stay together in a six-inch nest. The nests of single rats are elongated, about two or three inches wide by five to six inches long and much more carelessly and loosely woven than the nursery homes.

Marsh rice rats devour as much as one-quarter of their own weight in food daily. To keep their feet dry, they eat on crude feeding platforms that they make by bending back tall grasses. Here they bolt down succulent plants, berries and seeds, some insects, snails and crustaceans such as fiddler crabs. In rice fields, as Audubon and Bachman wrote, they eat or destroy quantities of the crop. Although they prefer swamp meadows and marshes (both fresh and salt water), they also live on dry upland slopes if vegetation is rank. Scurrying along, they make networks of runways over their territories which, for individuals, average one-half to one acre. (Females have slightly less.)

A high birth rate is required to offset the many casualties from hawks and owls, weasels, skunks, snakes and probably snapping turtles. Although rice rats in the South breed throughout the year, the average length of life is only seven months. During their short lives, like other rodents, they are plagued by parasites and diseases; some are known to have typhus. Breeding rapidly and living well in confinement, they are used in many laboratories for medical and nutritional experiments.

The marsh rice rat is 9 to 12 inches long, including the 4- to 6-inch tail. Its range extends from southern New Jersey and Florida west to southeastern Kansas and Texas. Southward to Panama, some 20 species of rice rats have been described and South America has many more. The group's scientific name of *Oryzomys* is from two Greek words, *oryza* meaning rice, and *mys* — mouse.

MUS MINIMUS, AUD & BACH.

LITTLE HARVEST MOUSE.

By the casual observer, this diminutive little species, on being started from its retreat in the long grass, or under some fence or pile of brushwood, might be mistaken for the young of the white-footed mouse *(Mus /now Peromyscus/ leucopus)*, or that of the jumping mouse *(Meriones Americanus /presumably Zapus hudsonius/)*. It however differs widely from either, and bears but a general resemblance to any of our American species.

About twenty years ago, whilst we /Bachman/ were endeavouring to make ourselves acquainted with the species of smaller rodentia existing in the Southern States, we discovered this little Mouse in the grass fields and along the fences of the plantations a few miles from Charleston, S.C. We procured it in the way in which field mice and other small quadrupeds in all countries can be most easily obtained, by having what are denominated figure of 4 traps, set along fences and ditches in the evening, baited with meat and seeds of various kinds. On the following morning we usually were rewarded with a number of several interesting species. We on two occasions preserved this Mouse in a domestic state, once for a year, during which time it produced two broods of young: the first consisting of four were born in May, the second of three in July. They reared all their young. We fed them at first on pea or ground nuts, *(Hypogea arachis /Arachis hypogaea/,)* cornmeal, (maize,) the latter they preferred boiled, but after having tempted their appetites with the seeds of the Egyptian Millet, *(Pennisitum tiphoideum /now P. glaucum,* pearl millet/,) we discovered that they relished it so well, we allowed it finally to become their exclusive food. They refused meat on all occasions. They were very gentle, allowed themselves to be taken into the hand, and made no attempt to bite, or scarcely any to escape. The young, when born, were naked and blind, but in a very few days became covered with hair, and at a week old were seen peeping out of their nests. We did not discover that the female dragged the young, attached to the teats, in the manner of the white-footed mouse. We placed a female in a cage with a male of the white-footed mouse: they lived on tolerably good terms for six months, but produced no young. We then placed the same female with the male of the common mouse. The latter immediately commenced fighting with our little pet, and in the morning she was found dead in the cage, bitten and mutilated in various places.

This to us is a rare species; after a search of twenty years we have obtained only a dozen specimens from the fields. The nests, which we have oftener seen than their occupants, were placed on the surface of the ground among the long grass, composed of soft withered grasses, and covered over in the manner of the nest of WILSON's meadow mouse. We have also seen the nests of this species under brush-heaps and beneath the rails of fences, similarly constructed.

We doubt whether this species is of much injury to the farmer. It consumes but little grain, is more fond of residing near grass fields, on the seeds of which it subsists, than among the wheat fields. We have observed in its nest small stores of grass seeds — the outer husks and other remains of the Broom grass *(Andropogon dissitiflorum /now A. virginicus/)*— also that of the Crab grass *(Digitaria sanguinalis,)* and small heaps of the seeds of several species of *paspalum* /a pasture grass/, *poa* /bluegrass/ and *panicum,* especially those of *panicum Italicum /Setaria italica,* foxtail millet/.

The specimen from which this description was taken was a little the largest of any we have seen. It was a female captured on the 10th December, and containing four young in its matrix; we presume therefore that this species, like the field mice in general, produce young several times during the summer.

EASTERN HARVEST MOUSE

Reithrodontomys humulis humulis (Audubon and Bachman)

The harvest mouse inhabits waste places and fields where grass and weeds are thick. Home is a soft, globular nest woven of shredded plants, about six or seven inches in diameter, with a single entrance. In dry places, the nest is located on the ground or occasionally in a shallow burrow or crevice; if wet, it is woven into plants or shrubs several inches above the ground. The young number two to seven (usually four); each weighs approximately one twenty-eighth ounce and is only about one-quarter inch long from head to end of tail. Although the young begin to explore their surroundings when 10 days old, they probably remain a while longer with the mother. Since the breeding season extends from April to October, a female may rear several litters in a season.

An agile climber, the mouse goes up stems to gather tender shoots and seeds, storing some in its nest. Occasionally it will rest on a lateral branch with its very long, thinly-haired tail hanging straight down. After eating, like most rodents, it washes its forepaws and entire length of tail, and grooms its fur. Very rarely it has been heard to bugle at a shrill high pitch barely discernable to humans. It is active the year round, tunneling under snow when necessary. Living chiefly in untilled corners, the species seldom does any harm to man's interests.

Bachman discovered the harvest mouse near his home in Charleston, South Carolina, and in 1841 he and Audubon described it as a new species, *humulis* (meaning humble or lowly), in the same genus with the house mouse and white-footed mouse *(Mus)*. A keen observer, Bachman noticed differences (grooves) in the teeth and was not satisfied with his classification. Later naturalists established a new genus for this and 15 additional species of harvest mice. (The species name of *humulis* had to be retained.)

The eastern harvest mouse is 4¼ to 5¼ inches long, including the 1¾- to 2½-inch tail, and weighs about 1/3 ounce. The species ranges from Maryland and Florida north to Ohio and west to eastern Texas. It is not as scarce as Bachman thought; in favorable habitats it is common and sometimes even abundant.

MUS LEUCOPUS, RAFF.
WHITE FOOTED MOUSE.

Next to the common /house/ mouse, this is the most abundant and widely diffused species of mouse in North America. We have received it (under various names) from every State in the Union, and from Labrador, Hudson's Bay, and the Columbia River. Being nocturnal in its habits, it is far more common than is generally supposed. In familiar localities, where we had never known of its existence, we found it almost the only species taken in traps at night. . . .

In New-Jersey their favourite resorts are isolated cedars growing on the margins of damp places, where green briars *(Smilax rotundifolio* /i.e., *rotundifolia/* and *S. herbacea* /the carrion flower/) connect the branches with the ground, and along the stems of which they climb expertly.

When started from their nests in these trees, they descend along the vines in safety to the earth. When thus disturbed, however, if the nest is at some distance from the ground, they hesitate before they come down, and go out on a branch perhaps, to scrutinize the vicinity, and, if not farther molested, appear satisfied, and again retreat to their nests. They have been known to take possession of deserted bird's nests — such as those of the cat-bird, red-winged starling /blackbird/, song thrush, or red-eyed flycatcher.

In the northern part of New-York we could always obtain specimens from under the sheaves of wheat that were usually stacked in the harvest fields for a few days before they were carried into the barn. We have also occasionally found their nests on bushes, from five to fifteen feet from the ground. They are in these cases constructed with nearly as much art and ingenuity as the nests of the Baltimore Oriole. . . .

When we first discovered this kind of nest we were at a loss to decide whether it belonged to a bird or a quadruped; on touching the bush, however, we saw the little tenant of this airy domicile escape. At our next visit she left the nest so clumsily and made her way along the ground so slowly, that we took her up in our hand, when we discovered that she had four young about a fourth grown, adhering so firmly to the teats that she dragged them along in the manner of the jumping mouse *(Meriones Americanus* /now *Zapus hudsonius/),* or of the Florida rat /eastern wood rat/. We preserved this little family alive for eighteen months, during which time the female produced several broods of young. During the day they usually concealed themselves in their nests, but as soon as it was dark they became very active and playful, running up and down the wires of their cages, robbing each other's little store-houses of various grains that had been carried to them, and occasionally emitting the only sound we ever heard them utter — a low squeak resembling that of the common mouse. . . .

In its wild state it is continually laying up little stores of grain and grass seeds. We have seen it carrying in its mouth acorns and chinquepins. In the Northern States, these little hoards are often composed wholly of wheat; in the South, of rice. This species, like all rats and mice, is fond of Indian-corn, from which it only extracts the choicest sweetest portions, eating the heart and leaving the rest untouched.

In thickly settled parts of the United States this Mouse avoids dwellings, and even out-houses, and either confines itself to the woods, or keeps near fences, stone-heaps, &c.; but in partially deserted houses, or in newly formed settlements, it seems to take the place of the common mouse. RICHARDSON states that in the fur countries it becomes an inmate of the dwelling houses. . . .

This is a timid and very gentle species; we have seldom known it to bite when taken into the hand, and have observed that in a state of confinement it suffered itself to be killed by the very carnivorous cotton-rat *(Sigmodon hispidum* /i.e., *S. hispidus/)* without making any resistance.

We are disposed to believe that this species produces at least two litters of young in a season, in the Northern States, and three, in the Southern. In the State of New-York we have seen the young every month from May to September; and in Carolina a female that was kept in confinement had young three times, first having three, at a second litter five, and having six at a third. . . .

150

WHITE-FOOTED MOUSE

Peromyscus leucopus leucopus (Rafinesque)

When disturbed, the white-footed mouse stamps its front feet very rapidly. On dead leaves or a hard surface, the repeated thumps make a sharp buzz. Under stress the animal may squeak and race off with a series of leaps. The "song" of the white-footed mouse is a faint, high-pitched "prolonged ditty." It is a rare mouse that "sings" and a rare observer who hears it. Bachman and many zoologists have not.

Unlike most rodents, a pair of white-footed mice will sometimes build a home together and remain in it. During the winter, several mice occasionally live in one nest. This species wash and scrub themselves every day but otherwise they are untidy. As soon as a nest becomes soiled, however, the owner moves to another. This may be in a tunnel that the mouse itself digs or in burrows abandoned by other animals, in the hollow of a tree or even up among the branches. Sometimes the mouse roofs over the bird or squirrel nests that Bachman mentions on the opposite page.

Mating is chiefly in spring and fall but may occur at other seasons if food is plentiful. Although gestation normally requires 21 to 23 days, the period is sometimes extended if the female continues to nurse the previous brood. The first litter is born during April and even in the north may be followed by two or three more before November. The female often breeds within a few hours of delivery. As soon as one litter is weaned, another is born. Each litter usually contains five and rarely seven. Wrinkled, transparent, blind and deaf, but with vibrissae quivering, they weigh about one-fifteenth ounce each. At three weeks the young are weaned and furred with gray above and white beneath. Although not full grown at two months, they are ready to mate. During the first moult, the gray is replaced by pale to rich reddish brown. An extraordinarily lucky animal that escapes owls, weasels, foxes, and snakes may live three or even four years. Usually they die before they are two years old.

White-footed mice subsist on nuts and seeds, from acorns and beechnuts to cherry pits and seeds of raspberry and blueberry. Considerable amounts are stored in holes and crevices for winter use. During summer the animals eat great numbers of beetles and caterpillars, with occasional snacks of centipedes, even birds, other mice and carrion.

This species is 6¼ to 8¼ inches long, including the 2½- to 4-inch tail; it weighs about one ounce. The range extends from Nova Scotia and central Montana south to central Georgia, Arizona and southeastern Mexico.

* * * *

Due to prolific reproduction and adaptation to laboratory life, white-footed mice and their relatives are used in great numbers for genetic and medical studies.

MUS AUREOLUS, AUD. & BACH.

ORANGE COLORED MOUSE.

In symmetry of form and brightness of colour, this is the prettiest species of *Mus* inhabiting our country. It is at the same time a great climber. We have only observed it in a state of nature in three instances in the oak forests of South Carolina; it ran up the tall trees with great agility, and on one occasion concealed itself in a hole (which apparently contained its nest,) at least thirty feet from the ground. The specimen we have described, was shot from the extreme branches of an oak, in the dusk of the evening, where it was busily engaged among the acorns. It is a rare species in Carolina, but appears to be more common in Georgia, as we received from Major LE CONTE, three specimens obtained in the latter State.

/Editor's Comment: Early American naturalists, noting only superficial resemblances, regarded this "orange-colored mouse" as merely another of the many species of deer mice and lumped them all togther with the Old World house mouse in the genus Mus. *Later, on the basis of marked differences in both structure and appearance, the American species of deer mice were given a generic name of their own:* Peromyscus. *Since then and comparatively recently, the "orange-colored mouse," today called golden mouse, has been set apart in still another genus,* Ochrotomys. *It not only has different skull, tooth and skeletal characters, but its bright coloring and extremely dense, soft fur differ from that of all the nearly 60 species of deer mice./*

GOLDEN MOUSE

Ochrotomys nuttalli aureolus (Audubon and Bachman)

The golden brown coat, with the white feet and under-parts splashed with orange, explains the Audubon and modern names of this handsome little mammal. Young animals with long tails will wrap their appendages around the mother's neck when she is carrying them. In this species, even the adult's tail is somewhat prehensile and is used when climbing trees.

Uncommon, the golden mouse lives in almost impenetrable (to humans) thickets of shrubs interlaced with thorny greenbrier and honeysuckle. It has also been found in canebreaks, but never in very dry places.

These mice weave compact nests of leaves with linings of finely shredded inner bark, milkweed-seed down and other soft material. Nests are six to nine inches in diameter with a single entrance which is usually closed. Sometimes they are in the ground under logs but more often in forks or hollows of trees or in tangles of vines up to 15 feet high.

A second type of structure is the roughly built feeding platforms with arched covers and one or two large entrances which are never closed. Abandoned bird nests often serve as foundations. In their large, nearly transparent internal cheek pouches, the mice carry to the platforms seeds of sumac, wild cherry, dogwood, greenbrier and other plants. Even such tiny seeds as sweet clover and bedstraw are broken open with ease and dexterity before they are eaten. Apparently birds on the nest or asleep may be caught and devoured.

Golden mice forage at night over a small territory (1½ acres in Texas), racing nimbly through the thickets and trees, and balancing themselves with their long, golden brown tails. Several males and females have been known to share a nest but a female with young will not tolerate the close presence of other adults. She may have up to three litters annually between February and October. The one to five (average three) young are born after a gestation of 23 or 30 days. Their eyes open at 11 to 15 days and they are sexually mature when two or three months old. The average life span is believed to be about six months, although individuals are known to have lived in the wild at least 2½ years.

Golden mice are 6 to 7½ inches long, including the 2¾- to 3¾-inch tail, and weigh about 1 ounce. They are found from central Florida and Virginia to eastern Oklahoma and Texas. In captivity they are docile and make attractive pets.

MUS MISSOURIENSIS, AUD. & BACH

MISSOURI MOUSE.

...This pretty little animal was discovered for us by Mr DENIG, during our sojourn at, and in the neighbourhood of Fort Union in 1843. It was in full summer pelage, having been killed on the 14th of July. At that time being in quest of antelopes and large animals, we did not give it that close attention, which we should have done. A glance at our plate, or an examination of our description, will suffice to convince any one of its being entirely new. This species is much larger, and has a thicker and shorter tail than *mus* /now *Peromyscus*/ *leucopus* /the white-footed mouse/.

Expecting to get more of them we did not make any notes of the habits of those killed at that time, and which had doubtless been observed by the hunters, who procured them. The next day after they were brought in, we left the fort on an expedition to the Yellow-Stone river, from which we did not return for some time. ...

As there is little grain of any kind grown in this part of the country, the Missouri Mouse no doubt exists on the seeds and roots of wild plants entirely, of which it is able to lay up a store for the winter in holes in the ground. It may, however, possibly resort to the patches of corn planted by the squaws of some of the Indian tribes, at the time that grain is ripe. We brought with us from this country, when we returned home, some ears of a very small corn, (maize,) which ripens early, and bears its fruit near the ground. Having planted it on our place, we found that it was advanced enough to be eaten at table as a vegetable, several weeks before the ordinary kinds of corn known about New-York. We, therefore, distributed some of the seed among our farming neighbours, and likewise sent some to England to Lord DERBY and other friends, but this was unfortunately lost. We incline to believe that this corn would ripen well in the climate of England or Scotland. Unluckily, ours has become mixed by having been planted too near common corn, and is now depreciated or reduced to nearly the same thing as the latter.

NORTHERN GRASSHOPPER MOUSE

Onychomys leucogaster missouriensis (Audubon and Bachman)

Unlike most rodents, the grasshopper mouse is primarily a meat-eater. It stalks its prey at night, sniffing the trails and listening for the unwary. Leaping upon its victim, it shuts its eyes and lays back its ears. After one or more lethal bites it devours the prey head first. Carried away with the zest of the chase, it will stand up on its hind legs, point its nose to the heavens, open its mouth and squeak repeatedly. This shrill hunting-call is tiny, but eloquent; surprisingly it can be heard a hundred feet away. Grasshoppers and other arthropods, beetles and larvae of many species are easy game. Small kangaroo rats, other mice and even their own race, require more effort and skill. Active the year round, the grasshopper mouse puts on fat, especially in its tail, before the winter season of poor hunting arrives.

To grasshopper mice, dust is necessary. Without dust baths, their fur becomes oily and matted and they are very uncomfortable. Accordingly, these mice live in arid grassland, or among shrubs of western America. Preferring loamy and sandy soils where digging is easy, they avoid rocky places. The genus name is a combination of two Greek words: *onycho* meaning nail or claw, and *mys* for mouse.

The gestation period varies widely from 29 to 47 days according to demands on the mother's milk supply. The time is short for females without young and longest for those with large litters still to be fed — up to six young. An average brood contains three or four. At birth they are blind and hairless, nearly two inches long and weigh less than one-tenth ounce. They are well furred at 12 days of age. The eyes open at 19 or 20 days when weaning is almost completed. The gray upper parts of the juvenile coat change to the tawny adult pelage at five or six months of age. Eventually, when nearing the end of their normal life span of three to four years, many of the surviving mice become gray again. Thus they complete a color cycle from youth to old age.

In southern, hot deserts when food is abundant, females may breed practically the year round. The shortest gestation period, followed by the relatively brief rearing time, makes it possible for one mouse to bear seven litters in a calendar year — with a total of 20 to 30 offspring.

Despite their carnivorous diet, they make gentle pets in captivity. They are deliberate and much less nervous than, for instance, white-footed mice, and are coolly curious about strange objects and occurrences. They have a variety of chirping and barking notes as well as a hunting "howl."

Grasshopper mice depend more on agility than speed to escape from owls, foxes, coyotes and other meat-eaters. Skunks and badgers dig them from their tunnels, which have been excavated by the mice or adapted from burrows vacated by previous owners. Because of the diet, the species is almost entirely beneficial to man.

The northern grasshopper mouse is 4¾ to 7½ inches long, including the tail which is 1¼ to 2½ inches. The mouse weighs about 2 ounces. Although never abundant, it occurs from central Saskatchewan to northern Tamaulipas and from western Minnesota and central Texas westward to central Oregon. The slightly smaller southern species occupies the region from southern Nevada and adjacent California southeastward to San Luis Potosí.

ARVICOLA HISPIDUS, SAY & ORD.

COTTON RAT.

This is the most common wood-rat /cotton rat/ existing in the Southern States, being even more abundant than any of the species of meadow-mice in the Northern and Eastern States. It is however a resident rather of hedges, ditches, and deserted old fields, than of gardens or cultivated grounds; it occasions very little injury to the planter. Although its paths are everywhere seen through the fields, it does not seem to destroy many plants or vegetables. It feeds on the seeds of coarse grasses and leguminous plants, and devours a considerable quantity of animal food. In its habits it is gregarious. We have seen spots of half an acre covered over with tall weeds, (*Solidago* /goldenrod/ and *Eupatorium* /boneset/,) which were traversed in every direction by the Cotton-Rat, and which must have contained several hundred individuals.

Although this species does not reject grains and grasses, it gives the preference in all cases to animal food, and we have never found any species of rat more decidedly carnivorous. Robins, partridges, or other birds that are wounded and drop among the long grass or weeds in the neighbourhood of their burrows are speedily devoured by them. They may sometimes be seen running about the ditches with crayfish (*Astacus Bartoni*) in their mouths, and have been known to subsist on Crustacea, especially the little crabs called fiddlers, (*Gelasimus vocans.*) /now *Eca pugilator,* the sand fiddler, and *E. pugnax,* the mud fiddler/. . .

Although the Cotton-Rat is nocturnal in its habits, it may frequently be seen by day; and in places where it is seldom disturbed, it can generally be found at all hours.

The galleries of this species often run twenty or thirty yards under ground, but not far beneath the surface; and the ridges thrown up as the animals excavate their galleries, can often be traced along the surface of the earth for a considerable distance, like those formed by the common shrew-mole /eastern mole/.

Each burrow or hole contains apparently only one family, a pair of old ones with their young; but their various galleries often intersect each other, and many nests may be found within the compass of a few yards; they are composed of withered grasses, are not very large, and may usually be found within a foot of the surface. In summer the nests are often seen in a cavity of the earth, on the surface in some meadow, or among rank weeds.

This is a very prolific species, producing young early in spring, and through all the summer months, till late in autumn. We have on several occasions known their young born and reared in cages. They produce from four to eight at a litter. The young are of a bright chesnut-brown colour, and at the age of five or six days begin to leave the nest, are very active and sprightly, and attain their full growth in about five months.

This species has no other note than a low squeak, a little hoarser than that of the common mouse; when captured it is far more savage than the Florida rat. On one occasion, while seizing one of them, we were bitten completely through a finger covered by a buckskin glove.

The Cotton-Rat is fond of burrowing in the old banks of abandoned rice-fields. In such situations we have, during freshets, observed that it could both swim and dive like the water-rat /or water vole, *Arvicola terrestris*/ of Europe, and WILSON's meadow-mouse of the Middle States.

This species supplies a considerable number of animals and birds with food. Foxes and wild-cats especially, destroy thousands; we have observed minks coursing along the marshes in pursuit of them, and have frequently seen them with one of these Rats in their mouth. Marsh-hawks, and several other species, may be constantly seen in the autumn and winter months sailing over the fields, looking out for the Cotton-Rat. No animal in the Southern States becomes more regularly the food of several species of owls than this. . . .

The Cotton-Rat has obtained its name from its supposed habit of making its nest with cotton, which it is said to collect for the purpose in large quantities. We have occasionally, although very seldom, seen cotton in its nest, but we have more frequently found it composed of leaves and withered grasses. Indeed, this species does not appear to be very choice in selecting materials for building its nest, using indiscriminately any suitable substance in the vicinity. . . .

HISPID COTTON RAT

Sigmodon hispidus hispidus Say and Ord

The cotton rat is one of the most prolific of all American mammals. When overpopulation causes crowding, it apparently develops serious neuroses. Males, especially, are extremely quarrelsome. Adults are often disfigured by new or old scars from fighting. Backs are cut open and tails may be amputated. Any cotton rat that strays from its own territory is virtually certain to be attacked and bitten, or even killed.

Throughout much of the range, breeding is year-long, although less rapid in winter. Twenty-seven days after mating, the litter of one to 12 (usually five to seven) young are born and the female breeds again within a few hours. Weaning is often completed before the young are two weeks old. Although they are not full-grown until four or five months, juvenile males are sexually mature when three to four weeks old and females one to two weeks later.

Populations fluctuate widely and at intervals of two to five years there may be 500 cotton rats to the acre. At these peaks, they cause great destruction to sugar cane, cotton, truck, grain and forage crops. During these periods all kinds of carnivorous reptiles, birds and mammals concentrate on the teeming prey. This acts temporarily as a buffer for game birds and other species. Fungus and other diseases may also help to decimate the rat population within a few months.

When J. W. Audubon was in Texas in 1845-6, he secured specimens of the "Texan Meadow-Mouse," from which he painted Figure 3 in Plate 147 (page 67) and which eventually proved to be only a paler and slightly smaller form of the cotton rat. Audubon recorded (Vol. 3, p. 230) "Not being very numerous, it is difficult to procure. . ." and he forecast that specimens would be scarce in museum collections "for some time to come."

Apparently Audubon happened on one of those population nadirs and concluded that he had found a scarce species. At another time, in the same Brazos Valley where Audubon had collected specimens with such difficulty, four persons caught 40 cotton rats in less than an hour.

These rodents seek densely grassy fields and weed-grown places to construct their labyrinths of shallow tunnels and surface runways. Nervous, and active chiefly at night, they ordinarily spend their lives within 50 feet of their respective nests. Although Bachman's captive cotton rats were bloodthirsty, the principal food in the wild is actually vegetation. Of course meat in any form whenever available is devoured. They have been accused of heavy depredations on quail eggs and young.

During the mid-eighteenth century, the common name "wood-rat" was applied in South Carolina to both cotton rats and wood rats. (Actually they are quite different animals and are divided into two genera.) Although Bachman was very well acquainted with both species, he uses the "wood-rat" term in the first paragraph on the opposite page. His description of the "Texan Meadow-Mouse" collected by J. W. Audubon mentions its similarity to the cotton rat. It is not surprising, because of its smaller size and resemblance to a large meadow mouse, that Bachman erroneously identified it as a meadow mouse rather than a subspecies of the cotton rat.

Cotton rats are used extensively for research on typhus, diphtheria, polio and other diseases.

The hispid cotton rat is 9 to 14½ inches long, including the 2¼- to 6¾-inch tail, and weighs 4 to 8½ ounces. It is found from Virginia, Kansas and California to Panama.

Neotoma Floridana. Say et Ord.

Florida Rat

The specimens from which we /John J. Audubon/ drew the figures we have given on our plate, which represents this species in various ages and attitudes on the branch of a pine tree, were obtained in South Carolina, and were preserved alive for several weeks in cages having wire fronts. They made no attempt to gnaw their way out. On a previous occasion we preserved an old female with three young (which latter were born in the cage a few days after the mother had been captured) for nearly a year; by which time the young had attained the size of the adult. We fed them on corn, potatoes, rice, and bread, as well as apples and other fruit. They seemed very fond of corn flour, (Indian meal,) and for several months subsisted on the acorns of the live oak. (*Quercus virens* /now *Q. virginiana*/.)

They became very gentle, especially one of them which was in a separate cage. It was our custom at dark to release it from confinement, upon which it would run around the room in circles, mount the table we were in the habit of writing at, and always make efforts to open a particular drawer in which we kept some of its choicest food. . . .

About fifteen years ago, on a visit to the grave-yard of the church at Ebenezer, Georgia, we were struck with the appearance of several very large nests near the tops of some tall evergreen oaks (*Quercus aquaticus* /now *Q. nigra*/); on disturbing the nests, we discovered them to be inhabited by a number of Florida rats of all sizes, some of which descended rapidly to the ground, whilst others escaped to the highest branches, where they were concealed among the leaves. These nests in certain situations are of enormous size. We have observed some of them on trees, at a height of from ten to twenty feet from the ground, where wild vines had made a tangled mass over head, which appeared to be larger than a cart wheel and contained a mass of leaves and sticks that would have more than filled a barrel. . . .

This is a very active rat, and in ascending trees, exhibits much of the agility of the squirrel, although we do not recollect having observed it leaping from branch to branch in the manner of that genus.

The Florida rat is, in Carolina, a very harmless species; the only depredation we have known it to commit, was an occasional inroad on the corn-fields when the grain was yet juicy and sweet. We have seen several whole ears of Indian corn taken from one of their nests, into which they had been dragged by these animals the previous night. They appear also to be very fond of the Chinquapin (*Castania pumila*), and we have sometimes observed around their nests traces of their having fed on frogs and cray-fish.

This species is nocturnal, or at least crepuscular, in its habits. In procuring specimens we were only successful when the traps had been set over night. Those we had in captivity scarcely ever left their dark chambers till after sunset, when they came forth from their dormitories and continued playful and active during a great part of the night. They were mild in their dispositions, and much less disposed to bite when pursued than the common and more mischievous Norway rat.

Whilst the young are small they cling to the teats of the mother, who runs about with them occasionally without much apparent inconvenience; and even when older, they still, when she is about to travel quickly, cling to her sides or her back. Thus on a visit from home, she may be said to carry her little family with her, and is always ready to defend them even at the risk of her life. . . .

From three to six are produced at a litter, by this species, which breeds generally twice a year; we have seen the young so freqeuntly in March and August, that we are inclined to the belief that these are the periods of their reproduction. We have never heard them making any other noise than a faint squeak, somewhat resembling that of the brown rat. The very playful character of this species, its cleanly habits, its mild, prominent, and bright eyes, together with its fine form and easy susceptibility of domestication, would render it a far more interesting pet than many others that the caprice of man has from time to time induced him to select.

EASTERN WOOD RAT

Neotoma floridana floridana (Ord)

Similar to Norway or house rats, this American species has soft, smooth fur with light underparts instead of being all gray, its ears are furred and the tail is haired. Wood rats are clean creatures and much more attractive than the Old World rodents that populate our city garbage dumps.

Most eastern wood rats live in rather dry, rocky, deciduous woods. Somewhere in a structure of masses of sticks is a nest cavity five to eight inches in diameter.

Generally hostile, wood rats breed briefly from February to August in the north and year-long in the extreme south. The young, usually two or three (rarely one to six) are born between 33 and 42 days later. During much of their first three weeks, they hold firmly to the mother's teats by means of a temporary diamond-shaped space between the four incisors. If disturbed, the entire brood (still clamped to the mother) may be dragged 100 yards or more to a place of safety. The young are independent at 10 weeks and sexually mature at nine months of age.

Wood rats are vegetarians, feeding on almost all parts of plants growing within a few yards of the nest. Naturalists have not found them eating crayfish (as stated opposite).

Adults are 14 to 17 inches long, including the 6- to 8-inch tail. The range extends from the Gulf states to the Black Hills and southern New York.

NEOTOMA DRUMMONDII, RICH.

ROCKY MOUNTAIN NEOTOMA.

We regret that from personal observation, we have no information to give in regard to the habits of this species, having never seen it in a living state. It was, however, seen by /Captain Meriwether/ LEWIS and /William/ CLARKE, by DRUMMOND, DOUGLASS, NUTTALL, and TOWNSEND. According to the accounts given by these travellers, this Neotoma appears to have nearly the same general habits as the smaller species, *(N. Floridana,)* the Florida rat, but is much more destructive than the latter. It has a strong propensity to gnaw, cut to pieces, and carry to its nest every thing left in its way. The trappers dread its attacks on their furs more than they would the approach of a grizzly bear. These rats have been known to gnaw through whole packs of furs in a single night. The blankets of the sleeping travellers are sometimes cut to pieces by them, and they carry off small articles from the camp of the hunter.

"Mr. DRUMMOND," says RICHARDSON, "placed a pair of stout English shoes on the shelf of a rock, and as he thought, in perfect security; but on his return, after an absence of a few days, he found them gnawed into fragments as fine as saw-dust."

Mr. DOUGLASS, who unfortunately lost his life in ascending Mouna Roa /Mauna Loa/, in the Sandwich /Hawaiian/ Islands, by falling into a pit for catching wild bulls, where he was gored by one of those animals, was one of the most indefatigable explorers of the Western portions of our continent, and kept a journal of his travels and discoveries in natural history. It was never published, but a few copies were printed some time after his death, by his friend and patron, Sir WILLIAM HOOKER /famous English botanist/, who presented one of them to us. In it we found the following account of this animal: —

"During the night I was annoyed by the visit of a herd of rats, which devoured every particle of seed I had collected, ate clean through a bundle of dried plants, and carried off my soap, brush, and razor. As one was taking away my inkstand, which I had been using shortly before, and which lay close to my pillow, I raised my gun, which, with my faithful dog, always is placed under my blanket by my side with the muzzle to my feet, and hastily gave him the contents. When I saw how large and strong a creature this rat was, I ceased to wonder at the exploits of the herd in depriving me of my property. The body and tail together measured a foot and a half; the hair was brown, the belly white; it had enormous ears three quarters of an inch long, and whiskers three inches in length. Unfortunately the specimen was spoiled by the shot which in my haste to secure the animal and recover my inkstand, I did not take time to change; but a female of the same sort venturing to return some hours after, I handed it a smaller shot, which did not destroy the skin. It was in all respects like the former, except being a little smaller." This identical specimen is in the museum of the Zoological Society of London, where we examined it.

Mr. TOWNSEND has kindly furnished us with some remarks on this species, from which we make the following extracts: — "I never saw it in the Rocky Mountains, but it is very common near the Columbia river. It is found in the storehouses of the inhabitants, where it supplies the place of the common rat, which is not found here. It is a remarkably mischievous animal, destroying every thing which comes in its way — papers, books, goods, &c. It has been known not unfrequently to eat entirely through the middle of a bale of blankets, rendering the whole utterly useless; and like a pet crow carries away every thing it can lay its *hands* on. Even candlesticks, porter-bottles, and large iron axes, being sometimes found in its burrows."

The food of this species consists of seeds and herbage of various kinds; it devours also the small twigs and leaves of pine trees, and generally has a considerable store of these laid up in the vicinity of its residence.

It is said by DRUMMOND to make its nest in the crevices of high rocks. The nest is large, and is composed of sticks, leaves, and grasses. The abode of this Rat may be discovered by the excrement of the animal, which has the colour and consistence of tar, and is always deposited in the vicinity. It is stated by those who have had the opportunity of observing, that this species produces from three to five young at a time.

BUSHY-TAILED WOOD RAT

Neotoma cinerea drummondii (Richardson)

The tail of this wood rat is almost squirrel-like compared to that of the preceding species, but habits and disposition are very similar.

All of the more than 20 species of wood rats are avid collectors. The young botanist (opposite page) was only one of many travelers in western America who lost belongings to those small robbers.

While foraging, the wood rat picks up and carries off any useless (to the rat) object that momentarily attracts it. A few of the innumerable additions to Bachman's list are bones, pebbles, scraps of paper, broken glass, shotgun shells, anything shiny like silverware, and even the dried droppings of other animals. If, on the way home the rat comes across another object that is more appealing, it drops what it is carrying and hurries off with the new find. This habit has led to the alternate names of pack rat and trade rat. Accumulations of loot are cached in the mass of debris which surrounds the nest, or in rock crevices nearby.

Although normally solitary, a pair of wood rats share the same nest during courtship. While the male nuzzles the female, he makes a peculiar buzzing or humming sound. This does not last long, for both are fiery tempered and the mating period is stormy. When fighting, wood rats may stand on their hind legs, grate their teeth, squeal, box and claw.

Gestation requires 27 to 32 days. Most litters contain three young. Some females are able to nurse only four at a time; the rest of the young generally perish. Weaned at about a month, they go through at least three changes of pelage before they are sexually mature and a year old. In colder localities, females have one litter annually but in the south two may be reared.

The cup- or ball-shaped nest is about a foot in diameter. Barricades of sticks, bones and other debris threaten to impale any invader; it is remarkable that more occupants are not damaged themselves. Depending on location and numbers of generations that have occupied it, the "fort" sometimes becomes very large. Droppings with a musty odor are everywhere except in the nest. Here there are stolen treasures and leftover food. Wood rats are clean about their bodies; from time to time they clear out their dwelling. Usually this is built in a narrow rock crevice or on a shelf; sometimes in a hollow tree or, rarely, in a thicket.

When alarmed, a wood rat thumps its feet and vibrates its tail. It drinks little and climbs well, although there is seldom need for the latter. Since the bushy-tailed cannot tolerate the heat of southwestern deserts it ranges as high as the summit of Pikes Peak, 14,110 feet above sea level.

During late summer and early autumn, great quantities of vegetation are cut, dried and stored between rocks for winter food. Small amounts are also stored at all times to eat in the nest during daylight or on moonlit nights when foraging would be dangerous. Wood rats are not entirely nocturnal however; they have been seen abroad at midday.

When reared in captivity, they may become so tame that they can be handled safely.

Bushy-tailed wood rats are 12 to 19 inches long, including the 5- to 9-inch tail. They occur from New Mexico and the Sierra Nevada north to North Dakota and the Yukon.

ARVICOLA PENNSYLVANICUS, ORD.

WILSONS MEADOW MOUSE

We have had opportunities in New-York, Pennsylvania, and the New-England States, of learning some of the habits of this species. It is, in fact, the common Meadow-Mouse of the Northern and Eastern States.

Wherever there is a meadow in any of these States, you may find small tortuous paths cut through the grass, appearing as if they had been partially dug into the earth, leading to the roots of a stump, or the borders of some bank or ditch. These are the work of this little animal. Should you dig around the roots, or upturn the stump, you may find a family of from five to ten of this species, and will see them scampering off in all directions; and although they do not run fast, they have so many hiding places, that unless you are prompt in your attack, they are likely to escape you. Their galleries do not run under ground like those of the shrew mole /eastern mole/, or the mischievous pine-mouse, (of LECONTE,) but extend along the surface sometimes for fifty yards. . . .

We doubt whether this active little arvicola ever does much injury to the meadows; and in the wheat-fields it is not often a depredator, as it is seldom seen on high ground. . . . In very severe winters, when the ground is frozen, and there is no covering of snow to protect the roots of its favourite grasses, it resorts for a subsistence to the stems of various shrubs and fruit trees, from which it peals off the bark, and thus destroys them. We possessed a small but choice nursery of fruit trees, which we had grafted ourselves, that was completely destroyed during a severe winter by this Meadow-Mouse . . .

The nests of this arvicola are always near the surface; sometimes two or three are found under the same stump. We have frequently during summer observed them on the surface in the meadows, where they were concealed by the overshadowing grasses. They are composed of about a double handful of leaves of soft grasses, and are of an oval shape, with an entrance on the side.

WILSON's Meadow-Mouse swims and dives well. During a freshet which covered some neighbouring meadows, we observed several of them on floating bunches of grass, sticks, and marsh weeds, sitting in an upright posture as if enjoying the sunshine, and we saw them leaving these temporary resting places and swimming to the neighbouring high grounds with great facility; a stick thrown at them on such occasions will cause them to dive like a musk-rat.

This species does not, in any part of the United States, visit dwellings or outhouses, although RICHARDSON states that it possesses this habit in Canada. We have scarcely ever met with it on high grounds, and it seems to avoid thick woods.

It produces young three or four times during the summer, from two to five at a birth. As is the case with the Florida /eastern wood/ rat and the white-footed mouse, the young of this species adhere to the teats, and are in this way occasionally dragged along by the mother. We would, however, here remark, that this habit, which is seen in the young of several animals, is by no means constant. It is only when the female is suddenly surprised and driven from her nest whilst suckling her young, that they are carried off in this manner. The young of this species that we had in confinement, after satisfying themselves, relinquished their hold, and permitted the mother to run about without this incumbrance.

This species is easily caught in wire-traps baited with a piece of apple, or even meat; we have occasionally found two in a trap at the same time. When they have become accustomed to the confinement of a cage they are somewhat familiar, feed on grass and seeds of different kinds, and often come to the bars of the cage to receive their food.

They frequently sit erect in the manner of marmots or squirrels, and while in this position clean their faces with their paws, continuing thus engaged for a quarter of an hour at a time. They drank a good deal of water, and were nocturnal in their habits. During the day-time they constantly nestled under some loose cotton, where they lay, unless disturbed, until dusk, when they ran about their place of confinement with great liveliness and activity, clinging to the wires and running up and down in various directions upon them, as if intent on making their escape.

MEADOW VOLE

Microtus pennsylvanicus pennsylvanicus (Ord)

This little animal (commonly called meadow mouse) is one of the most prolific mammals in the world. During warm weather, females may produce litters of five to seven young every three weeks — all growing up and dispersing before the birth of the next litter. Breeding when a little over three weeks old, one new offspring can, under ideal conditions, produce 17 litters of three to 10 young in a year. The populations rise to a peak every three to four years when more than 200 mice may occupy an acre — then drop abruptly to only 15 to 30.

Meadow voles live in grassy places — wet, moist or dry, large and small. Here they make a labyrinth of tiny highways for most of their foraging. About an inch wide, the travel ways are formed by clipping off plants at ground level; tender parts are eaten and the rest, cut into short lengths, are stacked tidily in little heaps by the road.

Scampering up and down their paths, some mice are friendly and touch noses in greeting. Others feel mean enough to chase and nip at the heels of any passerby. Dispositions are affected by abundance and scarcity of food due to overcrowding. In times of plenty they are generally tolerant with each other. When times are bad, fighting breaks out and both adults and young are eaten. Antagonists grind their teeth, squeal, growl, paw the earth and may even dance and waltz around like the British field vole or a very fancy boxer.

Winter nests are usually placed above ground, while summer ones are often below. Woven so compactly that they are waterproof, they have one or two entrances.

Field mice dash about day and night the year round, and eat 80% of their weight in food every day. Roots, bark, shoots and seeds of a vast array of plants from succulent creepers to woody trees are devoured. Cranberries, raisins (drying in fields) and some other fruits are taken for their seeds alone; the pulp of the fruit is discarded.

Spreading over practically the entire continent, from the Arctic islands to southern Mexico, voles are an important food for carnivores. Even bears enjoy these tidbits. Although the swarming prey destroys many weeds, they also ruin millions of dollars worth of crops and orchards every year.

The species measures 5½ to 7¾ inches in total length (including the tail which is 1¼ to 2½ inches), and weighs up to 4 ounces. It has a vast transcontinental range, from within the Arctic Circle south to Georgia, New Mexico and northern Washington. It is suspected that the field voles *(Microtus agrestis)* of Europe and Asia are actually but subspecies of a single species.

ARVICOLA XANTHOGNATHUS, LEACH.

YELLOW CHEEKED MEADOW MOUSE.

The descriptions of its habits given by the few writers who have referred with positive certainty to this species, are very meagre, but all the arvicolae, with slight variations, are similar in habit; they live in low grounds, usually preferring meadows; burrow in the banks of ponds and near water-courses, feed on grasses and seeds, have a considerable number of young at a birth, are somewhat nocturnal, and make galleries of various lengths, which enable them to traverse the neighbourhood of their nestling places and procure the roots of grasses and plants.

This species, as is mentioned by RICHARDSON and other observers, makes its long galleries under the mossy turf, on the dry banks of lakes and rivers, and also in the woods; the specimens brought by us /J. J. Audubon/ from Labrador were obtained from beneath large masses of moss growing on the rocks.

In some portions of the far north these hardy little animals are abundant: they were common in Labrador, and were easily captured by turning up some of the patches of moss, as just mentioned, when they were knocked over by the young men of our party.

We are told that this species has seven young at a time.

/Editor's Comment: This species does not occur east of Hudson Bay. The authors apparently confused the rock vole, Microtus chrotorrhinus, with the yellow-cheeked vole. Both species have a spot of yellowish color on each side of the nose, but the rock vole is much the smaller animal. The specimens on which the error was made were obtained by Audubon during his stay in southern Labrador during the summer of 1833./

YELLOW-CHEEKED VOLE

Microtus xanthognathus (Leach)

Conspicuous yellow or chestnut patches on the cheeks give this large mouse its name. (Flecks of the same color are near the ears.) The animal lives on the tundra and in open boreal forests of black and white spruces, birch, cottonwood and larch. It occurs on both high and low ground but prefers the latter. Its runways wind through the thick mats of sphagnum moss and lichens in which grow horsetail, sedge and cottongrass with such shrubs as blueberry, crowberry and dwarf birch. These mice seem to prefer wet, soggy areas to dry or well-drained terrain. Puddles and small ponds are scattered about and the mice run or swim across these places as part of their normal environment — easily taking them in their stride!

Colonies of yellow-cheeked voles build earth mounds, as much as 10 feet in diameter and two feet high, in which they dig a maze of tunnels. Here the nests can be elevated above ground-water level, which in summer is close to or at the surface because moisture cannot drain down through the permafrost. This species of vole is distributed most unevenly, being rare or completely absent over extensive tracts. At the crest of its population cycle, however, it becomes very abundant locally.

The animals are most active in the evening and at night, but in a region where daylight lasts nearly 24 hours for several months the mice are also abroad during the day. While the favorite food seems to be horsetail and lichens, it is assumed that many kinds of succulent vegetation are eaten as well. Litters may contain as many as 10 to possibly 11 young. Known enemies are the marten and great gray owl; undoubtedly numerous other carnivores such as weasel, fox and wolf can be added to the list.

This is one of the biggest of the *Microtus*. Total length is 7½ to 9 inches, including the 1¾- to 2¼-inch tail. Large adults weigh as much as 6 ounces. In the late Pleistocene, yellow-cheeked voles occurred as far south as Virginia; now the range has shrunk to the region between Hudson Bay and central Alberta, thence north and west to northern Yukon and central Alaska. Relatively few specimens are in museum collections and much remains to be learned of their life history.

* * * *

The authors (opposite page) placed this species with the "Arvicolae." This was a large group of rodents which included at that time a number which have since been given the rank of genera: rice rats, deer mice, cotton rats, bog lemmings, collared lemmings and the voles. Today the genus *Arvicola* includes only one species — the water vole of Europe and Asia.

ARVICOLA RICHARDSONII, AUD. & BACH.

RICHARDSON'S MEADOW MOUSE.

DRUMMOND, who procured this Meadow-Mouse, states that its habits are analogous to those of the common water-rat /or water vole/ of Europe *(Arvicola amphibius),* with which it may be easily confounded, although the shortness of its tail may serve as a mark by which to distinguish it.

It frequents moist meadows amongst the Rocky Mountains, and swims and dives well, taking to the water at once when pursued. All Meadow-Mice indeed are capital swimmers. We some time since amused ourselves watching one that had fallen into a circular cistern partly built up with stone and partly excavated out of the solid rock by blasting, and which was plastered with cement on the inside to make it water-tight. This cistern had about four feet of water in it. On one side there was a projecting rounded knob of stone some five or six inches long and about two wide, which slanted out of the water so that the upper edge of it was dry. Upon this little resting-place there was a large *Arvicola /Microtus/ Pennsylvanica* (Wilson's Meadow-Mouse) seated very quietly, having probably tumbled in the preceding night. When we approached the edge and looked down into the clear element we at first did not observe the Rat, but as soon as we espied him he saw us, immediately dived, and swam around underneath the surface quite rapidly; he soon arose, however, and regained his position on the ledge, and we determined to save him from what had been his impending fate—drowning or starving, or both. We procured a plank, and gently lowering one end of it towards the ledge, thought he would take advantage of the inclined plane thus afforded him, to come out; but in our awkwardness we suffered the plank to slip, and at the plash in the water the little fellow dived and swam around several times before he again returned to his resting place, where we now had the end of the board fixed, so that he could get upon it. As soon as he was on it, we began to raise the plank, but when we had him about three feet above the surface he dashed off into the water, making as pretty a dive as need be. He always looked quite dry, and not a hair of his coat was soiled or turned during these frequent immersions, and it was quite interesting to see the inquistive looks he cast towards us, turning his head and appearing to have strong doubts whether we meant to help, or to make an end of him. We put down the plank again, and after two attempts, in both of which his timidity induced him to jump off it when he was nearly at the edge of the cistern, he at last reached the top, and in a moment disappeared amid the weeds and grasses around. . . .

We have named this Arvicola in honour of Sir JOHN RICHARDSON, who in describing it (Fauna Boreali Americana, p. 120), applied to it, with a doubt, the name of *Arvicola riparius,* ORD */Microtus pennsylvanicus,* the meadow vole/, from which it differs so much as to render a comparison here unnecessary.

/Editor's Comment: Richardson described the water vole in his Fauna Boreali-Americana, *published in 1829. He assumed, however, that the animal was merely an oversize meadow vole. Other zoologists, reading his description, thought it quite unlike that eastern mouse. Audubon and Bachman, in their* Quadrupeds of North America, *listed the animal as an entirely different species and named it in honor of Richardson. Oddly, they seem to have overlooked the fact that years earlier, in 1842, DeKay had redescribed Richardson's specimens as a new species and had anticipated them by giving it the same name,* richardsoni./

WATER VOLE

Microtus richardsoni richardsoni (DeKay)

Although a fast swimmer, the water vole is rather clumsy and does a good deal of splashing. If thoroughly frightened, it swims for some distance well below the surface. On land, its well-worn trails, four inches wide, go directly to the edge of creeks and ponds, and reappear on the opposite side. The many landing places where the mice come ashore, dripping water, are conspicuous.

The water vole's burrow may be dug in the bank of a stream or river with the entrance under water. More often the opening is just above the water line or even higher and is placed at the edge of a rock to lessen danger of cave-ins. The tunnel is about three inches in diameter and excavated earth is dumped in a heap at the mouth. This vole is an energetic digger and in a colony the tunnel systems are quite extensive.

In the winter it builds a large grass nest on top of the ground and hurries about under the snow. The mass of grass is so loosely woven that it falls apart soon after the snow melts. Subterranean nests used in summer, and probably the year round, are the birth and rearing places of the two to four young. (Females carrying five to nine embryos have been recorded.) Judging from trapped specimens, they breed before maturity, and younger animals have smaller litters. Lactating mothers with embryos indicate that the litters come in fast succession.

The principal food the year round is grass and sedge. In winter these plants are cut off at ground level under the snow. In summer, discarded sections of grass-blades litter the small pools where the mice have been feeding. Many warm-weather plants and fall seeds of conifers are eaten.

Water voles live in high mountain marshes and wet short-grass meadows, usually above 7,000 feet in the south. The species is the largest of the voles and one of the largest of all American microtines — 8 to 10½ inches long, including the 2¾ - to 3¾-inch tail; weight, 4 to 7 ounces. It is found in two separate areas: (1) the Coast Range from southern Oregon to British Columbia and (2) the northern Rockies from central Utah to Alberta and British Columbia.

167

ARVICOLA PINETORUM, LECONTE

LECONTES PINE MOUSE.

The manners of this species do not differ very widely from those exhibited by many other field mice. They however, avoid low grounds, so much the resort of the meadow mice, and prefer higher and drier soils.

This mouse is rather an inhabitant of cultivated fields than of woods, and is seldom found in the forest far removed from the vicinity of plantations, to which it resorts, not only to partake of the gleanings of the fields, but to lay its contributions on the products of the husbandman's labours, claiming a share before the crops are gathered. In the Northern states, it is found in potato fields and in vegetable gardens, gnawing holes into the sides of the potatoes, carrots, ruta-baga, and common turnips, following the rows where green peas and corn have been planted . . . In the South it is, next to the Norway rat, the most troublesome visitant of the cellars and banks in which the sweet potato is stored, destroying more than it consumes, by gnawing holes into the tubers, and causing them to rot. Wherever a bed of Guinea corn, Egyptian millet /*Sorghum* spp./, or Guinea grass /*Panicum maximum;* however, the authors may have given three alternate vernacular names for one *Sorghum*/ is planted, there you will soon observe numerous holes and nests of this species. We have recently seen an instance where a large bed of kohlrabi was was nearly destroyed by it . . . A number of small holes at the root of a stump, in the garden, indicated the true author of these depredations, and on digging, about a dozen of LECONTE's field Mice were captured. This species is particularly fond of the pea or ground nut, (hypogea.) /*Arachis*/ On examining the beds where this nut is cultivated, we have observed the rows on whole acres perforated in every direction by small holes, giving evidence that this troublesome little pest had been at work. In endeavouring to save and collect the seeds of the Gama grass, (*Tripsacum dactyloides,*) we generally found ourselves forestalled by this active and voracious little rat.

This species has young three or four times during the summer. One which we had in confinement, produced young three times, having three, seven, and four, in the different broods. The young were nearly all raised, but, when full-grown, became pugnacious and persecuted each other so much that we were obliged to separate them. They were almost exclusively fed on ground nuts, corn meal and sweet potatoes, but seemed to relish both boiled rice and bread. We have seen nine young taken from one nest. /See comments on reproduction, opposite page./

The nest of this species is generally found under ground, at the distance of about a foot from the surface; it is small, and composed of light, loose materials, collected in the vicinity.

This prolific field rat possesses many enemies to diminish its numbers. The house cat not only watches for it about the fields and gardens, but is fond of devouring it, whilst the bodies of shrews and ground moles are not eaten. The very common /barred/ Owl, (*Syrnium nebulosum* /*Strix varia*/,) the Barn Owl (*Strix Americana* /*Tyto alba*/,) the Weasel, Ermine, and Mink, all make this species a considerable part of their subsistence. /See comment on enemies, opposite page./

The only note we have ever heard from this mouse is a low squeak, only uttered when it is either struck suddenly or greatly alarmed. . . .

We do not feel warranted in changing the specific name of LE CONTE, but that name is not expressive of one of its characteristics, as, although it may have been found in the pine woods, we have never, in a single instance, detected it in such localities. We have always found it either in the open fields, or along fences, in the vicinity of gardens and farms. . . .

/*Editor's Comment: Another member of this group, first identified by Bachman as the Oregon Meadow Mouse,* Arvicola oregoni, *was painted by J. W. Audubon as Figure 2 in Plate 147. It is now known as the creeping vole,* Microtus oregoni oregoni (Bachman). *The species lives in dry grassy areas up to 6,000 feet or more above sea level from southern British Columbia to northwestern California.*/

PINE VOLE

Microtus pinetorum pinetorum (LeConte)

Although it weighs less than an ounce, the pine vole is a bundle of energy and is constantly extending its network of tunnels. In undisturbed loam, it digs as fast as 15 inches in a minute. The one-inch tunnels surface often, run under the leaves for a few inches and descend again, but seldom deeper than three or four inches. In addition to its own burrow system, the pine vole uses those of shrews, moles and other mice.

The little animal (also called pine mouse) is formed for subterranean life. The body is slender, eyes and ears tiny, vibrissae long and sensitive (for feeling the way in dark tunnels), mouth small and adapted to exclude dirt, and tail very short. Dirt does not adhere to its glossy, velvety fur.

So accustomed is the animal to low ceilings that even in a relatively spacious cage a captive does not sit up on its haunches like a meadow mouse. Instead, when eating, it holds food against the floor with its forepaws.

During courting season, the female may make advances. In captivity she sometimes grasps the male's hip with her teeth and repeatedly drags him backward as a preliminary to mating. In some cases breeding in the wild occurs all year; ordinarily there is a lapse, from October to January.

The tunnel nest has three or four entrances. Several litters of two or three young (sometimes one or four) are born usually between March and October but occasionally during other months. (The litter of nine that Bachman found were probably young meadow voles.) If the mother is frightened from home, the nestlings hang onto the teats with even greater tenacity than meadow mice. When six days old, fur appears and teeth are cut. Two days later ears unfold and the eyes open in about 10 days. At three weeks the young are weaned and are ready to breed at two months.

Most of the food is gathered below ground. Under snow, the mice go above and eat the bark of trees and shrubs, often killing them. Storage rooms in the burrow contain up to a gallon of fleshy rootstocks and are closed with earth. When captured, some pine voles are placid while others become frenzied and almost vicious. They have a wide variety of vocal notes, are poor climbers and jumpers but can float and swim when flooded out of their tunnels.

These mice are captured underground by snakes, shrews, small weasels and diggers like skunks. Peak populations are reduced by epizootic disease, but perhaps not before the voles have done great damage to orchards and gardens. Often they are afflicted by internal and external parasites; thousands of louse nits may infest the vibrissae, facial hairs and body of a single pine mouse.

This animal is 4¼ to 5¾ inches long, including the ¾- to 1-inch tail. It occurs over the eastern half of the United States except Maine, Florida and Minnesota.

FIBER ZIBETHICUS . CUVIER.

MUSK-RAT, MUSQUASH.

Reader! If you are a native of, or have sojourned in any portion, almost, of our continent, and have interested yourself in observing the "beasts of the field" in our woods or along our streams, to the slightest degree, you have probably often seen the Musk-Rat; or should you have been confined to the busy marts of commerce, in our large cities, you may even there have seen his *skin,* and thought it a beautiful fur. It is, in fact, when the animal is killed in good season, superior to very many other materials for making *beaver* (?) hats, as well as for other purposes, and thousands of Musk-Rat skins are annually used in the United States, while still greater numbers are shipped to Europe, principally to Great Britain. . . .

Musk-Rats are lively playful animals when in their proper element the water, and many of them may be occasionally seen disporting on a calm night in some mill-pond or deep sequestered pool, crossing and recrossing in every direction leaving long ripples in the water behind them, whilst others stand for a few moments on little knolls or tufts of grass, or on stones or logs, on which they can get footing above the water, or on the banks of the pond, and then plunge one after another into the water; at times, one is seen lying perfectly still on the surface of the pond or stream, with its body widely spread out, and as flat as it can be. Suddenly it gives the water a smart flap with its tail, somewhat in the manner of the beaver, and disappears beneath the surface instantaneously — going down head foremost — and reminding one of the quickness and ease with which some species of ducks and grebes dive when shot at. At the distance of ten or twenty yards, the Musk-Rat comes to the surface again, and perhaps joins its companions in their sports; at the same time others are feeding on the grassy banks, dragging off the roots of various kinds of plants, or digging underneath the edge of the bank. These animals thus seem to form a little community of social playful creatures, who only require to be unmolested in order to be happy. . . .

. . . .A pond supplied chiefly if not entirely by springs and surrounded by low and marshy ground, is preferred by the Musk-Rats; they seem to be aware that the spring-water it contains, probably will not be solidly frozen, and there they prepare to pass the winter. Such a place, as you may well imagine, cannot without great difficulty be approached until its boggy and treacherous foundation has been congealed by the hard frosts and the water is frozen over; before this time the Musk-Rats collect coarse grasses and mud, with which, together with sticks, twigs, leaves, and any thing in the vicinity that will serve their purpose, they raise their little houses from two to four feet above the water the entrance being always from below. We have frequently opened these nests and found in the centre a dry comfortable bed of grass, sufficiently large to accommodate several of them. When the ponds are frozen over, and a slight fall of snow covers the ground, these edifices resemble small hay-cocks. . . .

Although the Musk-Rat does not seem to possess any extraordinary instincts by which to avoid or baffle its pursuers, we were witnesses of its sensibility of approaching danger arising from a natural cause, manifested in a way we think deserving of being recorded. . . . After an unusual drought, succeeded by a warm Indian-summer, as we were one day passing near a mill-pond inhabited by some families of Musk-Rats, we observed numbers of them swimming about in every direction, carrying mouthfuls of withered grasses, and building their huts higher on the land than any we had seen before. We had scarcely ever observed them in this locality in the middle of the day, and then only for a moment as they swam from one side of the pond to the other; but now they seemed bent on preparing for some approaching event, and the successive reports of several guns fired by some hunters only produced a pause in their operations for five or ten minutes. Although the day was bright and fair, on that very night there fell torrents of rain succeeded by an unusual freshet and intensely cold weather.

This species has a strong musky smell; to us this has never appeared particularly offensive. . . .

170

MUSKRAT

Ondatra zibethicus zibethicus (Linnaeus)

The muskrat, smaller than the beaver, dives with less disturbance, often noiselessly. It dog-paddles backward as well as forward. The narrow, vertically flattened tail acts as a rudder; the fringed, slightly webbed hind feet are propellers. Although it can make only two or three miles an hour in the water (as on land), it can stay under the surface as long as 17 minutes, and travel 60 yards before coming up for air. Sight, smell and hearing are poor, but their sense of direction is excellent.

Unless they are victims of highway traffic, muskrats are seldom seen. Their presence is advertised by their signs: houses in marshes, channels in mud leading to bank burrows, narrow excavated canals, covered feeding platforms, defecating posts, floating pieces of cut vegetation, trails through marsh growth, and tracks. The latter resemble the "hand" imprints of beaver and raccoon but are much smaller. Muskrats live in fresh, brackish and salt water marshes, and along margins of all types of ponds, lakes and streams, except those with very swift currents and rocky shores.

They eat practically everything — including poison ivy! Their favorite foods are aquatic plants, including cattail, arrowhead, rushes, sedges and pondweed. Clams, mussels, crayfish, snails and dead or dying fish are devoured when available. In winter they sometimes nibble part of their houses and occasionally will kill another for food.

In the north, the breeding season is April to July; on the Gulf Coast, it is nearly year long. One female muskrat may produce more than 25 young in a year, another only four. The litter of one to 11 (average six) are born after a gestation of about 30 days. In 10 days, before their eyes open, they can swim and dive. (Sometimes adult males rescue them.) As soon as they are weaned at three to four weeks, the mother drives them out to make way for the next litter.

Mink and raccoons tunnel into muskrat houses to eat the young. Muskrats that survive are subject to disease including pasteurellosis, tularemia, hepatitis, pneumonia, occasional gallstones, and even leukemia. Sick muskrats may not eat, but their teeth still keep growing. The lower incisors of one of these cut off the upper incisors and the end of its nose. In spite of many calamities, such a prolific species becomes overcrowded — critically about every 10 years in Canada. Trapping, predation, floods, droughts and disease are population controls.

Named for its perineal glands, this species is the most lucrative of all fur bearers. Adults are 16 to 25 inches long, including the 7- to 12-inch tail, and weigh 18 to 55 ounces. The range blankets the United States and Canada except the far north and extreme northeast.

GEORYCHUS HELVOLUS, RICH.

TAWNY LEMMING.

Mr. DRUMMOND, who obtained this animal, procured no further information in regard to its habits than that it was found in Alpine swamps. It bears a strong resemblance to the Norway Lemming, and we may presume does not differ widely from that species in its habits, which it is said are migratory to a surprising extent, and about which some curious stories are related that we do not consider necessary to place in our work.

This Lemming is one of those animals we have never seen except the stuffed specimens. Our figure was drawn in London by J. W. AUDUBON from the original skin procured by Mr. DRUMMOND /probably from the headwaters of a southern tributary of the Peace River/.

This Lemming was found in the spring season at Great Bear Lake, by Sir JOHN FRANKLIN, burrowing under the thick mosses which cover a large portion of the ground in high northern latitudes.

As soon as the surface of the ground had thawed, the little animal was observed at work making his progress beneath, and actively engaged in hunting for food.

In the winter it travels under the snow in semi-cylindrical furrows, very neatly cut to the depth of two inches and a half in the mossy turf; these hollow ways intersect each other at various angles, but occasionally run to a considerable distance in a straight direction; from their smoothness it was evident that they were not merely worn by the feet, but actually cut by the teeth; their width is sufficient to allow the animal to pass with facility.

The food of this Lemming seems to consist entirely of vegetable matters; it inhabits woody spots.

A female killed on Point Lake /Mackenzie/, June 26, 1821, contained six young, fully formed, but destitute of hair.

This animal was discovered by Captain BACK on the borders of Point Lake, in latitude 65°, on Sir JOHN FRANKLIN's first expedition. Mr. EDWARDS, the surgeon of the Fury, on Captain PARRY's second expedition, brought a specimen from Igloolik /on Melville Peninsula/, in latitude 69⅓°; and specimens were obtained on Sir JOHN FRANKLIN's second expedition, on the shores of Great Bear Lake.

/Editor's Comment: The above two "species" are now regarded as two subspecies of the brown lemming. Any differences of form and structure are inappreciable or the result of normal variation between individuals of the same species. Richardson's tawny lemming (now Lemmus trimucronatus helvolus (Rich.), *a bright tawny animal, inhabits the Canadian Rocky Mountain region; Back's lemming (L.t. trimucronatus (Rich.)) is more grizzled and occurs eastward to Hudson Bay and Baffin Island. Several other subspecies are found in Alaska./*

Fig. 1

Fig. 2
Fig. 3

BROWN LEMMING

Lemmus trimucronatus (ssp.)

The lemming tribe has achieved unhappy fame for its periodic population explosions that are followed by even more violent die-offs. Every three or four years, the population of the brown lemming builds up to a peak. Breeding then continues through the winter instead of stopping as usual in late fall. In northern Alaska, lemmings have increased a hundred times in a single winter. Sometimes, but not always, the resulting masses of rodents devour not only all of their own food, but that of the reindeer and caribou in their area. During the final spring and summer the lemmings rush aimlessly about. No vast, concerted migrations take place in North America as have occurred in northern Europe. Foxes, weasels, owls, ravens, gulls, jaegers and other carnivorous creatures gorge on the lemmings and increase their own populations. Suddenly it is over. In a few weeks the hordes of swarming lemmings are finally devoured, wiped out by starvation, or dead of disease. (At Barrow, Alaska, the toll by assembled owls and jaegers once brought the rodent population back to normal size without further catastrophe.) After the usual crash, however, there begins the cyclic decline — starvation or emigration of the predators

which have fed with such gluttony.

Brown lemmings make a network of runways both underground and on the surface which they share with each other. From the upper travel ways, spurs run to feeding places where the lemmings eat sedges, leaves, blossoms and berries.

Six-inch globular nests of shredded grass, lined with moss, plant fibers and feathers, are placed in grassy hummocks, under rocks or in a burrow. Females start bearing young before they are full grown and have several litters from May through September. Gestation probably takes about 21 days. As soon as the three to possibly nine young are weaned, the mother moves to another nest or den nearby.

In winter the long thumb claw is more noticeable and the fur is much longer, especially on the ankles and wrists. When threatened, the lemming chatters, squeals and fights with its forefeet.

Brown lemmings are 4¾ to 6½ inches long, including the ¾- to 1-inch tail, and weigh up to 4 ounces. They occur from Baffin Island to the Bering Sea, south from the Arctic coast to the tree line and, in the west, to central British Columbia.

ARVICOLA BOREALIS, RICH.

NORTHERN MEADOW-MOUSE,

We have little to say in regard to the present species. RICHARDSON states that its habits are very similar to those of *A. xanthognatha /Microtus xanthognathus,* the yellow-cheeked vole/, and in our article on that species we have given an account of the general habits of the Arvicolae . . . /microtines, see p. 164/, to which we refer our readers.

The northern Arvicolae do not appear to become dormant from the effect of cold, but during the long Arctic winter dig galleries under the deep snows, in which they are enabled to search for seeds, grasses, or roots suited to their wants. We have ascertained by an examination of the bodies of several, more southern species of Arvicolae, possessing similar habits, that so far from suffering in winter and becoming lean, they are usually in good case, and sometimes quite fat, during that season.

The length of the fur on the back of the present species (ten twelfths of an inch) is somewhat remarkable for so small an animal.

This species was found in numbers at Great Bear Lake, living in the vicinity of *Arvicola xanthognatha.* We have not been able to ascertain the extent of its range towards the south or west. We /J. J. Audubon/ did not discover this Meadow-Mouse or hear of it on our expedition to the Yellow Stone and Upper Missouri rivers, nor has it been found, so far as we know, anywhere west of the Rocky Mountains. /See opposite page./

NORTHERN BOG LEMMING

Synaptomys borealis borealis (Richardson)

Not a true lemming, this little rodent has the alternate name of lemming mouse. Long thick hair covers its ears and body, and claws on the front toes thicken in winter. It looks rather like a small, stocky, grizzled meadow mouse with a large head and short tail. Glands in the groin (and also hips of the males) are much more active during mating season and leave an identifying secretion. The genus name, *Synaptomys,* is from two Greek words, *synapto* (to unite) and *mys* (mouse). The term refers to the concept that the bog lemming is a link between the meadow vole and the true lemmings.

Because it is largely limited to far northern sphagnum bogs (an unappealing habitat for most naturalists) and its small colonies are widely scattered, little is known about the northern bog lemming and its way of life. Occasionally it has been found in burrows and runways on dry grassland instead of bogs. A biologist who trapped more than 700 microtines in northern Manitoba discovered only six bog lemmings in his catch. Even those expert predators, hawks and owls, fared no better. Out of 437 victims examined in the predators' stomachs, only one was a bog lemming.

Except for the long winter claws, this boreal rodent is very similar in appearance and habits to its close relative, the southern bog lemming. This better-known animal, active at all hours and seasons, also generally keeps to its burrows in bogs and damp meadows, and only occasionally moves into dry fields and wet woods. When crossing water, the lemming mouse dog-paddles vigorously. Although colonial, it is ex-

tremely nervous and likely to quarrel and bite one of its own kind. At the entrance and inside its runways are bundles of dry grass, cut two to three inches long, and many tiny, green fecal pellets. When captured, although the bog lemming displays little fear and usually can be handled without gloves, it often dies in a short time from shock. Besides grass stems, it eats leaves and seeds and, since it spends most of the time in the maze of tunnels, probably roots and bulbs. Some food besides grass is stored.

In size and color, the female can be distinguished from the male only when the latter is old and has white hairs growing out of the center of its hip glands. The nest is an enlargement of a tunnel to six or eight inches in diameter and is lined with grass and other plants. In Wisconsin, the southern bog lemming breeds from early March to November. (Its northern relative probably has a somewhat shorter season.) The gestation period is about 21 days and a female bears three and perhaps four litters a year containing three to four (rarely two to five) young. She carries them by their bellies. Her tone when comforting them is very different from her courting or quarreling voice.

Northern bog lemmings are 4¾ to 5½ inches long, including the tail which is 1 inch or a little less. The species is found south of the tree limit from western Alaska and the Pacific Coast of Canada east to Labrador and the Gulf of St. Lawrence, with extensions to northern Washington, Montana, Minnesota and New Hampshire.

MYODES HUDSONIUS, RICH.

HUDSON'S BAY LEMMING

Our only acquaintance with this species is through the works of the old writers and the Fauna Boreali Americana, we /John J. Audubon/ having failed to meet with it at Labrador. The first specimen we saw of it was in the museum of the Royal College of Surgeons at Edinburgh. Our drawing was made from specimens in the British Museum. Dr. RICHARDSON did not meet with this Lemming in the interior of America, and thinks it has hitherto been found only near the sea.

"Its habits are still imperfectly known. In summer, according to HEARNE, it burrows under stones in dry ridges, and Captain SABINE informs us that in winter it resides in a nest of moss on the surface of the ground, rarely going abroad."—*Fauna Boreali Americana*, p. 132.

HEARNE states that this little species is very inoffensive, and so easily tamed that if taken even when full grown it will in a day or two be perfectly reconciled, very fond of being handled, and will creep of its own accord into its master's neck or bosom.

/Editor's Comment: Bachman used an outdated classification in grouping the three lemmings (pp 172, 176) in the genus Georychus. *(The latter now contains only one species,* G. capensis, *the Cape mole-rat of South Africa.) Already two new genera had been established for these small rodents of the northern polar and subpolar regions of North America, Europe and Asia. Their characteristics are described on pages 173 and 177.*

North America has two species of Lemmus, *the true lemmings. The scientific name is New Latin and is derived from the Norwegian* lemja — *to maim or strike. There are three species of* Dicrostonyx, *the varying or collared lemmings, in the New World. This genus name was formed from two Greek words:* dikroos, *forked, and* onyx, *claw — a reference to the double-clawed appearance of the middle toes on the forefeet in winter./*

LABRADOR COLLARED LEMMING

Dicrostonyx hudsonius (Pallas)

The collared lemmings are the only true rodents that turn white in the winter, thus explaining the alternate name, varying lemmings. Probably because there is comparatively little snow on the Aleutian Islands in Alaska, the collared or varying lemmings there stay brown the year round. An indistinct ruff, which is recognizable only in summer and is completely absent in winter, is responsible for the name — collared lemming. Two more names — "banded" and "pied" — come from the patches of white winter hairs that appear here and there in a slow and somewhat haphazard molt instead of the more orderly progression along the body as in most mammals.

Another unique distinction of this lemming is the thick horny growth that develops each autumn on the underside of the claws of the third and fourth toes of the forefeet. Presumably these shields, which are shed in spring, strengthen the claws and protect them from excessive wear while the animal tunnels through packed or crystalline snow.

The collared lemming often digs through the upper layers of snowdrifts while the brown lemming, which lacks the horny winter pads, works under the snow along the surface of the ground. Both species live in the treeless Arctic although usually in different habitats. (The collared lemming prefers dry sand or gravelly areas, while the brown lemming is found most often in wet bogs.) Neither lemming hibernates but runs about under the snow all winter.

Collared lemmings make numerous short tunnels as well as many shallow runways on the surface. Tunnel nests sometimes have a defecating room nearby. Winter nests, about eight inches in diameter, are often placed above ground among rocks and in snowdrifts. Mainly vegetarians, these lemmings may eat insects and meat if available.

They have at least two litters of young a year and sometimes breed in winter. Gestation requires about 21 days. The young are usually three or four, although up to 11 embryos have been counted in a related species. Eskimos use the white fluffy winter fur for trimming garments, and little girls often make individual skins into doll parkas.

This species does not range over as extensive an area as the brown lemming and it does not have such extreme peaks of abundance. However, the population fluctuates on the same three- or four-year cycle and it sometimes becomes very numerous. The animals hurry about, migrate individually and in different directions — just anywhere is good enough. Some drown or are eaten by fish; most are devoured by predators of land and air, or die of starvation and disease.

The Labrador collared lemming is about 6 inches long, including the ¾-inch tail. It occurs from the Atlantic Coast of Labrador to Hudson Bay.

MUS RATTUS ET VAR. LINN.
BLACK RAT.

The character of this species is so notoriously bad, that were we to write a volume in its defence we would fail to remove those prejudices which are every where entertained against this thieving cosmopolite. Possessing scarcely one redeeming quality, it has by its mischievous propensities caused the world to unite in a wish for its extermination.

The Black Rat is omnivorous, nothing seeming to come amiss to its voracious jaws — flesh, fowl or fish, and grain, fruit, nuts, vegetables, &c., whether raw or cooked, being indiscriminately devoured by it. It is very fond of plants that contain much saccharine or oleaginous matter.

The favourite abodes of this species are barns or granaries, holes under out-houses or cellars, and such like places; but it does not confine itself to any particular locality. We have seen its burrows under cellars used for keeping the winter's supply of sweet potatoes in Carolina, in dykes surrounding rice-fields sometimes more than a mile from any dwelling. . .

In the neighbourhood of the small streams which are the sources of the Edisto river, we found a light-coloured variety, in far greater numbers than the Black, and we have given three figures of them in our Plate. They were sent to us alive, having been caught in the woods, not far from a mill-pond. We have also observed the same variety in Charleston, and received specimens from Major LECONTE, who obtained them in Georgia.

During the summer season, and in the autumn, many of these rats, as well as the common or Norway rat, (*Mus decumanus* /now *Rattus norvegicus*/,) and the common /house/ mouse, (*Mus musculus,*) leave their hiding places near or in the farmer's barns or hen-houses, and retire to the woods and fields, to feed on various wild grasses, seeds, and plants. We have observed Norway rats burrowing in banks and on the borders of fields, far from any inhabited building; but when the winter season approaches they again resort to their former haunts, and possibly invite an additional party to join them. The Black Rat, however, lives in certain parts of the country permanently in localities where there are no human habitations, keeping in crevices and fissures in the rocks, under stones, or in hollow logs. . . .

Like the Norway rat this species is fond of eggs, young chickens, ducks, &c., although its exploits in the poultry house are surpassed by the audacity and voraciousness of the other.

We have occasionally observed barns and hen-houses that were infested by the Black Rat, in which the eggs or young chickens remained unmolested for months together; when, however, the Rats once had a taste of these delicacies, they became as destructive as usual, and nothing could save the eggs or young fowls but making the buildings rat-proof, or killing the plunderers. . . .

The Black Rat, although capable of swimming, seems less fond of frequenting the water than the brown rat. It is a more lively, and we think a more active, species than the other; it runs with rapidity, and makes longer leaps; when attacked, it shrieks and defends itself with its teeth, but we consider it more helpless and less courageous than the brown or Norway rat. . . .

We have occasionally found both species existing on the same premises, and have caught them on successive nights in the same traps; but we have invariably found that where the Norway rat exists in any considerable numbers the present species does not long remain. The Norway rat is not only a gross feeder, but is bold and successful in its attacks on other animals and birds. We have known it to destroy the domesticated rabbit by dozens; we have seen it dragging a living frog from the banks of a pond; we were once witnesses to its devouring the young of its own species, and we see no reason why it should not pursue the Black Rat to the extremity of its burrow, and there seize and devour it. Be this as it may, the latter is diminishing in number in proportion to the multiplication of the other species, and as they are equally prolific and equally cunning, we cannot account for its decrease on any other supposition than that it becomes the prey of the more powerful and more voracious Norway rat.

The Black Rat brings forth young four or five times in a year; we have seen from six to nine young in a nest, which was large and composed of leaves, hay, decayed grasses, loose cotton, and rags of various kinds . . .

BLACK RAT

Rattus rattus (ssp.)

The black rat is smaller and, as Audubon and Bachman pointed out, much less aggressive than its cousin the Norway (brown) rat. Consequently, on this continent, it has lost out generally in the fierce struggle for existence. Two characteristics, however, have permitted considerable numbers to survive in the southeastern and Gulf states, on the west coast north to San Francisco, and in Central America.

Much better climbers than the Norway rats, these rodents occupy the upper portions of warehouses and other buildings in seaports, while their larger competitors, the Norway rats, take over the basements and lower floors. (For this reason the black rats are often called "roof rats.") These climbers are also better adapted to field living and frequently spend their entire lives outside of and some distance from man's habitations. (When Norway rats burrow in fields, they usually move into barns and houses with the advent of cold weather.) In other respects, the life histories of the two species are quite similar.

The black rat is a native of Asia and is still very numerous in the tropics. It was brought to Spanish America about 1554, and arrived in the English colonies, starting with Jamestown, Virginia, in 1609. Captain John Smith recorded that the settlers of the tiny village were driven to distraction in their generally futile efforts to guard their precious provisions from the voracious rodents which came ashore from the ships and swiftly multiplied.

At least three identifiable subspecies of the black rat have established themselves in North America, although in many areas they have interbred with other species until distinctive features have been lost:

1. The typical black rat [*Rattus rattus rattus* (Linnaeus)] is black or dark slate-colored above and lighter and less glossy underneath. Apparently this was the subspecies which was first introduced to the New World; it is now generally rare but has been reported to be rather numerous at Halifax and Vancouver, Canada.

2. The Alexandrine or roof rat [*R. r. alexandrinus* (E. Geoffroy-Saint-Hilaire)] is reddish-brown above and grayish-white below. It is scarce over most of the United States but fairly common in the south.

3. The fruit rat [*R. r. frugivorus* (Rafinesque)] is similar to the preceding except that its underparts are white. These rodents are plentiful in southern seaports and have moved inland with shipping to such cities as St. Louis and Kansas City. They live to a large extent on ripe oranges, grapefruit and other fruits when available, and they often inhabit densefoliaged trees such as palms.

Black rats have fewer litters per year than Norway rats, with a maximum of 10 young in each litter. Although their more open way of life tends to foster fewer ectoparasites, black rats are still highly dangerous to man as carriers of the louse which can transmit plague, typhus and other deadly diseases. Adults of the species are 13 to 18 inches long, including the 6½- to 10-inch tail, and weigh 5 to 12 ounces.

MUS DECUMANUS, LINN

BROWN, OR NORWAY RAT.

The brown rat is unfortunately but too well known almost in every portion of our country, and in fact throughout the world, to require an elaborate account of its habits, but we will give such particulars as may we hope be interesting. It is one of the most prolific and destructive little quadrupeds about the residences of man, and is as fierce as voracious. Some cases are on record where this rat has attacked a man when he was asleep, and we have seen both adults and children who, by their wanting a piece of the ear, or a bit of the end of the nose, bore plainful testimony to its having attacked them while they were in bed; it has been known to nibble at an exposed toe or finger, and sometimes to have bitten even the remains of the shrouded dead who may have been exposed to its attacks.

The Norway Rat is very pugnacious, and several individuals may often be seen fighting together, squealing, biting, and inflicting severe wounds on each other. On one occasion, we saw two of these rats in furious combat, and so enraged were they, that one of them whose tail was turned towards us, allowed us to seize him, which we did, giving him at the same time such a swing against a gate post which was near, that the blow killed him instantly — his antagonist making his escape. . . .

The Brown or Norway Rat was first introduced in the neighbourhood of Henderson, Kentucky, our /Audubon's/ old and happy residence for several years, within our recollection.

One day a barge arrived from New-Orleans (we think in 1811) loaded with sugar and other goods; some of the cargo belonged to us. During the landing of the packages we saw several of these rats make their escape from the vessel to the shore, and run off in different directions. In a year from this time they had become quite a nuisance; whether they had been reinforced by other importations, or had multiplied to an incredible extent, we know not. Shortly after this period we had our smokehouse floor taken up on account of their having burrowed under it in nearly every direction. We killed at that time a great many of them with the aid of our dogs, but they continued to annoy us, and the readers of our Ornithological Biography are aware, that ere we left Henderson some rats destroyed many of our valued drawings. . . .

The Norway Rat is quite abundant in New-York and most other maritime cities, along the wharves and docks, and becomes very large. These animals are frequently destroyed in great numbers, while a ship is in port, after her cargo has been discharged, by smoking them; the fumes of sulphur and other suffocating materials, being confined to the hold by closing all parts, windows and hatches. After a thorough cleaning out, a large ship has been known to have had many thousands on board. . . .

The Brown Rat brings forth from 10 to 15 young at a litter, and breeds several times in a year. Fortunately for mankind, it has many enemies: weasels, skunks, owls, hawks, &c., as well as cats and dogs. We have never known the latter to eat them, but they may at times do so. Rats are also killed by each other, and the weak ones devoured by the stronger.

This species becomes very fat and clumsy when living a long time in mills or warehouses. We have often seen old ones so fat and inactive that they would fall back when attempting to ascend a staircase.

We will take our leave of this disagreeable pest, by saying, that it is omnivorous, devouring with equal voracity meat of all kinds, eggs, poultry, fish, reptiles, vegetables, &c. &c. It prefers eels to other kinds of fish, having been known to select an eel out of a large bucket of fresh fish, and drag it off to its hole. In vegetable gardens it devours melons, cucumbers, &c., and will eat into a melon, entering through a hole large enough to admit its body, consuming the tender sweet fruit, seeds and all, and leaving the rind almost perfect. Where rats have gained access to a field or vegetable garden, they generally dig holes near the fruits or vegetables, into which they can make an easy retreat at the approach of an enemy.

We have represented several of these rats in our plate about to devour muskmelons, for which they have a strong predilection.

NORWAY RAT

Rattus norvegicus norvegicus (Berkenhout)

The Norway rat is called the brown rat, barn rat, sewer rat, wharf rat — and much worse! It shares the distinction, with its smaller and weaker relative the black rat, of being the most feared and hated mammal in the world. As prolific as it is aggressive, the Norway rat often outnumbers human residents, and has spread everywhere except in the very coldest regions. It carries some of the most virulent diseases of man and animals, including plague and typhus, which have killed more people than all the wars in history. Voracious, the rat devours or destroys property worth possibly one-half billion dollars every year in the United States alone.

Named through a mistaken notion as to its place of origin, the Norway rat actually spread from central Asia into Europe. It reached the east coast of North America about 1775 and the Pacific coast around 1851. Although most abundant in and around man's habitations and refuse dumps, it also occurs in fields but usually comes in for shelter during cold periods. It digs tunnels two or three inches in diameter and up to a foot deep, with chambers for nests and eating places. In the wild, as in buildings, rats often form colonies which are dominated by certain individuals and any strange rats are driven out.

Although chiefly nocturnal, Norway rats sometimes are abroad in daylight. They feed mostly soon after dark and shortly before dawn. Omniverous, they eat all vegetable and animal matter, and miscellany including paper, soap and insulation on wiring. Rats kill and devour poultry, young lambs and swine, rabbits, snakes, black rats and their own kind. They eat as much as one-third of their own weight daily and require considerable water.

In the tropics, Norway rats can breed year-long but in the temperate zone, most reproduction is in spring and fall. Gestation requires 21 days. The average adult female has five litters a year containing seven to 11 young. In a laboratory, a pair of rats and offspring have produced 1,500 animals in a year.

At birth, the young weigh about one-fifth ounce. They are "on their own" in four weeks and can breed at three to four months of age. They have many enemies and few reach the potential life span of two to three years.

Adults are 13 to 18½ inches long, including the 5- to 8½-inch tail, and weigh 7 to 17 (rarely 30) ounces. The species occurs in most inhabitable areas of North America except the coldest parts of Alaska and Canada.

MUS-MUSCULUS, LINN.
COMMON MOUSE.

We have attempted to shew a portion of a shelf in a pantry, on which stands a china jar, with its indigo-blue peaked mountains, its fantastic trees and its (take them altogether) rather remarkable landscapes, reminding us more of the sweetmeats it contains than of aught in the way of nature; and we have also portrayed a plate, with a piece of hard old cheese in it, on which a Mouse is standing in the act of listening, while another in the plate, and two more on the shelf, likewise appear a little startled, and are expecting to be disturbed ere they can make their intended meal; the little rascals have reason to fear, for the careful housekeeper has heard them of late, squealing in their squabblings with each other, has found the marks of their teeth on the bread and butter, and is determined to get rid of them instanter, if possible; she is calling now to her faithful pussy cat, and inquiring for the trap.

But although the thievish Mouse is often frightened, and may be said to eat his dinner with "a cat" over his head, although he is assailed with pokers, broomsticks, &c., whenever he unluckily runs across the floor, and in fact is killed as often as his death can be compassed by the ingenuity of man, or the cunning and quickness of his ally the cat, the Mouse will not retire from the house, and even where the supply of food for him is small, or in rooms that have long been shut up, he may be found; and would he let our drawings and books alone, we should willingly allow him the crumbs from our table. . . . He in his turn frightens man at times, and should the hard-hearted hoarding wretch who has made gold his God, while with aged, trembling hands, locked in his inmost chamber, he counts his money-bags, but hear a little Mouse; what a feeling of terror shoots through his frame; despair seems for an instant to be written on his face, and he clutches convulsively the metal to which he is a slave; another moment, and he recovers, but he is still agitated, and hastily secures with locks and bolts the treasure which is to him more precious than the endearments of a wife, the love of children, the delights of friendship and society. . . .

Many a young lady will scream at sight of a poor little Mouse, and many a brave young man might be startled in the stillness of the night by the noise made by this diminutive creature, especially if given to the reading of the "Mysteries of Udolpho" or the "Castle of Otranto," late in the hours of darkness, alone in a large old lumbering house.

The Common Mouse is a graceful, lively little animal — it is almost omnivorous, and is a great feeder, although able to live on but little food if the supply is scanty. This species has from four to ten young at a litter, and the female suckles her young with tender care. When first born, they are very small, almost naked, and of a pinkish colour. The Mouse has several litters every year. We kept a pair in confinement, which produced four times, having from four to nine in each litter. Dr. GODMAN quotes Aristotle, who says that "a pregnant female being shut up in a chest of grain; in a short time a hundred and twenty individuals were counted."

On examining our corn-crib in the spring, and cleaning it out; although it was constructed with a special view to keep off rats and vermin, being on posts, and the floor raised from the ground some three feet, with boards outside inclining downwards all round, we found and killed nearly fifty Mice. A basket in the crib, hanging by a rope from a cross-beam, in which we had put some choice corn for seed, had been entered by them, and every grain of corn in it devoured. We found in the basket nothing but husks, and the remains of a Mouse's nest. The animal must therefore have climbed up to the roof of the crib, and then descended the cord by which the basket of corn was suspended.

The activity, agility, and grace of the Mouse, have made it a favourite pet with the prisoner in his solitary cell, and it has been known to answer his call, and come out of its hiding places to play with the unfortunate captive, showing the greatest fondness for him, and eating out of his hand without fear.

Of late years, white Mice have been in request in London, where they are taught various tricks, and are exhibited by boys in the streets. It is stated that in order to increase the number of this variety, persons exclude them from the light, this they pretend causes a great many of them to be born albinos. We are however satisfied from personal experience that a pair of albinos, accidently produced, would continue to propagate varieties of the same colour without the aid of darkness; as is the case in the albino variety of the English rabbit.

HOUSE MOUSE

Mus musculus brevirostris Waterhouse

A native of Asia, the house mouse colonized the Mediterranean region even before Rome became its center, and from there was given free transportation throughout the world. Reaching America about the time of the Revolution, house mice have accompanied humans almost everywhere on the continent. Rats outnumber humans, and there are twice as many house mice as there are rats. In the south, some individuals live independently in fields and marshes, but in the northern and central states house mice take shelter in buildings during winter. In colder parts of Canada and Alaska, the species is dependent on human shelter the year round.

House mice are sociable animals and gather in colonies. Each family, consisting of a dominant male with one or more females and young, live in a nest of paper, rags or other trash or, if out-of-doors, grass. They are chiefly nocturnal and when food is plentiful travel only a few yards from the nest. They are skillful climbers, jumpers and swimmers. When thoroughly alarmed, they scurry as fast as 12 feet a second. The vocal repertoire is extensive — many squeaks, chirps, chitters, and a "song" of two to six notes a second which ranges through two octaves.

Domesticated strains of house mice, used for medical and other research, reproduce the year round. Wild mice, however, breed mostly from early spring to late fall, raising from five to 10 litters. The two to 12 young (usually five to seven) are born after a gestation of 19 days — or longer if the female is still nursing a litter. The young are blind, naked and weigh less than one-half ounce, but they are weaned in three weeks and are capable of bearing young when six weeks old. Few live longer than one year. Under favorable conditions of temperature and food, house mice may become extremely numerous and then starve or are decimated by diseases.

In addition to eating and fouling food, fabrics and other property, house mice harbor parasites which carry typhus, spotted fever and other deadly viruses. Long before there was proof, mankind vaguely recognized a connection between disease and these rodents. One of the Greek gods, Apollo Smintheus, was believed to ward off disease and also to be a destroyer of mice.

The house mouse can be distinguished from the white-footed and other deer mice by the *gradual* shading of color from back to belly, instead of a sharp division between gray or brown flank and white underparts.

House mice are 5½ to 8 inches long, half of this length being tail. In the New World, they occur from the Arctic Ocean to the southern tip of South America.

MERIONES AMERICANUS, BARTON.

JUMPING MOUSE.

This species was familiar to us /John Bachman/ in early life, and we possessed many opportunities of studying its peculiar and very interesting habits. We doubt whether there is any quadruped in the world of its size, that can make its way over the ground as rapidly, or one that can in an open space so quickly evade the grasp of its pursuers. The ploughman in the Northern and Middle States, sometimes turns up this species from under a clod of earth, when it immediately commences its long leaps. He drops his reins and hurries after it; whilst the little creature darts off with great agility, pursuing an irregular zig-zag direction, and it requires an active runner to keep pace with it, as it alternately rises and sinks like the flying-fish at sea, and ere the pursuer is aware, is out of sight, hidden probably behind some clod, or concealed under a tuft of grass. . . .

We experienced no difficulty in capturing this species in box-traps, and preserved a female in a cage from spring to autumn; she produced two young a few days after being caught; she reared both of them, and they had become nearly of full size before autumn, when by some accident our pets escaped. We placed a foot of earth at the bottom of the cage, in this they formed a burrow with two outlets. They used their feet and nails to advantage, as we observed them bury themselves in the earth, in a very short time. They were usually very silent, but when we placed a common /house/ mouse in the cage, squeaked with a loud chattering noise, like some young bird in pain. They skipped about the cage, were anxious to make their escape from the mouse, and convinced us that this species is very timid. They were in their habits strictly nocturnal, scarcely ever coming out of their holes during the day, but rattling about the wires of the cage throughout the night.

We observed that every thing that was put into their cage, however great might be the quantity, was stored away in their holes before the next morning. . . .

We are inclined to believe that this species produces several times during the summer, as we have seen the young on several occasions in May and August; They are from two to four; we have usually found three. . . .

The domicil of the Jumping Mouse in summer, in which her young are produced, we have always found near the surface, seldom more than six inches under ground, sometimes under fences and brushwood, but more generally under clods of earth, where the sward had been turned over in early spring, leaving hollow spaces beneath, convenient for the summer residence of the animal. The nest is composed of fine grass, mixed with which we have sometimes seen feathers, wool, and hair.

We are, however, under an impression that the Jumping Mouse in winter resorts to a burrow situated much deeper in the earth, and beyond the influence of severe frosts, as when fields were ploughed late in autumn, we could never obtain any of this species. It may be stated as a general observation, that this animal is a resident of fields and cultivated grounds; we have, however, witnessed two or three exceptions to this habit, having caught some in traps set at night in the woods, and once having found a nest under the roots of a tree in the forest, occupied by an old female of this species with three young two-thirds grown; this nest contained about a handful of chestnuts, which had fallen from the surrounding trees.

It is generally believed, that the Jumping Mouse, like the Hampster /hamster/ of Europe, *(Cricetus vulgaris* /now *C. cricatus/),* and the Marmots, *(Arctomys* /now *Marmota/),* hibernates, and passes the winter in a profound lethargy. Although we made some efforts many years ago, to place this matter beyond a doubt by personal observation, we regret that our residence /Charleston, South Carolina/, being in a region where this species does not exist, no favourable opportunity has since been afforded us. . . .

To us the Jumping Mouse has not been an abundant species in any part of our country. Being, however, a nocturnal animal, rarely seen during the day unless disturbed, it is in reality more numerous than is generally supposed. . . .

This species, feeding on small seeds, does very little injury to the farmer; it serves, like the sparrow, to lessen the superabundance of grass seeds, which are injurious to the growth of wheat and other grains . . .

MEADOW JUMPING MOUSE

Zapus hudsonius americanus (Barton)

Although the jumping mouse has internal cheek pockets and long hind legs like those of the kangaroo rat, it lives in moist — not arid — places. Across a meadow, a damp field, or even a marsh, the jumping mouse picks its way in a slow walk or a series of leisurely one- to six-inch hops. When frightened, however, it springs away in a series of leaps — the first of which some naturalists declare stretch eight to 10 or even 13 feet. While the jumps average only about a foot in a lengthy chase, they give a false impression of speed. Timed at eight feet per second, this mouse travels only three-quarters as fast as the scurrying house mouse.

The tail, which is considerably longer than head and body, serves as a balance when the mouse is jumping. If much is cut off by accident, fighting, or in escaping a carnivore, the animal falls all over itself. In water, the mouse holds its forefeet against its chest, propels its big hind feet, and keeps its head up by the long balancing tail.

During a flight, the mother may lose one or more of the offspring clinging to her teats. The "drop-offs" squeal loudly until she comes back and takes them home. Her warm-weather nest is a woven ball of grass with an entrance on one side; it is usually on the ground or attached to the lower stems in a tussock of grass. Apparently most females bear two litters during the summer, but some may have three. Gestation requires only 18 days. The average number of young is five or six with extremes of one to nine.

Born weighing one-thirtieth ounce, with only half a tail and not a single whisker, they squeak noisily. In three weeks they are weaned and disperse shortly afterward. The mice that are born early in the season may breed in late summer; others are not sexually mature until the following spring.

In autumn, the jumping mouse moves to nearby higher ground and digs a solitary hibernating den in well-drained soil. The short burrow may descend nearly six feet, or merely go under a log. In any case, the baseball-sized grass nest must be placed below frost line. Instead of storing food, the jumping mouse becomes very fat — doubling its spring weight. It gets more and more drowsy and then ceases to eat. The digestive tract is emptied. Curling into a ball, the little animal folds forepaws over belly, hooks hind legs behind ears, winds the long tail around itself and goes to sleep. Hibernation may last as long as seven months, although some individuals rouse briefly and venture from the tunnel.

When above ground, the jumping mouse climbs surely and skillfully. Although a vegetarian, it drinks a good deal of water. It likes to wet its forepaws and clean itself from head to end of tail. Individuals have sometimes been seen dancing — as with deer mice, this may be a form of epilepsy. The jumping mouse makes a variety of clucking and squeaking noises. It also "drums" by vibrating its tail rapidly against ground or dry leaves. Not pugnacious, it seldom fights with its own kind.

The meadow jumping mouse is 7 to 9½ inches long, including the 4- to 5¾-inch tail, and weighs ½ to 1 ounce. It occurs from the tree line south to Alabama, Colorado and southern British Columbia. A relative, the woodland jumping mouse lives under trees and brush in the eastern part of this range.

HYSTRIX DORSATA, LINN.

CANADA PORCUPINE.

The Canada Porcupine, of all North American quadrupeds, possesses the strangest peculiarities in its organization and habits. In its movements it is the most sluggish of all our species. . . . Under such circumstances the inquiry arises, what protection has this animal against the attacks of the wolverene, the lynx, the wolf, and the cougar? and how long will it be before it becomes totally exterminated? But a wise Creator has endowed it with powers by which it can bid defiance to the whole ferine race, the grizzly bear not excepted. If the skunk presents to its enemies a formidable battery, that stifles and burns at the same time, the Porcupine is clothed in an impervious coat of mail bristling with bayonets.

We /Bachman/ kept a living animal of this kind in a cage in Charleston for six months, and on many occasions witnessed the manner in which it arranged its formidable spines, in order to prove invulnerable to the attacks of its enemies.

It was occasionally let out of its cage to enjoy the benefit of a promenade in the garden. It had become very gentle, and evinced no spiteful propensities; when we called to it, holding in our hand a tempting sweet-potatoe or an apple, it would turn its head slowly towards us, and give us a mild and wistful look, and then with stately steps advance and take the fruit from our hand. It then assumed an upright position, and conveyed the potatoe or apple to its mouth with its paws. If it found the door of our study open, it would march in, and gently approach us, rubbing its sides against our legs, and looking up at us as if supplicating for additional delicacies. We frequently plagued it in order to try its temper, but it never evinced any spirit of resentment by raising its bristles at us; but no sooner did a dog make his appearance, than in a moment it was armed at all points in defence. It would bend its nose downward, erect its bristles, and by a threatening sideway movement of the tail, give evidence that it was ready for the attack. . . .

On a visit to the western portion of the county of Saratoga, New-York, in the winter of 1813, a farmer residing in the vicinity carried us in his sleigh to show us a Porcupine which he had frequently seen during the winter, assuring us that he could find it on the very tree where he had observed it the previous day. We were disappointed, finding that it had deserted the tree; we however traced it in the snow by a well beaten path, which it seemed to have used daily, to a beech tree not far distant, which we cut down, and at the distance of twenty feet from the root we found the object of our search in a hollow part. . . . Our friend killed it by a blow on the nose, the only vulnerable part as he informed us. . . . It had fed principally on hemlock bark, and had destroyed upwards of a hundred trees. The observations made on this occasion incline us to doubt the correctness of the statement that the Canada Porcupine does not leave a tree until it has eaten off all the bark, and that it remains for a week or more on the same tree; we were on the contrary led to suppose that the individual we have just spoken of, retired nightly to its comfortable domicile and warm bed in the hollow beach /beech/, in which we discovered it.

The Porcupine we kept in Charleston did not appear very choice in regard to its food. It ate almost any kind of vegetable we presented to it. . . . We occasionally heard it during the night, uttering a shrill note, that might be called a low querulous shriek. . . .

We have mentioned in our article on the Canada lynx, that one of those animals was taken in the woods in a dying state, owing to its mouth being filled with Porcupine quills. We have heard of many dogs, some wolves, and at least one panther, that were found dead, in consequence of inflammation produced by seizing on the Porcupine.

Its nest is found in hollow trees or in caves under rocks. It produces its young in April or May, generally two at a litter; we have however heard that three, and on one occasion four, had been found in a nest.

The Indians residing in the North, make considerable use of the quills of the Porcupine; moccasins, shot-pouches, baskets made of birch bark, &c., are ingeniously ornamented with them, for which purpose they are dyed of various bright colours.

The flesh of this species is sometimes eaten, and is said to have the taste of flabby pork. . . .

PORCUPINE

Erethizon dorsatum dorsatum (Linnaeus)

When threatened, the porcupine turns its rear to the enemy and thrashes its tail. Thirty thousand barbed quills are raised and ready to penetrate the hide of any attacker. Some predators have learned to upset the porcupine and attack its unprotected throat and belly. Quills inflicted on a carnivore often work through the muscles and out, or are absorbed or blunted by body chemicals. They rarely work into vital organs and cause death.

From October to December, the porcupine's unique courtship is marked by amorous sounds and gestures. After seven months the single young is born with its eyes wide open and body covered with hair. The quills, in full array, are one-fourth to one inch long and harden as they dry. The mother keeps her quills clamped flat to her body to avoid impaling the young.

A porcupine may spend days or weeks on tree branches eating cambium, and sometimes killing the tree. Adults measure 26 to 40 inches (tail 6 to 12) and weigh 12 to 25 up to a maximum 43 pounds. The range covers most of Canada and the United States except the southeast.

CANIS LATRANS, SAY,
PRAIRIE WOLF.

We /J.J. Audubon/ saw a good number of these small wolves on our trip up the Missouri river, as well as during our excursions through those portions of the country which we visited bordering on the Yellow Stone.

This species . . . . is also found on the Saskatchewan. It has much the appearance of the common grey Wolf in colour, but differs from it in size and manners.

The Prairie Wolf hunts in packs, but is also often seen prowling singly over the plains in search of food. During one of our morning rambles near Fort Union, we happened to start one of these wolves suddenly. It made off at a very swift pace and we fired at it without any effect, our guns being loaded with small shot at the time; after running about one hundred yards it suddenly stopped and shook itself violently, by which we perceived that it had been touched; in a few moments it again started and soon disappeared beyond a high range of hills, galloping along like a hare or an antelope.

The bark or howl of this wolf greatly resembles that of the dog, and on one occasion the party travelling with us were impressed by the idea that Indians were in our vicinity, as a great many of these wolves were about us and barked during the night like Indian dogs. We were all on the alert, and our guns were loaded with ball in readiness for an attack.

In Texas the Prairie Wolves are perhaps more abundant than the other species /gray or red wolf/ they hunt in packs of six or eight, which are seen to most advantage in the evening, in pursuit of deer. It is amusing to see them cut across the curves made by the latter when trying to escape, the hindmost Wolves thus saving some distance, and finally striking in ahead of the poor deer and surrounding it, when a single Wolf would fail in the attempt to capture it. By its predatory and destructive habits, this Wolf is a great annoyance to the settlers in the new territories of the west. Travellers and hunters on the prairies, dislike it for killing the deer, which supply these wanderers with their best meals, and furnish them with part of their clothing, the buck-skin breeches, the most durable garment, for the woods or plains. . . .

This Wolf feeds on birds, small and large quadrupeds, and when hard pressed by hunger, even upon carrion or carcasses of buffaloes, &c. It is easily tamed when caught young, and makes a tolerable companion, though not gifted with the good qualities of the dog. We had one once, which was kept in a friend's store in the west, and we discovered it to be something of a rat catcher. This individual was very desirous of being on friendly terms with all the dogs about the premises . . . One day we missed our pet from his accustomed place near the back part of the ware-house, and while we were wondering what had become of him, were attracted by an unusual uproar in the street. In a moment we perceived the noise was occasioned by a whole pack of curs of high and low degree, which were in full cry, and in pursuit of our Prairie Wolf. The creature thus hard beset, before we could interfere, had reached a point opposite a raised window, and to our surprise, made a sudden spring at it and jumped into the warehouse without touching the edges of the sills, in the most admirable manner, while his foes were completely baffled.

After this adventure the Wolf would no longer go out in the town and seemed to give up his wish to extend the circle of his acquaintance.

The barking or Prairie Wolf digs its burrows upon the prairies on some slight elevation, to prevent them from being filled with water. These dens have several entrances, like those of the red fox. The young, from five to seven and occasionally more in number, are brought forth in March and April. They associate in greater numbers than the larger Wolves, hunt in packs, and are said by RICHARDSON to be fleeter than the common Wolf. A gentleman, an experienced hunter on the Saskatchewan, informed him that the only animal on the plains which he could not overtake when mounted on a good horse, was the prong-horned antelope, and that the Prairie Wolf was next in speed.

All our travellers have informed us, that on the report of a gun on the prairies, numbers of these Wolves start from the earth, and warily approach the hunter, under an expectation of obtaining the offal of the animal he has killed.

The skins of the Prairie Wolves are of some value, the fur being soft and warm; they form a part of the Hudson Bay Company's exportations, to what extent we are not informed. . . .

COYOTE

Canis latrans latrans Say

Similar in size and color to the small red wolf, this little "prairie wolf" has been shot, trapped and poisoned over its entire range. Unspeakable, noxious lures have been successful — on the other hand, so was a scented powder puff that successively caught nine coyotes in the same spot. Although clever, they let curiosity get the better of them. Sometimes an individual "plays possum" before pouncing on prey. Coyotes endure great pain and, like some other animals, may even chew off a foot to get free from a trap. Contrary to Audubon's opinion, the coyote when caught young does not make a good pet for any length of time at all. It is too nervous and unreliable.

Probably only a small percentage of coyotes have learned how easy it is to catch domesticated (unwary, stupid, slow) stock. Most large, wild prey are sick, injured, aged or have already died of starvation or disease. In addition to culling (thus improving wildlife) and cleaning up carrion, coyotes destroy vast numbers of range-depleting rodents. They eat almost any part of an animal and even dried leather. (A famous zoologist seriously doubts a developed sense of taste!)

When running, their tails tend to droop instead of floating outward like those of wolves. Hunting in relays (their groups are much smaller than wolf packs), coyotes may go up to 45 miles an hour in short spurts. The variety of notes in their nocturnal chorus of howls and wails is a thrilling part of the prairie.

The pups are born furred, but blind, in a den with or without nest, depending on climate and the mother's solicitude. The male (coyotes frequently mate for life) brings food to the mother while she is first nursing. She spends much time nosing, licking and playing with her young. When they are about to be weaned, both parents may bring meat in their stomachs and regurgitate it, partially digested, for the pups. When greeting his mate, the coyote may touch her nose and lick her face. If disturbed by enemy or infestation of fleas, the pair will move the family to another den.

The species is 44 to 54 inches long, including the 12- to 16-inch tail, and weighs 20 to 50 pounds. The range (which has expanded eastward and northward during this century) is from northwestern Alaska and eastern Ontario to Costa Rica.

189

CANIS FAMILIARIS, LINN. VAR BOREALIS, DESM.

ESQUIMAUX DOG.

So much has been written about the admirable qualities of the dog, that it would be quite useless for us to enter upon the subject; we shall also avoid the question of the origin of the various races, which in fact have been so intermixed that it would be an almost Quixotic task to endeavour to trace the genealogy of even the "noblest" of them. Those, however, that have, like the Esquimaux Dog, for centuries retained their general characters, and have not been exposed to any chance of "amalgamation" with other races, exhibit habits as well as forms and colours sufficiently permanent to warrant the naturalist in describing them, and in many cases their history is exceedingly interesting.

The Esquimaux Dogs are most useful animals to the savages of our Arctic regions, and when hitched to a sled many couples together, will travel with their master over the ice and snow at great speed for many miles without much fatigue, or draw heavy burthens to the huts of their owners. When on the coast of Labrador we /John J. Audubon/ had the following account of the mode in which these dogs subsist, from a man who had resided in that part of the world for upwards of ten years. . . .

. . . During spring and summer they ramble along the shores, where they meet with abundance of dead fish, and in winter they eat the flesh of the seals which are killed and salted in the spring or late in the autumn when these animals return from the north. This man informed us also that when hard pushed he could relish the fare he thus provided for his Dogs just as much as they did themselves. We found several families inhabiting the coast of Labrador, all of whom depended entirely on their Dogs to convey them when visiting their neighbours, and some of whom had packs of at least forty of these animals. On some parts of the coast of Labrador the fish were so abundant during our visit that we could scoop them out of the edge of the water with a pocket-handkerchief: at such times the Esquimaux Dogs catch them, wading in and snapping at them with considerable dexterity as the surf retires; when caught they eat them at once while they are still alive.

We were informed that when these Dogs are on a journey, in winter, should they be overtaken by a severe snow-storm, and thereby prevented from reaching a settlement within the calculated time, and if the provisions intended for them in consequence give out, in their ravenous hunger they devour the driver, and even prey upon one another. Such cases were related to us, as well as others in which, by severe whipping and loud cries the Dogs were forced into a gallop and kept on the full run until some house was reached and the sleigh-driver saved.

These animals are taught to go in harness from the time they are quite young pups, being placed in a team along with well trained Dogs when only two or three months old, to gain experience and learn to obey their master, who wields a whip of twenty or thirty feet length of lash, with a short, heavy handle.

On a man approaching a house where they are kept, these Dogs sally forth with fierce barkings at the intruder, and it requires a bold heart to march up to them, as with their pointed ears and wiry hair they look like a pack of wild wolves. They are in fact very savage and ferocious at times, and require the strictest discipline to keep them in subjection. . . .

We have been induced, in our account of American animals, to give figures and descriptions of this peculiar variety of Dog, inasmuch as it appears to have been a permanent variety for ages, and is one of the most useful animals to the Indians residing in the polar regions. Whether it be an original native Dog, or derive its origin from the wolf, is a subject which we will not here discuss, farther than to state, in opposition to the views of Dr. RICHARDSON, that our figures do not represent these animals, as very closely allied to the wolf; on the contrary, their look of intelligence would indicate that they possess sagacity and aptitude for the service of man, equal at least to that of many favourite breeds of Dog. The fact also of their breeding at all seasons of the year, their manner of placing the tail in sport, and their general habits, give evidence of their being true Dogs and not Wolves, the only difference between them and some other varieties consisting in their having erect pointed ears, which are peculiar to the Dogs of savage nations, and not altogether absent in some of our common breeds, as we have witnessed in the shepherd's Dog of Europe and some cur Dogs in America, erect ears of a similar character.

ESKIMO DOG

Canis familiaris Linnaeus

As primitive man moved into the Arctic, he probably brought along his dogs. By natural selection they became large, extremely hardy and, with a minimum of food, capable of pulling heavy loads. Because Eskimos rarely bartered their dogs, the animals were inbred. During the era of white exploration of the Arctic (1700–1910), other breeds were introduced. Many of the resulting crosses did not have the necessary stamina and died out. However the present-day sled dog differs considerably from the original stock of three or four centuries ago.

Bitches may come in heat at any time of year, but generally mate in spring or fall. The litter contains 7 to 8, with extremes of 3 to 12 pups. They are usually vari-colored,—dirty white, grays and black. Eskimo dogs do not bark except for a short yapping when sensing an unfamiliar object. Instead they emit a sad, monotonous howl. This voice and some physical characters have led to a belief that wolf blood is predominant in the heredity. (Audubon and Bachman were correct in rejecting this opinion.) Although many Eskimos consider matings with wolves desirable, crossbreeding seldom occurs and any resulting hybrids are generally intractable and poor sled dogs.

A spectacular use of Eskimo dogs, especially by Greenlanders, is in polar bear hunting. On sighting the prey, the driver slips his dogs from their harness. Racing after the fleeing bear, the dogs nip at its rear and eventually bring it to bay. The driver then kills the bear with spear or gun. During the skinning of the carcass, the dogs lie quietly awaiting their reward of meat or at least entrails. Like man, the dogs are susceptible to poisoning by the heavy concentration of vitamin C in the bear's liver.

Unsheltered, Eskimo dogs are fed every day or so when traveling, every three days when at home, and less often in warm weather. Audubon's informants in Labrador gave him an extreme example of the dog's unreliability (see preceding page). Possibly dangerous when it is starving, it is usually a faithful and gentle slave, and has become rather popular among white dog fanciers.

The typical Eskimo dog is about 57 inches long, stands 24 inches high at the shoulder, and weighs 65 to 85 pounds. The original "range" coincided with Eskimo territory; in America, the continent's northern rim from Labrador to the Kuskokwim River in western Alaska, as well as islands of the Arctic Ocean; also western Greenland north to Smith Sound. In the Old World, the same or a slightly smaller breed of arctic dog was used by natives in the far north from Kamchatka Peninsula and Kolyma River areas in eastern Siberia, west to European Russia and Lapland.

191

CANIS FAMILIARIS, LINN. (VAR LAGOPUS.)

HARE-INDIAN DOG.

This animal is more domestic than many of the wolf-like Dogs of the plains, and seems to have been entirely subjugated by the Indians north of the great lakes, who use it in hunting, but not as a beast for burthen or draught.

Sir JOHN RICHARDSON says (F.B.A. /Fauna Boreali-Americana/, p. 79): "The Hare-Indian Dog is very playful, has an affectionate disposition, and is soon gained by kindness. It is not, however, very docile, and dislikes confinement of every kind. It is very fond of being caressed, rubs its back against the hand like a cat, and soon makes an acquaintance with a stranger. Like a wild animal it is very mindful of an injury, nor does it, like a spaniel, crouch under the lash; but if it is conscious of having deserved punishment, it will hover round the tent of its master the whole day, without coming within his reach, even if he calls it. Its howl, when hurt or afraid, is that of the wolf; but when it sees any unusual object it makes a singular attempt at barking, commencing by a kind of growl, which is not, however, unpleasant, and ending in a prolonged howl. Its voice is very much like that of the prairie wolf /coyote/.

"The larger Dogs which we had for draught at Fort Franklin, and which were of the mongrel breed in common use at the fur posts, used to pursue the Hare-Indian Dogs for the purpose of devouring them; but the latter far outstripped them in speed, and easily made their escape. A young puppy, which I purchased from the Hare Indians, became greatly attached to me, and when about seven months old ran on the snow by the side of my sledge for nine hundred miles, without suffering from fatigue. During this march it frequently of its own accord carried a small twig or one of my mittens for a mile or two; but although very gentle in its manners it showed little aptitude in learning any of the arts which the Newfoundland Dogs so speedily acquire, of fetching and carrying when ordered. This Dog was killed and eaten by an Indian, on the Saskatchewan, who pretended that he mistook it for a fox."

The most extraordinary circumstance in this relation is the great endurance of the puppy, which certainly deserves special notice. Even the oldest and strongest Dogs are generally incapable of so long a journey as nine hundred miles (with probably but little food), without suffering from fatigue.

It is stated by Sir JOHN RICHARDSON that this species exists only among the different tribes of Indians that frequent the borders of Great Bear lake and the Mackenzie river.

From the size of this animal it might be supposed by those who are desirous of tracing all the Dogs to some neighbouring wolf, hyena, jackal, or fox, that it had its origin either from the prairie wolf or the red fox, or a mixture of both.

The fact, however, that these wolves and foxes never associate with each other in the same vicinity, and never have produced an intermediate variety, or, that we are aware of, have ever produced a hybrid in their wild state, and more especially the fact that the prairie wolf, as stated by RICHARDSON, does not exist within hundreds of miles of the region where this Dog is bred, must lead us to look to some other source for its origin. /The range of the coyote has expanded during the twentieth century until it has reached the lower Mackenzie River and vicinity of Great Bear Lake./

Its habits, the manner in which it carries its tail, its colour, and its bark, all differ widely from those of the prairie wolf.

We have never had an opportunity of seeing this animal and examining it, except in the stuffed specimen from which our drawing was made; we are therefore indebted to Sir JOHN RICHARDSON for all the information we possess in regard to its habits, and have in this article given the results of his investigations mostly in his own language.

INDIAN DOG

Canis familiaris Linnaeus

In pre-Columbian times, most North American Indians had only one domesticated animal — the dog. (An exception: Basket-makers or "Cliff-dwellers" of the Southwest kept turkeys.) Indians used dogs when hunting — for flushing and driving game into ambushes or traps.

Small types were used for food. While many Indian tribes abhorred dog-eating, the Siouan group and those of the bison area had no such aversion. The dog dance of the Dakotas was climaxed by eating the livers of newly killed dogs. The participants believed that it would make them shrewd as well as brave. Indian and half-breed employees of the North West Fur Company in the late 18th and early 19th centuries bred a small type of dog specifically for the table. One Canadian perhaps drooled as he recorded in his diary that his Indian wife cooked a meal of "5 Indian dogs, bear, beaver, mountain cat & raccoon, boiled in bear's grease and mixed with huckleberries."

The dog was the only draft animal in North America before the horse. Although limited in usefulness by size, dogs carried packs and pulled loads for numerous tribes in the caribou, bison and inland-salmon areas. In 1832, the artist George Catlin watched a cavalcade of Sioux, numbering 600 lodges (groups), trek across the rolling plains near the mouth

of the Yellowstone River. Bringing up the rear were at least 3,000 dogs, most pulling loads. In western Canada, Indian blanket weavers bred dogs for hair to use in textiles.

Three types of dogs existed in North America at the time of its discovery by Europeans. The largest was the wolf-like Eskimo dog of the Arctic described in the preceding account. At the other end of the scale were terrier-size animals which occurred mostly from Mexico into South America. In between — both geographically and in physical bulk — was a medium-size type with erect ears and a drooping tail. This was the Indian Dog.

Audubon and Bachman described only the Eskimo and Indian dogs. These and all other primitive "breeds" in the three groups were either obliterated or greatly altered by crossing with European introductions.

The "Hare-Indian dog" of northwestern Canada which was a rather small version of the medium-size type, disappeared early in the 19th century. J. W. Audubon had to use a mounted specimen as a model for his painting (above). It may have been one kept in the London Zoo until it died when its skin and skull were turned over to the British Museum. This animal was 51 inches long, including the 15-inch tail and stood 14 inches high at the shoulder.

CANIS LUPUS, LINN, (VAR ATER.)

BLACK AMERICAN WOLF.

Not an individual of the party saw a Black Wolf during our /J. J. Audubon's/ trip up the Missouri, on the prairies near Fort Union, or along the shores of that portion of the Yellow Stone River that we visited. Mr. SAY speaks of its being the most common variety on the banks of the Missouri, but, unfortunately, does not state precisely where.

Wolves of this colour were abundant near Henderson, Kentucky, when we removed to that place, and we saw them frequently during our rambles through the woods after birds.

We found a Black Wolf in one of our wild turkey pens, early one morning. He observed us, as we approached, but instead of making his escape, squatted close down, like a dog which does not wish to be seen. We came up within a few yards of the pen, and shot him dead, through an opening between the logs. This Wolf had killed several fine turkeys, and was in the act of devouring one, which was, doubtless, the reason he did not attempt to make his escape when we approached him.

There is a strong feeling of hostility entertained by the settlers of the wild portions of the country, toward the Wolf, as his strength, agility, and cunning, (in which last qualification, he is scarcely inferior to his relative, the fox,) tend to render him the most destructive enemy of their pigs, sheep, or young calves, which range in the forest; therefore, in our country, he is not more mercifully dealt with than in any other part of the world. Traps and snares of various sorts are set for catching him in those districts in which he still abounds. . . . Although Wolves are bold and savage, few instances occur in our temperate regions of their making an attack on man; and we have only had one such case come under our own notice. Two young negroes, who resided near the banks of the Ohio, in the lower part of the State of Kentucky, about thirty years ago /were attacked by a wolf pack/ . . .Both struggled manfully against their foes, but in a short time one of the negroes had ceased to move; and the other, reduced in strength and perhaps despairing of aiding his unfortunate comrade or even saving his own life, threw down his axe, sprang on to the branch of a tree, and speedily gained a place of safety amid the boughs. Here he passed a miserable night, and the next morning the bones of his friend lay scattered around on the snow, which was stained with his blood. Three dead wolves lay near, but the rest of the pack had disappeared; and Scipio sliding to the ground, recovered the axes and returned home to relate the terrible catastrophe.

About two years after this occurrence, as we were travelling between Henderson and Vincennes, we chanced to stop for the night at the house of a farmer. . . . we accompanied him across the fields to the skirts of the adjoining forest, where he had three pits within a few hundred yards of each other. They were about eight feet deep, broadest at the bottom, so as to render it impossible for the most active animal to escape from them. . . ./Next morning/ on examining the second pit, we discovered three famous fellows safe enough in it, two black and one brindled, all of good size. They were lying flat on the earth, with their ears close down to their heads, their eyes indicating fear more than anger. To our astonishment, the farmer proposed descending into the pit to hamstring them, in order to haul them up, and then allow them to be killed by the dogs, which, he said, would sharpen his curs for an encounter with the wolves, should any come near his house in /the/ future. . . .The woodman stretched out their hind legs, in succession, and with a stroke of the knife cut the principal tendon above the joint, exhibiting as little fear, as if he had been marking lambs. . . . We now hauled the terrified animal up; and motionless with fright, half choked, and disabled in its hind legs, the farmer slipped the rope from its neck, and left it to the mercy of the dogs, who set upon it with great fury and worried it to death. The second was dealt with in the same manner; but the third, which was probably oldest, showed some spirit the moment the dogs were set upon it, and scuffled along on its forelegs, at a surprising rate, snapping all the while furiously.at the dogs, several of which it bit severely; and so well did the desperate animal defend itself, that the farmer, apprehensive of its killing some of his pack, ran up and knocked it on the head with his axe. . . .

GRAY WOLF

Canis lupus occidentalis Richardson

Lurid tales of the American wolf's attacks on man have chilled the hearts of generation after generation. The gray (timber) wolf has been hated and feared and a price set upon its head for over 300 years. During the present century many attempts failed to secure indisputable proof of unprovoked attacks. Only one, apparently, has produced complete, documentary evidence. On December 29, 1942, in northern Ontario, a railroad foreman, riding his speeder at 10 miles an hour, was yanked off the tracks — speeder and all — by a wolf. He was able to keep the wolf at bay with an axe until help came on a passing train.

In contrast to this incident, a famous naturalist crawled through an entrance tunnel to a wolf den in Alaska and kidnapped one of the pups while the parents stood off, watched, barked and howled but made no attack. Actually, if a wolf passes your tent in the wilderness, he is less likely to be unpleasant than is your next door neighbor back home.

Of course there have been many famous wolves like old Three Toes in South Dakota which reputedly killed $50 thousand worth of stock while 150 hunters and trappers tried for 13 years to catch him. Such cattle raiders were the cause of the bounty trapping system. Seventeen years ago, it was estimated that more than $100 million had been spent in the United States on bounties paid over the years in money, tobacco, liquor, pigs, cattle and other commodities. Since then, most states have concluded that bounty trapping had been futile, often corrupt, and expensive, and have stopped it. In much of Canada, however, a bounty trapper can still make money hunting by airplane.

Some wolves die from food shortages, interspecific strife, and injuries received when attacking big game. Mange, rabies, tularemia, distemper, trichinosis, cancer, arthritis, smallpox (reported), and encephalitis also take a toll. Man, however, is the wolf's most important enemy. By reducing wilderness, in addition to trapping and poisoning, he has nearly exterminated wolves from all of North America south of the spruce-fir forest and east of the Canadian Rockies.

A gray wolf may be black, gray, brownish, all white (in the north) or a mixture of colors and patterns, and have no two pups alike. When running (see plate), its tail is held up rather than down like the coyote's.

Disregarding exceptionally large animals of northwestern America (under next plate), most male wolves measure 55 to 66 inches, including the 13- to 18-inch tail. Weight is 60 to 100 pounds. Females are 15 to 20 percent smaller. The original range of the species included practically all of North America north of 20° north latitude except the Gulf States and the driest deserts. Today, south of the Canadian boundary, only small remnant populations exist precariously in northern Michigan, Wisconsin and Minnesota, and in wild areas of Mexico including the extensive Sierra Madre Occidental. (Continued)

195

CANIS LUPUS, LINN (VAR ALBUS.)

WHITE AMERICAN WOLF.

The White Wolf is far the most common variety of the Wolf tribe to be met with around Fort Union, on the prairies, and on the plains bordering the Yellow Stone river. When we first reached Fort Union we found Wolves in great abundance, of several different colours, white, grey, and brindled. A good many were shot from the walls during our residence there, by EDWARD HARRIS, Esq., and Mr. J. G. BELL. . . .

. . . These animals were in the habit of coming at almost every hour of the night, to feed in the troughs where the offal from the Fort was deposited for the hogs. On one occasion, a wolf killed by our party was devoured during the night, probably by other prowlers of the same species.

The white wolves are generally fond of sitting on the tops of the eminences, or small hills in the prairies, from which points of vantage they can easily discover any passing object on the plain at a considerable distance. . . .

These animals are extremely abundant on the Missouri river, and in the adjacent country. On our way up that extraordinary stream, we first heard of wolves being troublesome to the farmers who own sheep, calves, young colts, or any other stock on which these ravenous beasts feed, at Jefferson city, the seat of goverment of the State of Missouri; but to our great surprise, while there not a black wolf was seen.

Wolves are said to feed at times, when very hard pressed by hunger, on certain roots which they dig out of the earth with their fore-paws, scratching like a common dog in the ground. When they have killed a Buffalo or other large animal, they drag the remains of the carcass to a concealed spot if at hand, then scrape out the loose soil and bury it, and often lie down on the top of the grave they have thus made for their victim, until urged again by hunger, they exume the body and feast upon it. . . .

Some days while ascending the river, we saw from twelve to twenty-five wolves; on one occasion we observed one apparently bent on crossing the river, it swam toward our boat and was fired at, upon which it wheeled round and soon made to the shore from which it had started. . . .

We were assured at Fort Union that wolves had not been known to attack men or horses in that vicinity, but they will pursue and kill mules and colts even near a trading post, always selecting the fattest. The number of tracks or rather paths made by the wolves from among and around the hills to that station are almost beyond credibility, and it is curious to observe their sagacity in choosing the shortest course and the most favourable ground in travelling.

We saw hybrids, the offspring of the wolf and the cur dog, and also their mixed broods: some of which resemble the wolf, and others the dog. Many of the Assiniboin Indians who visited Fort Union during our stay there, had both wolves and their crosses with the common dog in their trains, and their dog carts (if they may be so called) were drawn alike by both.

The natural gait of the American wolf resembles that of the Newfoundland dog, as it ambles, moving two of its legs on the same side at a time. When there is any appearance of danger, the wolf trots off, and generally makes for unfrequented hilly grounds, and if pursued, gallops at a quick pace, almost equal to that of a good horse . . .

Wolves are frequently deterred from feeding on animals shot by the hunters on the prairies, who, aware of the cautious and timid character of these rapacious beasts, attach to the game they are obliged to leave behind them a part of their clothing, a handkerchief, &c., or scatter gun powder around the carcass, which the cowardly animals dare not approach although they will watch it for hours at a time, and as soon as the hunter returns and takes out the entrails of the game he had left thus protected, and carries off the pieces he wishes, leaving the coarser parts for the benefit of these hungry animals, they come forward and enjoy the feast. . . .

The wolves of the prairies form burrows, wherein they bring forth their young, and which have more than one entrance; they produce from six to eleven at a birth, of which there are very seldom two alike in colour. The wolf lives to a great age and does not change its colour with increase of years.

GRAY WOLF

Canis lupus occidentalis Richardson

The largest timber wolves live in Alaska and the Mackenzie River region. Nearly seven feet long, including tail, they are up to 38 inches tall at the shoulder and may weigh 175 pounds. These gray wolves may be all white or black the year round; most are grayish or tawny gray.

Young wolves mate for the first time when two or three years old, and the pair usually remain together for life. A den is chosen, or excavated if necessary, in an earthen slope, a rocky ledge or in a hollow tree or fallen snag. The four to 14 (usually six or seven) young are born between March and early June after 60 to 63 days gestation. They are furred but blind for the first five to nine days. The father guards the family and brings meat to the mother. When she goes out to meet him, she may enthusiastically caper about, wag her tail and put her forepaws on his shoulders. The pups subsist entirely on milk for about three weeks. Then, sometimes assisted by other members of the pack, both parents bring back food, partially digested. The den is abandoned when the pups are about two months old but the family hunt together through the first winter or longer.

The typical family group or pack often includes several adult relatives, but rarely totals more than 15 individuals. Food controls the size — larger groups cannot get enough to eat from carcasses of even the big prey. Lone animals that try to join a pack are frequently driven off or even killed. Within the group, friendship is strong and visibly expressed by touching of noses and wagging of tails.

Hunting over a roughly circular route, sometimes several hundred miles long, wolves may travel up to 60 miles (rarely) in one night. They have great endurance, and tend to wear out rather than outrun their prey. Twenty-eight miles an hour for only a few yards is considered their top speed; one wolf, however, was clocked between 35 and 40 miles an hour for four miles. Traveling through snow, a band of wolves often trot in single file, each animal carefully stepping in the leader's tracks.

The old, the young, the weak, the sick and the injured are culled from the big game herds because they are easier to catch A determined doe with fawns, and her rear protected by a cliff, has been known to kill a wolf. Often wolves will not pursue fleeing prey into water; one wolf, however, was seen treading water while it fed on a partly submerged, very ripe moose.

When hungry, a wolf can eat meat equivalent to almost one-fifth its weight — enough to last for three days or more. Surplus food may be cached.

CANIS LUPUS, LINN, VAR RUFUS.
RED TEXAN WOLF.

This variety is by no means the only one found in Texas, where Wolves, black, white and gray, are to be met with from time to time. We do not think, however, that this Red Wolf is an inhabitant of the more northerly prairies, or even of the lower Mississippi bottoms, and have, therefore, called him the Red Texan Wolf.

The habits of this variety are nearly similar to those of the black and the white Wolf, which we have already described, differing somewhat, owing to local causes, but showing the same sneaking, cowardly, yet ferocious disposition.

It is said that when visiting battle-fields in Mexico, the Wolves preferred the slain Texans or Americans, to the Mexicans, and only ate the bodies of the latter from necessity, as owing to the quantity of pepper used by the Mexicans in their food, their flesh is impregnated with that powerful stimulant. Not vouching for this story, however, the fact is well known that these animals follow the movements of armies, or at least are always at hand to prey upon the slain before their comrades can give them a soldier's burial, or even after that mournful rite; and if anything could increase the horrors displayed by the gory ensanguined field, where man has slain his fellows by thousands, it would be the presence of packs of these ravenous beasts disputing for the carcasses of the brave, the young, and the patriotic, who have fallen for their country's honour!

No corpse of wounded straggler from his troop, or of unfortunate traveller, butchered by Camanches, is ever "neglected" by the prowling Wolf, and he quarrels in his fierce hunger in his turn over the victim of similar violent passions exhibited by man!

The Wolf is met on the prairies from time to time as the traveller slowly winds his way. We will here give an extract from the journal kept by J. W. AUDUBON while in Texas, which shows the audacity of this animal, and gives us a little bit of an adventure with a hungry one, related by POWELL, one of the gallant Texan Rangers.

". . . .as I rode by the side of POWELL we started no deer, nor came to a 'water hole,' but a Red Wolf jumped up some two or three hundred yards from us, and took to the lazy gallop so common to this species; 'Run you------,' cried POWELL, and he sent a yell after him that would have done credit to red or white man for its shrill and startling effect, the Wolf's tail dropped lower than usual, and now it would have taken a racer to have overtaken him in a mile; a laugh from POWELL, and another yell, which as the second reached the Wolf made him jump again, and POWELL turned to me with a chuckle, and said, 'I had the nicest trick played me by one of those rascals you ever heard of.' The simple, how was it, or let's have it, was all that he wanted and he began at the beginning. 'I was out on a survey about 15 miles west of Austin, in a range that we didn't care about shooting in any more than we could help, for the Camanches were all over the country; and having killed a deer in the morning, I took the ribs off one side and wrapping them in a piece of the skin, tied it to my saddle and carried it all day, so as to have a supper at night without hunting for it; it was a dark, dismal day, and I was cold and hungry when I got to where I was to camp to wait for the rest of the party to come up next day; I made my fire, untied my precious parcel, for it was now dark, with two sticks put up my ribs to roast, and walked off to rub down and secure my horse, while they were cooking; but in the midst of my arrangements I heard a stick crack, and as that in an Indian country means something, I turned and saw, to my amazement, for I thought no animal would go near the fire, a large Red Wolf actually stealing 'my ribs' as they roasted; instinct made me draw a pistol and 'let drive' at him; the smoke came in my face and I saw nothing but that my whole supper was gone. So not in the most philosophical manner I lay down, supperless, on my blanket; at daylight I was up to look out for breakfast, and to my surprise, my half-cooked ribs lay within twenty feet of the fire, and the Wolf about twenty yards off, dead; my ball having been as well aimed as if in broad daylight."

We have represented a fine specimen of this Wolf, on a sand-bar, snuffing at the bone of a buffalo, which, alas! is the only fragment of "animal matter" he has in prospect for breakfast.

RED WOLF

Canis niger rufus Audubon and Bachman

The red wolf may be black, brown, tan or red. Usually it is reddish or buffy. The species was first described and given its scientific name by William Bartram in his *Travels,* published in 1791. His type specimen, obtained in Florida, evidently was a black animal *(niger).* The first description of the western subspecies by Audubon established *rufus* (meaning "red") as a part of this animal's scientific name. In early days, naturalists named a number of "varieties" of animals, including wolves, on the basis of color; it was some time before they learned that many shades and combinations did not endure through successive generations. (Example: Both of Audubon's black and white wolves are now called the gray wolf.)

While the red wolf sometimes resembles the gray wolf in color, it has been designated a separate species because of differences in the teeth, smaller foot and ankle pads and generally more slender proportions.

In the western part of its range (Texas-Oklahoma), a *small* red wolf may be mistaken for a large coyote. The wolf is more stocky, its ears are shorter and more rounded, its nose pad usually wider, and its hair is coarser. Furthermore, the legs are relatively long and slender, fitting the animal for long distance running.

Young red wolves are born earlier in the year than gray wolves. The litters may contain three to a dozen pups. The red wolf lives on rabbits, squirrels and other rodents, ground-nesting birds and young deer. On the coast of Texas, it has been known to eat fiddler crabs.

Like the gray species, red wolves occasionally become stock killers. Often the most persistent robbers are animals that have been injured in traps. In eastern Texas, a government trapper spent two and one-half months before he succeeded in catching a crippled red wolf which had killed more than a hundred sheep and goats on one ranch. The predator had lost a forefoot, two toes from a hind foot, and its other rear foot had been broken.

Both species of wolves are vocal and their wailing howl is variously regarded as "sad and dismal" or as the "true and most thrilling voice of the wilderness." The red wolf of Texas is more prone than the gray wolf to vary the tone, which results in a ventriloquial effect. The howl of a single animal may sound like a chorus made by an entire pack.

Bartram lay asleep one night in Florida while wolves stole an entire string of fish from over his bed, and was awakened only as the last fish was taken. In Louisiana, an aged hunter was skinning alligators by the light of a carbide lamp when it went out. A wolf pack circled him for two hours while the terrified man slapped the water with his pirogue paddle, yelled and fired his few shotgun shells. Unable to reach the alligator carcasses (apparently their sole objective), the wolves left at daybreak.

Red wolf males are 56 to 60 inches long, including the 16-inch tail and weigh 50 to (rarely) 80 pounds; females are materially smaller. A relatively few animals survive in east Texas and Louisiana; originally the species occurred east to Florida and north to Illinois and South Carolina.

VULPES LAGOPUS, LINN.

ARCTIC FOX,

. . . this animal is well adapted to endure the severest cold. In winter its feet are thickly clothed with hair, even on the soles, which its movements on the ice and snow do not wear away, as would be the case if it trod upon the naked earth. These softly and thickly haired soles serve the double purpose of preserving its feet from the effects of frost and enabling it to run briskly and without slipping over the smooth icy tracts it must traverse.

The Arctic Fox is a singular animal, presenting rather the appearance of a little stumpy, round-eared cur, than that of the sharp and cunning-looking Foxes of other species which are found in more temperate climes. The character (for all animals have a character) and habits of this species are in accordance with its appearance; it is comparatively unsuspicious and gentle, and is less snappish and spiteful, even when first captured, than any other Fox with which we are acquainted.

At times there is seen a variety of this Fox, which has been called the Sooty Fox /a color phase; see opposite page/, but which is in all probability only the young, or at any rate is not a permanent variety, and which does not turn white in winter, although the species generally becomes white at that season. It is said likewise that the white Arctic Foxes do not all assume a brown tint in the summer. RICHARDSON says that only a majority of these animals acquire the pure white dress even in winter; many have a little duskiness on the nose, and others, probably young individuals, remain more or less coloured on the body all the year. On the other hand, a pure white Arctic Fox is occasionally met with in the middle of summer, and forms the variety named *Kakkortak* by the Greenlanders.

Mr. WILLIAM MORTON, ship's steward of the Advance, one of Mr. HENRY GRINNELL's vessels sent in search of Sir JOHN FRANKLIN and his party, although not a naturalist, has furnished us with some account of this species. He informs us that whilst the vessels (the Advance and Rescue) were in the ice, the men caught a good many Arctic Foxes in traps made of old empty barrels set with bait on the ice: they caught the same individuals in the same trap several times, their hunger or their want of caution leading them again into the barrel when only a short time released from captivity.

They were kept on board the vessels for some days, and afterwards let loose; they did not always appear very anxious to make their escape from the ships, and those that had not been caught sometimes approached the vessels on the ice, where first one would appear, and after a while another, showing that several were in the neighbourhood. They were occasionally observed on the rocks and snow on the land, but were not seen in packs like wolves; they do not take to the water or attempt to swim.

These Foxes when they see a man do not appear to be frightened: they run a little way, and then sit down on their haunches like a dog, and face the enemy before running off entirely. . . .

RICHARDSON says . . . . they are unlike the red Fox in being extremely unsuspicious; and instances are related of their standing by while the hunter is preparing the trap, and running headlong into it the moment he retires a few paces. Captain LYON received fifteen from a single trap in four hours. The voice of the Arctic Fox is a kind of yelp, and when a man approaches their breeding places they put their heads out of their burrows and bark at him, allowing him to come so near that they may easily be shot.

They appear to have the power of decoying other animals within their reach, by imitating their voices. . . .

The trap in which the Arctic Fox is taken by the Esquimaux, is described by authors as simple: it consists of a little hut built of stones, with a square opening on the top, over which some blades of whalebone are extended nearly across so as to form an apparently secure footing, although only fastened at one end, so that when the animal comes on to them to get the bait they bend downward and the Fox is precipitated into the hut below, which is deep enough to prevent his jumping out, the more especially because the whalebone immediately rises again to its position, and the bait being fastened thereto, several Foxes may be taken successively. . . .

ARCTIC FOX

Alopex lagopus ungava (Merriam)

Every four or five years, when lemmings suddenly die by the millions, Arctic foxes face starvation. Many, probably the young, travel southward in desperation even as far as southern Labrador and central Manitoba. Few or none of these wanderers return to the Arctic or survive for long in the south. Most of the stay-at-homes starve or fall prey to hungry predators such as lynx, wolves and bears. The chain of misfortune has extended to the Eskimo trappers who depended heavily on income from fox pelts. These five-year cyclic depressions, however, were minor compared with the crash after World War II when fashion decreed against fox (and other long-haired) furs, and ruined the market.

Arctic foxes come in two colors. In the "white" phase, the winter coat is all white, while the summer coat is tawny. In the "blue" phase, the winter color is bluish-gray and the summer coat is brown. The "Sooty Fox" (opposite page) undoubtedly was the blue phase animal in its winter coat.

Yapping all year round, these foxes do not hibernate — even though the temperature goes down to 50° below zero and colder. Some of them go out on sea ice many miles from land and scavenge on the kills of the polar bear. Others stay on land and patrol the beaches for live food and carrion.

Any sea life that is washed ashore is eagerly devoured. Sometimes up to a hundred foxes gather around a large carcass such as walrus or whale. They also prey on birds and ptarmigans as well as the eggs and young.

Where terrain and soil are suitable, Arctic foxes den in colonies on slopes or bluffs, usually near the ocean or on tundra not far away. They prefer open country but may go into scrub forest, and occasionally they settle far inland. After a noisy courtship and 51 or 52 days of gestation, the young are born in May or June. They number up to 12 (average six or seven), weigh about two ounces and are clothed in fine, dark brown hair. In late summer, spawned-out salmon are sought on stream banks, while fruits (blueberries, etc.) also vary the diet. Both parents care for the pups until fall when the family breaks up.

Arctic foxes of both sexes measure 29 to 31 inches long, including the 12- to 13-inch tail, and 9½ to 12 inches in shoulder height. They weigh 6 to 12 pounds to a rare maximum of 20 pounds. The single species is circumpolar in distribution; in North America, western Greenland and from the Gulf of St. Lawrence around northern Canada (including the Arctic islands) and Alaska to the Alaska Peninsula.

VULPES FULVUS, (DESM.)

AMERICAN RED-FOX.

This Fox, in times gone by, was comparatively rare in Virginia, and farther south was unknown. It is now seldom or never to be met with beyond Kentucky and Tennessee. Its early history is not ascertained, it was probably for a long time confounded with the Gray Fox, (which is in many parts of the country the most abundant species of the two,) and afterwards was supposed to have been imported from England, by some Fox-hunting governor of one of the "colonies." It was first distinguished from the Gray Fox and hunted, in Virginia; but now is known to exist in all the Northern States, and we are somewhat surprised that it should so long have been overlooked by our forefathers. No doubt, however, the cultivation and improvement of the whole country, is the chief reason why the Red Fox has become more numerous than it was before the Revolution, and it will probably be found going farther south and west, as the woods and forests give place to farms, with hens, chickens, tame turkeys, ducks, &c., in the barn-yards.

The Red Fox is far more active and enduring than the Gray, and generally runs in a more direct line, so that it always gives both dogs and hunters a good long chase, and where the hounds are not accustomed to follow, it will frequently beat-out the whole pack, and the horses and huntsmen to boot. . . . .

The Red Fox brings forth from four to six young at a litter, although not unfrequently as many as seven. The young are covered, for some time after they are born, with a soft woolly fur, quite unlike the coat of the grown animal, and generally of a pale rufous colour. Frequently, however, the cubs in a litter are mixed in colour, there being some red and some black-cross Foxes together: when this is the case it is difficult to tell which are the red and which the cross Foxes until they are somewhat grown. In these cases the parents were probably different in colour.

This animal feeds upon rats, rabbits, and other small quadrupeds, and catches birds, both by lying in wait for them, and by trailing them up in the manner of a pointer dog, until watching an opportunity he can pounce or spring upon them. . . .

The Red Fox also eats eggs, and we have watched it catching crickets in an open field near an old stone wall. It is diverting to witness this — the animal leaps about and whirls round so quickly as to be able to put his foot on the insect, and then gets hold of it with his mouth; we did not see him snap at them; his movements reminded us of a kitten playing with a mouse. . . .

The Red Fox is taken in traps, but is so very wary that it is necessary to set them with great nicety.

Dr. RICHARDSON tells us that the best fox hunters in the fur countries use *assafoetida*, *castoreum*, and other strong smelling substances, with which they rub their traps and the small twigs set up in the neighbourhood, alleging that Foxes are fond of such perfumes.

The same author informs us that their flesh is ill tasted, and is eaten only through necessity. . . . .

Whilst the Gray Fox seldom is known to dig a burrow, concealing its young usually beneath the ledges of rocks, under roots, or in the hollow of some fallen tree, the Red Fox on the contrary, digs an extensive burrow with two or three openings. To this retreat the Fox only flies after a hard chase and as a last resort. If, as often happens, the burrow is on level ground it is not very difficult by ascertaining the direction of the galleries and sinking a hole at intervals of seven or eight feet, to dig out and capture the animal. When thus taken he displays but little courage — sometimes, like the Opossum, closing his eyes and feigning death.

The young, from four to six at a birth, are born in February and March, they are blind when born, and are not seen at the mouth of the den for about six weeks.

It is at this period, when the snows in the Northern States are still on the ground, that the Fox, urged by hunger and instinct, goes out in search of prey. At a later period, both the parents hunt to provide food for their young. They are particularly fond of young lambs, which they carry off for miles to their burrows. They also kill geese, turkeys, ducks, and other poultry, and have a bad reputation with the farmer. They likewise feed on grouse and partridges, as well as on hares, squirrels, and field-rats of various species, as we have previously mentioned.

RED FOX

Vulpes fulva fulva (Desmarest)

A red fox may be either red, black, silver or cross; all four types can occur in the same litter. Contrary to Audubon's supposition, a matched pair may produce a mixed litter. Since Audubon painted three of the "varieties" on separate plates, this life history of the one species is continued under each illustration.

Having no more weight nor strength than a big house cat, the red fox makes up in cleverness for what it lacks in size. An experienced fox will elude a whole pack of trained hunting dogs by taking to water, crossing a dry stone ledge which retains little scent, trotting on the top rail of a fence or on a stone wall. The same animal may be adept at avoiding traps, or even digging up and upsetting them. (For this one, the trap must be buried upside down!)

From the beginning of literature, the fox has been considered the craftiest of all the inhabitants of the animal kingdom. There are limits, however, to the animal's foresight. The semi-legendary fox that tolled the pack of hounds onto the railroad trestle and under the wheels of a speeding train may have been real. But he did it by (for him) a lucky chance — not by studied observation of the railroad's schedule.

Ninety percent of the red fox's diet consists of rabbits, mice and other rodents (ground squirrels, tree squirrels, woodchucks). The remainder includes many insects (grasshoppers, beetles) and fruit and berries (apples, plums, strawberries and June berries). Porcupines are killed, perhaps mostly by "specialists" which have developed the technique; occasionally an unlucky learner pays with infected quill-wounds or even its life. The fox captures, but usually will not eat, shrews and moles. Few game birds are taken. It devours a mouse from head to tail, crunched bones and all, but draws the line at feathers. When food is plentiful, the fox kills more than it needs, caches the surplus, returns from time to time to eat or play with the food and re-cache it. In the meantime, he is often an involuntary (and absent) host to other animals and predatory birds. (Continued)

CANIS (VULPES) FULVUS. DESMARET.
VAR. DECUSSATUS.
AMERICAN CROSS FOX.

. . . The Cross Fox is generally regarded as being more wary and swift of foot than the Red Fox; with regard to its greater swiftness, we doubt the fact. We witnessed a trial of speed between the mongrel greyhound . . . , and a Red Fox, in the morning, and another between the same dog and a Cross Fox, about noon on the same day. The former was taken after an hour's hard run in the snow, and the latter in half that time, which we accounted for from the fact that the Cross Fox was considerably the fattest, and . . . became tired out very soon. . . .

In regard to the cunning of this variety there may be some truth in the general opinion, but this can be accounted for on natural principles; the skin is considered very valuable, and the animal is always regarded as a curiosity; hence the hunters make every endeavour to obtain one when seen, and it would not be surprising if a constant succession of attempts to capture it together with the instinctive desire for self-preservation possessed by all animals, should sharpen its wits and render it more cautious and wild than those species that are less frequently molested. We remember an instance of this kind which we will here relate.

A Cross Fox, nearly black, was frequently seen in a particular cover. We offered what was in those days considered a high premium for the animal in the flesh. The fox was accordingly chased and shot at by the farmers' boys in the neighbourhood. The autumn and winter passed away, nay, a whole year, and still the fox was going at large. It was at last regarded by some of the more credulous as possessing a charmed life, and it was thought that nothing but a silver ball could kill it. In the spring, we induced one of our servants to dig for the young Foxes that had been seen at the burrow which was known to be frequented by the Cross Fox. With an immense deal of labour and fatigue the young were dug out from the side of a hill; there were seven. Unfortunately we were obliged to leave home and did not return until after they had been given away and were distributed about the neighbourhood.

Three were said to have been black, the rest were red. The blackest of the young whelps was retained for us, and we frequently saw at the house of a neighbour, another of the litter that was red, and differed in no respect from the Common Red Fox. The older our little pet became, the less it grew like the Black, and the more like the Cross Fox. It was, very much to our regret, killed by a dog when about six months old, and as far as we can now recollect, was nearly of the colour of the specimen figured in our work.

The following autumn, we determined to try our hand at procuring the enchanted fox which was the parent of these young varieties, as it could always be started in the same vicinity. We obtained a pair of fine fox-hounds and gave chase. The dogs were young, and proved no match for the fox, which generally took a straight direction through several cleared fields for five or six miles, after which it began winding and twisting among the hills, where the hounds on two occasions lost the scent and returned home.

On a third hunt, we took our stand near the corner of an old field, at a spot we had twice observed it to pass. It came at last, swinging its brush from side to side, and running with great rapidity, three-quarters of a mile ahead of the dogs, which were yet out of hearing. —A good aim removed the mysterious charm: we killed it with squirrel-shot, without the aid of a silver bullet. It was nearly jet-black, with the tip of the tail white. This fox was the female which had produced the young of the previous spring that we have just spoken of; and as some of them, as we have already said, were Cross Foxes and others Red Foxes, this has settled the question in our minds, that both the Cross Fox and the Black Fox are mere varieties of the Red.

J. W. AUDUBON brought the specimen he obtained at Niagara, alive to New-York, where it was kept for six or seven weeks. It fed on meat of various kinds: it was easily exasperated, having been much teased on its way from the Falls. It usually laid down in the box in which it was confined, with its head toward the front and its bright eyes constantly looking upward and forward at all intruders. Sometimes during the night it would bark like a dog, and frequently during the day its movements corresponded with those of the latter animal. It could not bear the sun-light shining into its prison, and continued shy and snappish to the last. . . .

RED FOX

Vulpes fulva fulva (Desmarest)

The cross fox variation (illustrated above) of the red fox is named for the dark band down the back and across the shoulders. Some cross foxes might be mistaken for small coyotes but tails always tell. Whether red, black, silver or cross, all red foxes have *white* tail tips — from the day they are born. The length of the white tip may vary from three inches to (rarely) only a few white hairs.

While the original text of *Quadrupeds* (not quoted) describes both the cross and the white-tipped tail, Audubon's painting does not show the first marking (perhaps because of the animal's position) — and the tail tip (or Audubon's brush!) may have been the exception to the rule.

In fall and early winter all phases of red foxes are solitary and sleep in the open. (They stay warm by curling into a ball and tucking nose and feet under the bushy tail.) Mating in January and February brings about considerable communication and some fighting. Vixens squall shrilly and dog foxes respond with a series of two or three short barks. The mating is monogamous for the season — sometimes for life.

The female chooses an existing den, digs a new one, or enlarges a woodchuck or other burrow to suit her require-ments. (A hibernating woodchuck owner may be eaten in the process.) Multiple entrances are necessary — sometimes up to 27. Occasionally there are storerooms for food. The one to 10 (usually about five) young are born in a grass-lined den during March or April after a gestation of 49 to 56 (average 52) days. They are blind but covered with fine, grayish-brown hair and weigh about four ounces. The dog fox brings meat to the mother during the first of her nursing.

The pair begin training the young to make their own living by giving them, first, prey with the underparts opened and then live food, crippled, on which to practice killing. Playful, they gambol around the entrance to the den with each other and with bones, dry droppings and feathers. The adults sometimes move the juveniles from den to den and may take the ripe-smelling "playthings" along.

Foxes in the same litter differ not only in color but in enterprise. Two litter mates, five months old, were captured in the University of Wisconsin Arboretum and Wildlife Refuge, marked with metal collars and released. About 10 months later, one was shot 245 miles away and the other was recaptured 300 yards from the original site. (Continued)

VULPES FULVUS, DESM. VAR ARGENTATUS, RICH.

AMERICAN BLACK OR SILVER FOX.

Our account of the habits of this beautiful Fox will be perhaps less interesting to many than our description of its skin; for, as is well known, the Silver-gray Fox supplies one of the most valuable furs in the world, not only for the luxurious nobles of Russia and other parts of Europe, but for the old-fashioned, never-go-ahead Chinese, and other Eastern nations.

In the richness and beauty of its splendid fur the Silver-gray Fox surpasses the beaver or the sea-otter, and the skins are indeed so highly esteemed that the finest command extraordinary prices, and are always in demand.

The Silver-gray Fox is by no means abundant, and presents considerable variations both in colour and size. Some skins are brilliant black (with the exception of the end of the tail, which is invariably white); other specimens are bluish-gray, and many are tinged with a cinereous colour on the sides: it perhaps is most commonly obtained with parts of its fur hoary, the shiny black coat being thickly interspersed with white or silvery-blue tipped hairs.

According to Sir JOHN RICHARDSON, a greater number than four or five of these Foxes is seldom taken in a season at any one post in the fur countries, though the hunters no sooner find out the haunts of one than they use every art to catch it. From what he observed, Sir JOHN does not think this Fox displays more cunning in avoiding a snare than the red one, but the rarity of the animal, and the eagerness of the hunters to take it, make them think it peculiarly shy.

This animal appears to be as scarce in northern Europe as in America; but we do not mean by this to be understood as considering the European Black Fox identical with ours.

The Black or Silver Fox is sometimes killed in Labrador, and on the Magdeleine Islands, and occasionally — very rarely — in the mountainous parts of Pennsylvania and the wilder portions of the northern counties of New York, where, however, PENNANT'S marten is generally called the "Black Fox," by the hunters and farmers.

It gives us pleasure to render our thanks to the Hon. Hudson's Bay Company for a superb female Black or Silver-gray Fox which was procured for us, and sent to the Zoological Gardens in London alive, where J. W. AUDUBON was then making figures of some of the quadrupeds brought from the Arctic regions of our continent for this work. Having drawn this beautiful animal, which was at the time generously tendered us, but thinking it should remain in the Zoological Gardens, as we have no such establishment in America, J. W. AUDUBON declined the gift in favor of the Zoological Society, in whose interesting collection we hope it still exists. When shall we have a Zoological Garden in the United States? /The first zoological park of consequence in this country was opened at Philadelphia in 1859. Others followed: Central Park, New York City, 1865; Cincinnati, 1875; the National Zoo in Washington, 1889, and the Bronx, New York, 1894./

This variety of the Fox does not differ in its propensities from the red Fox or the cross Fox, and its extraordinary cunning is often equalled by the tricks of these sly fellows.

The white tip at the end of the tail appears to be a characteristic of the Silver-gray Fox, and occurs in every specimen we have seen.

It is stated in MORTON'S New England Canaan (p. 79), that the skin of the Black Fox was considered by the Indians, natives of that part of the colonies, as equivalent to forty beaver skins; when offered and accepted by their kings, it was looked upon as a sacred pledge of reconciliation.

The present species has been seen "mousing" in the meadows, near Ipswich, Massachusetts, as we were informed by the late WILLIAM OAKES, who also wrote to us that "the common and cross Foxes were abundant about the White Mountains /of New Hampshire/, and that they were most easily shot whilst scenting and following game, when their whole attention appears to be concentrated on that one object."

This Fox is occasionally seen in Nova Scotia, and a friend there informs us that some have been shot in his vicinity.

RED FOX

Vulpes fulva fulva (Desmarest)

The melanistic (black) form of red fox occurs rather frequently in northwestern North America and rarely elsewhere on the continent. Some are sprinkled with white or white-tipped hairs, giving a "frosted" appearance; these are called "silver foxes." The few albino (white) red foxes apparently have died at birth or soon afterward. Another aberration — the Samson fox — is rare. Mutation produces woolly fur without guard hairs, which explains the Biblical name. This pelt of course has no commercial value.

Other red foxes have durable hides and long, handsome fur which, when in fashion, has been used for trimming, stoles, jackets, coats and coverlets for glamorous boudoirs. During the 1920's, great numbers of foxes were selectively bred and reared on fox farms. Later, unusual strains such as fawn, pearl, silvery red and platinum were developed. One platinum (pale smoky) fox pelt brought $11,000.

Although commercial trapping virtually stopped when long-haired furs went out of style, the species is still harassed. When foxes become over-abundant, more of them inevitably prey on poultry and sometimes on lambs and young pigs. Hunting, trapping and poisoning increase, and bounty trapping is threatened.

Sportsmen worry that the increase of foxes will decrease or exterminate cottontails, snowshoe hares, quail and pheasants. Foxes, however, rarely or never reduce their prey to an important extent. A more valid cause for alarm is rabies. The disease may flare into epidemic proportion when foxes become overly numerous, and diseased animals may bite and infect domestic stock, pets and people.

Annual spending for sport hunting of foxes has been estimated as high as $100,000,000. With this amount of money involved, much research into reproduction, food, range and disease has been financed by federal and state agencies. Among other methods, radio tracking has been used to determine use of cover and range. Foxes have been captured, fitted with collar-type transmitters, had their ears metal-tagged, and then released. The encumbrances caused no chafing nor change in habit.

Red foxes are 36 to 42 inches long, including the 14- to 16-inch tail, and weigh 8 to 12 pounds. They occur throughout Canada and the United States south of the Arctic Ocean except the southeast Coastal Plain, the Great Plains and eastern slopes of the Rocky Mountains, the southwestern deserts and a narrow strip along the Pacific Coast.

VULPES VELOX, SAY.

SWIFT FOX.

The First Swift Fox we /John J. Audubon/ ever saw alive was at Fort Clark /about 40 miles northwest of Bismarck, North Dakota/ on the upper Missouri river, at which place we arrived on the 7th of June, 1843. It had been caught in a steel-trap by one of its fore-feet, and belonged to Mr. CHARDON, the principal at the Fort, who with great kindness and politeness presented it to us; assuring us that good care would be taken of it during our absence, (as we were then ascending the river to proceed to the base of the Rocky Mountains,) and that on our return to the Mandan village, we might easily take it with us to New-York.

Mr. CHARDON informed us that this Fox was a most expert rat catcher, and that it had been kept in a loft without any other food than the rats and mice that it caught there. It was a beautiful animal, and ran with great rapidity from one side of the loft to another, to avoid us. On our approaching, it showed its teeth and growled much like the common red fox.

Soon after we left Fort Clark, between the western shore of the Missouri river and the hills called the "Trois mamelles" by the Canadian and French trappers, on an open prairie, we saw the second Swift Fox we met with on this journey. Our party had been shooting several buffaloes, and our friend ED. HARRIS, Esq., and ourself, were approaching the hunters apace. We were on foot, and Mr. HARRIS was mounted on his buffalo horse, when a Swift Fox darted from a concealed hole in the prairie almost under the hoofs of my friend's steed. My gun was unfortunately loaded with ball, but the Fox was chased by Mr. HARRIS, who took aim at it several times but could not draw sight on the animal; and the cunning fellow doubled and turned about and around in such a dexterous manner, that it finally escaped in a neighbouring ravine, and we suppose gained its burrow, or sheltered itself in the cleft of a rock, as we did not see it start again. This slight adventure with this (so called) Swift Fox convinced us that the accounts of the wonderful speed of this animal are considerably exaggerated; and were we not disposed to retain its name as given by Mr. SAY, we should select that of Prairie Fox as being most appropriate for it. . . . It is necessary to say, perhaps, that all the authors who have written about this fox (most of whom appear to have copied Mr. SAY's account of it) assert that its extraordinary swiftness is one of the most remarkable characteristics of the animal. GODMAN observes that the fleetest antelope or deer, when running at full speed, is passed by this little Fox with the greatest ease, and such is the celerity of its motion, that it is compared by the celebrated travellers above quoted, LEWIS and CLARK and Mr. SAY, "to the flight of a bird along the ground rather than the course of a quadruped." . . .

On our return to Fort Union after an excursion through a part of the adjacent country, we found at some distance from the stockade a young Swift Fox which we probably might easily have captured alive; but fearing that its burrow was near at hand, and that it would soon reach it and evade our pursuit, Mr. HARRIS shot it. This was the last specimen of this Fox that we were able to observe during our journey; we have given its measurement in a former part of this article. On our return voyage, we found on arriving at Fort Clark that the living Swift Fox given us by Mr. CHARDON was in excellent condition. It was placed in a strong wooden box lined in part with tin, and for greater security against its escape, had a chain fastened to a collar around its neck. During our homeward journey it was fed on birds, squirrels, and the flesh of other animals, and finally safely reached our residence, near New-York, where it was placed in a large cage box two-thirds sunk beneath the surface of the ground, completely tinned inside, and half filled with earth. When thus allowed a comparatively large space and plenty of earth to burrow in, the Fox immediately began to make his way into the loose ground, and soon had dug a hole large enough to conceal himself entirely. While in this commodious prison he fed regularly and ate any kind of fresh meat, growing fatter every day. He drank more water than foxes generally do, seemed anxious to play or wash in the cup which held his supply, and would frequently turn it over, spilling the water on the floor of the cage. . . .

SWIFT FOX

Vulpes velox velox (Say)

This shy, smallest, least crafty and most appealing of North American foxes was named for its speed. During the first hundred yards, it can probably run faster than any of our native animals. After that, it can depend only on its agility. Unfortunately, it is unsuspicious and has been slow to learn that man is a deadly enemy. Although its pelt has little commercial value, the swift fox has been decimated over much of its former range by traps and poison set out indiscriminately to control larger predators. As a result, the swift fox is one of the least known species to naturalists and laymen alike. Because of the animal's small size, it is also called the kit fox.

Largely nocturnal, the fox spends the day in its den. The twisting tunnel is nearly circular in outline, eight to 10 inches across and rarely over 10 feet long or five feet in depth. Ground around the entrance is often littered with bones, fur and scats, but the chamber is kept clean. The young, two to seven (averaging four or five), are born in February in the south, in March or April in the north. They are nursed for about 10 weeks during which the female stays in or close to the den and food is brought by the male. Swift foxes are usually monogamous throughout the year and probably for life. The young scatter in autumn to find their own territories.

When it hunts, the fox trots swiftly along until it spots a prospective victim. It then crouches for the stalk until close enough to pounce. Prey consists of rodents (especially kangaroo rats, ground squirrels and mice), ground-dwelling birds, lizards, snakes and many insects. The larger kills are carried home to be dismembered and eaten near the security of the den.

Adults are 24 to 32 inches long, of which the tail is 9 to 12 inches; weight is 4 to 6 pounds. The swift fox is a Great Plains animal; originally it occurred from west Texas to southern Saskatchewan. A very closely related fox is found in our Southwest from southeastern Oregon & central California south into Mexico.

CANIS (VULPES) VIRGINIANUS, GMEL.

GREY FOX

Throughout the whole of our Atlantic States, from Maine to Florida, and westwardly to Louisiana and Texas, there are but two *species* of fox known, viz., the red fox, *(V. fulvus,)* and the present species, *(V. Virginianus /Urocyon cinereoargenteus/,)* although there are several permanent *varieties*. The former may be regarded as a Northern, the latter as a Southern species. Whilst the Northern farmer looks upon the red fox as a great annoyance, and detests him as a robber who is lying in wait for his lambs, his turkeys, and his geese, the Gray Fox, in the eyes of the Southern planter, is the object of equal aversion. . . .

The Gray Fox is shy and cowardly, and the snap of a stick or the barking of a dog will set him off on a full run. Although timid and suspicious to this degree, his cunning and voracity place him in a conspicuous rank among the animals that prey upon other species weaker than themselves. The wild turkey hen often makes an excavation in which she deposits her eggs, at a considerable distance from the low grounds, or makes her nest on some elevated ridge, or under a pile of fallen logs covered over with scrub oaks, ferns, tall weeds and grasses; we have often seen traces of a violent struggle at such places; bunches of feathers scattered about, and broken egg-shells, giving sufficient evidence that the Fox has been there, and that there will be one brood of wild turkeys less that season. Coveys of partridges /quail/, which generally at the dusk of the evening fly into some sheltered place and hide in the tall grass, arrange themselves for the night in a circle, with their tails touching each other and their heads turned outward; the Gray Fox possessing a considerable power of scent, winds them like a pointer dog, and often discovers where they are thus snugly nestled, and pounces on them, invariably carrying off at least one of the covey.

. . . .Condemn not the Fox too hastily; he has a more strikingly carnivorous tooth than yourself, indicating the kind of food he is required to seek; he takes no wanton pleasure in destroying the bird, he exhibits to his companions no trophies of his skill, and is contented with a meal whilst you are perhaps not satisfied when your capacious bird-bag is filled. . . .

This species is not confined exclusively to animal food; a farmer of the State of New-York called our attention to a field of corn, (maize,) which had sustained no inconsiderable injury from some unknown animals that had been feeding on the unripe ears. The tracks in the field convinced us that the depredation had been committed by Foxes, which was found to be the case, and they were afterwards chased several successive mornings, and three of them, apparently a brood of the previous spring, were captured.

Although this Fox is nocturnal in his habits we have frequently observed him in search of food at all hours of the day; in general, however, he lies concealed in some thicket, or in a large tuft of tall broom-grass, till twilight invites him to renew his travels and adventures.

On a cold starlight night in winter, we have frequently heard the hoarse querulous bark of this species; sometimes two of them, some distance apart, were answering each other in the manner of the dog.

Although we have often seen this Fox fairly run down and killed by hounds, without his having attempted to climb a tree, yet it not unfrequently occurs that when his strength begins to fail he ascends one that is small or sloping, and standing on some horizontal branch 20 or 30 feet from the ground, looks down on the fierce and clamorous pack which soon comes up and surrounds the foot of the tree. . . .

. . . .Shortly after the railroad from Charleston to Hamburgh, South Carolina, had been constructed, the rails for a portion of the distance having been laid upon timbers at a considerable height from the ground, supported by strong posts, we observed a Fox which was hard pressed by a pack of hounds, mounting the rails, upon which he ran several hundred yards; the dogs were unable to pursue him, and he thus crossed a deep cypress swamp over which the railroad was in this singular manner carried, and made his escape on the opposite side. . . .

The Gray Fox produces from three to five young at a time. In Carolina this occurs from the middle of March to the middle of April; in the State of New-York they bring forth somewhat later. Gestation continues for about three months.

GRAY FOX

Urocyon cinereoargenteus cinereoargenteus (Schreber)

Not as smart nor as bold as the red fox with its more valuable pelt, the gray is the only climber in the family and has sometimes been called the tree fox. Occasionally it can be lured by faking the "caw" of a crow or the squeak of a mouse.

Wherever the gray fox is heavily hunted and trapped, the survivors are necessarily "shy and cowardly" as Bachman says. When not molested, it becomes confiding and curious about man. In broad daylight gray foxes have openly watched scientists working less than 30 yards away. At night they may visit camp garbage pits and eat within 30 feet of the campers.

Not liking to dig burrows, they sleep in hollow trees or logs, a burrow in a sawmill slab pile, a cavity in a rock heap or ledge, or sometimes an abandoned earth den.

The peak of mating is in February. One to seven young are born after a gestation period of about 63 days. They are blind, with blackish skin showing through thin fur. Contrary to Audubon and Bachman's belief, there is little difference in the birthing time date between north and south. When the pups are three weeks old, the father returns to help the mother feed and train them.

In late summer or fall, the young scatter — some travel as far as 50 miles while others stay much closer to the home territory. The most carnivorous of all the wild dogs, they eat considerable amounts of grass, fruit and nuts such as acorns. In addition to insects, rodents, rabbits, turkeys, quail and poultry (when the farmer is careless), gray foxes devour reptiles and amphibians with gusto.

Like its red relative, the gray fox falls prey to coyotes, bobcats and golden eagles, and is subject to rabies, distemper and other diseases. Life expectancy is rather short — probably five or six years. Only a rare (and perhaps toothless) individual may live as long as 10 years in the wild.

In comparison with the red fox, the yapping bark of the gray is louder and harsher and is not followed by a squall. It prefers the safety of wooded or brushy areas; the red fox keeps to the woodland borders with adjacent pastures and open fields.

Adults are 32 to 45 inches long, including the 11- to 18-inch tail. Males weigh 7 to 12 pounds (average 8½); females are 10 percent smaller. The species occurs throughout most of the United States except the northern Great Plains and Rockies, thence into South America.

URSUS AMERICANUS, PALLAS.

AMERICAN BLACK BEAR.

The Black Bear, however clumsy in appearance, is active, vigilant, and persevering, possesses great strength, courage, and address, and undergoes with little injury the greatest fatigues and hardships in avoiding the pursuit of the hunter. Like the deer it changes its haunts with the seasons, and for the same reason, viz. the desire of obtaining suitable food, or of retiring to the more inaccessible parts, where it can pass the time in security, unobserved by man, the most dangerous of its enemies.

During the spring months it searches for food in the low rich alluvial lands that border the rivers, or by the margins of such inland lakes as, on account of their small size, are called by us ponds. There it procures abundance of succulent roots and tender juicy plants, upon which it chiefly feeds at that season. During the summer heat, it enters the gloomy swamps, passes much of its time in wallowing in the mud like a hog, and contents itself with crayfish, roots, and nettles, now and then seizing on a pig, or perhaps a sow, a calf, or even a full-grown cow. As soon as the different kinds of berries which grow on the mountains begin to ripen, the Bears betake themselves to the high grounds, followed by their cubs.

In retired parts of the country, where the plantations are large and the population sparse, it pays visits to the corn-fields, which it ravages for a while. After this, the various species of nuts, acorns, grapes, and other forest fruits, that form what in the western States is called *mast,* attract its attention. The Bear is then seen rambling singly through the woods to gather this harvest, not forgetting, meanwhile, to rob every *bee-tree* it meets with, Bears being expert at this operation.

The Black Bear is a capital climber, and now and then *houses* itself in the hollow trunk of some large tree for weeks together during the winter, when it is said to live by sucking its paws. /This is one of the oldest fables or folk tales in American natural history!/ . . .

The female Black Bear generally brings forth two cubs at a time although, as we have heard, the number is sometimes three or four. The period of gestation is stated to be from six to seven weeks, but is mentioned as one hundred days by some authors. /The period is now known to be 200 to 210 days./ When born the young are exceedingly small, and if we may credit the accounts of hunters with whom we have conversed on the subject, are not larger than kittens. They are almost invariably brought forth in some well concealed den, or great hollow tree, and so cautious is the dam in selecting her place of accouchment, that it is extremely difficult to discover it, and consequently very rarely that either the female or her cubs are seen until the latter have obtained a much larger size than when born, are able to follow their dam, and can climb trees with facility.

Most writers on the habits of this animal have stated that the Black Bear does not eat animal food from choice, and never unless pressed by hunger. This we consider a great mistake, for in our experience we have found the reverse to be the case, and it is well known to our frontier farmers that this animal is a great destroyer of pigs, hogs, calves, and sheep, for the sake of which we have even known it to desert the pecan groves in Texas. At the same time, as will have been seen by our previous remarks, its principal food generally consists of berries, roots, and other vegetable substances. It is very fond also of fish, and during one of our expeditions to Maine and New Brunswick, we found the inhabitants residing near the coast unwilling to eat the flesh of the animal on account of its fishy taste. In our western forests, however, the Bear feeds on so many nuts and well tasted roots and berries, that its meat is considered a great delicacy, and in the city of New York we have generally found its market price three or four times more than the best beef per pound. The fore-paw of the Bear when cooked presents a striking resemblance to the hand of a child or young person, and we have known some individuals to be hoaxed by its being represented as such.

Perhaps the most acrid vegetable eaten by the Bear is the Indian turnip (*Arum /Arisaema/ triphyllum),* which is so pungent that we have seen people almost distracted by it, when they had inadvertently put a piece in their mouth. . . .

BLACK BEAR

Ursus americanus americanus Pallas

The smallest, most friendly and provoking of our bears is the black bear. It is brown, silvery, yellowish to reddish-brown, gray-blue, white — or black. Different colors may be in the same litter. (The blue-gray glacier bear is found in southeastern Alaska and the white Kermode's bear occurs in British Columbia.)

Intelligent, adaptable and man-like in form, bears were incorporated into the legends and folklore of Indians and early white settlers. Some tribes of red men apologized to the spirits of the bears they ate. Bears stand up on hind legs to peer around for better view, to fight each other, to hug their mates during courting season — even take a few steps in this position. They climb trees rapidly to escape or to shake down fruit and nuts. With forearms circling the trunk, their hind legs push them upward. They come down backward, tail first. Mothers protect the young from danger, play with them, discipline them with a slap of the paw and teach them to make a living. When in pain, adults cry out almost like humans.

Black bears are normally solitary and when they meet are unfriendly. During the two-week mating period in mid-summer, the male fights off any competitor with teeth and claws to the accompaniment of roars which are audible a mile away. Ripped ears, punctured hides, and sometimes death result. The cubs (two after the first pregnancy, occasionally three and very rarely four) are born in the winter den during late January or February. Embryonic development during the 200- to 210-day gestation is very slow and at birth the young weigh only six to eight ounces. In April, aged two months and weighing about five pounds, they leave the den with the mother. They continue to nurse, eat buds, leaves and grass. Sometimes the mother (and other adult bears) strip the bark of cedar and fir to eat the cambium, thus killing the trees. She shows them how to enjoy dust, mud and water baths, how to curry their fur on the grass and to lick themselves clean. Swinging their heads from side to side and toeing in their big feet, the family wander according to the food supply. Female bears usually stay within 10 miles of their home, but males may go much farther. One adventurous animal traveled 80 miles. Ordinarily each bear has its own range, marked by the trees that it claws and gashes. Black bears sometimes swim as much as five miles at a time. Not later than their second summer, the young bears scatter in search of new homes, whereupon the mother mates again.

The two-year breeding cycle of all bears means that they have the lowest reproduction potential of any American big game. (Continued)

213

URSUS AMERICANUS, PALLAS.

VAR CINNAMONUM, AUD & BACH.

CINNAMON BEAR.

... The Cinnamon Bear has long been known to trappers and fur traders, and its skin is much more valuable than that of the Black Bear. We have seen in the warehouse of Messrs. P. CHOUTEAU, JR., and Co., /fur traders and merchants/ in New York, some beautiful skins of this animal, and find that those gentlemen receive some every year from their posts near the Rocky Mountains. Being a permanent variety, and having longer and finer hair than the common Black Bear, we might possibly have elevated it into a distinct species but that in every other particular it closely resembles the latter animal. By the Indians (according to Sir JOHN RICHARDSON) it is considered to be an accidental variety of the Black Bear.

The Cinnamon Bear, so far as we have been able to ascertain, is never found near the sea coast, nor even west of the Ohio valley until you approach the Rocky Mountain chain, and it is apparently quite a northern animal.

Of the habits of this variety we have no accounts, but we may suppose that they do not differ in any essential particulars from those of the Black Bear ...

Our figures were made from living specimens in the gardens of the Zoological Society of London, which manifested all the restlessness usually exhibited by this genus when in a state of captivity. . . .

We have given a figure of this permanent variety of Bear, not because we felt disposed to elevate it into a species, but because it is a variety so frequently found in the collections of skins made by our fur companies, and which is so often noticed by travellers in the north-west, that errors might be made by future naturalists were we to omit mentioning it and placing it where it should be. . . . We have done this in the case of some species of squirrel, the otter, and the wolves, as well as this variety of Bear. . . .

/Editor's Comment: Because the authors had little information on their "cinnamon variety" and much concerning the black bear (same species), additional excerpts from the latter chapter are given below./

... In the State of Maine the lumbermen (wood-cutters) and the farmers set guns to kill this animal, which are arranged in this way: A funnel-shaped space about five feet long is formed by driving strong sticks into the ground in two converging lines, leaving both the ends open, the narrow end being wide enough to admit the muzzle of an old musket, and the other extremity so broad as to allow the head and shoulders of the Bear to enter. The gun is then loaded and fastened securely so as to deliver its charge facing the wide end of the enclosure. A round and smooth stick is now placed behind the stock of the gun, and a cord leading from the trigger passed around it, the other end of which, with a piece of meat or a bird tied to it (an owl is a favourite bait), is stretched in front of the gun, so far that the Bear can reach the bait with his paw. Upon his pulling the meat towards him, the string draws the trigger and the animal is instantly killed. . . .

The Black Bear is rather docile when in confinement, and a "pet" Bear is occasionally seen in various parts of the country. In our large cities, however, where civilization (?) is thought to have made the greatest advances, this animal is used to amuse the gentlemen of the fancy, by putting its strength and "pluck" to the test, in combat with bull-dogs or mastiffs. When the Bear has not been so closely imprisoned as to partially destroy his activity, these encounters generally end with the killing of one or more dogs; but occasionally the dogs overpower him, and he is rescued for the time by his friends, to "fight (again) some other day."

We are happy to say, however, that Bear-baiting and bull-baiting have not been as yet fully naturalized amongst us, and are only popular with those who, perhaps, in addition to the natural desire for excitement, have the hope and intention of winning money, to draw them to such cruel and useless exhibitions. . . .

BLACK BEAR

Ursus americanus americanus Pallas

Why do black bears and grizzlies frequently have tooth cavities, when most other wild carnivores do not? Probably because of their fondness for sweets. A bear will spend hours digging honey out of a bee-tree. Only an electric fence will keep it from knocking over an apiarist's hives and devouring the honey along with the bees. Although a vegetarian much of the time, it enjoys meat and carrion. It digs up ground squirrels and other rodents, laps up myriads of ants, and kills and eats any injured or weak animal that it can catch. Bears are usually too slow to overtake healthy deer. Their top speed is about 30 miles an hour for short distances, although a broad jump may carry them 18 feet. Sight is poor but hearing and smell are keen.

Bears in national forests and parks have developed appetites for ham sandwiches and soft drinks, thanks to the unwitting tourists who are intrigued by the animals' physical likeness to themselves. After being hand fed (unlawfully), bears reach out to claw food that is not there, and painful injuries may result. One woman was killed by a bear when she bumped into it in the dark as she went around the corner of a cabin. Having enjoyed hotel garbage heaps and tourist lunches, black bears have overturned autos, clawed open windows and trunks to get at food which they smell.

Early settlers and eastern Indians prized bear meat because of the fat. The oil was used for cooking, to relieve sore muscles and to repel insects. Bear paws were a great delicacy to Ojibways. White men started up an industry of catching young bears and fattening them for the table.

Bear oil was reputed to restore hair on the baldest pate; a "great chemist" in London's Haymarket ordered several cubs each year from America and fattened them for rendering. The bushiest pelts were imported for the manufacture of busbys for guard units in the British and Russian armies. Exports rose to 25,000 skins in 1803 and then diminished greatly due to growing scarcity. Bears became rare by the beginning of the 20th century, but with sensible protection, the species is once more numerous in forested regions.

Measurements vary in length from 4½ to 6½ feet, and in shoulder length from 25 to 40 inches. The weight, usually to 300 pounds, may reach a maximum of 500 pounds. Females are about 20% smaller. (They almost always have narrower skulls — less than 6¾ inches — and smaller canine teeth.) The range includes northern Mexico, the United States (except the Great Basin and northern and western Alaska) and Canada (except the extreme north, and Cape Breton and Prince Edward Islands).

URSUS-FEROX, LEWIS & CLARK.

GRIZZLY BEAR.

We /J. J. Audubon/ have passed many hours of excitement, and some, perchance, of danger, in the wilder portions of our country; and at times memory recalls adventures we can now hardly attempt to describe; nor can we ever again feel the enthusiasm such scenes produced in us. Our readers must therefore imagine, the startling sensations experienced on a sudden and quite unexpected face-to-face meeting with the savage Grizzly Bear — the huge shaggy monster disputing possession of the wilderness against all comers, and threatening immediate attack! . . .

The Indians, as is well known, consider the slaughter of a Grizzly Bear a feat second only to scalping an enemy, and necklaces made of the claws of this beast are worn as trophies by even the bravest among them.

On the 22d of August, 1843, we killed one of these Bears, and as our journals are before us, and thinking it may be of interest, we will extract the account of the day's proceedings. . . . ". . . .As we were approaching the boat we met Mr. SPRAGUE, who informed us that he thought he had seen a Grizzly Bear walking along the upper bank of the /Upper Missouri/ river, and we went towards the spot as fast as possible. Meantime the Bear had gone down to the water, and was clumsily and slowly proceeding on its way. It was only a few paces from and below us, and was seen by our whole party at the same instant. We all fired, and the animal dropped dead without even the power of uttering a groan. . . . Our 'patroon,' assisted by one of the men, skinned the Bear, which weighed, as we thought, about four hundred pounds. It appeared to be between four and five years old, and was a male. Its lard was rendered, and filled sundry bottles with 'real Bear's grease,' whilst we had the skin preserved by our accomplished taxidermist, Mr. BELL."

The following afternoon, as we were descending the stream, we saw another Grizzly Bear, somewhat smaller than the one mentioned above. It was swimming towards the carcase of a dead buffalo lodged in the prongs of a "sawyer" or "snag," but on seeing us it raised on its hind feet until quite erect, uttered a loud grunt or snort, made a leap from the water, gained the upper bank of the river, and disappeared in an instant amid the tangled briars and bushes thereabouts. . . .

The Grizzly Bear generally inhabits the swampy, well covered portions of the districts where it is found, keeping a good deal among the trees and bushes, and in these retreats it has its "beds" or lairs. . . . There are seasons during the latter part of summer, when the wild fruits that are eagerly sought after by the Bears are very abundant. These beasts then feed upon them, tearing down the branches as far as they can reach whilst standing in an upright posture. They in this manner get at wild plums, service berries, buffalo berries, and the seeds of a species of *cornus* or dog-wood which grows in the alluvial bottoms of the northwest. The Grizzly Bear is also in the habit of scratching the gravelly earth on the sides of hills where the vetgetable called "pomme blanche" /or Cree potato, *Psoralea esculenta*/ is known to grow, but the favourite food of these animals is the more savoury flesh of such beasts as are less powerful, fleet, or cunning than themselves. They have been known to seize a wounded buffalo, kill it, and partially bury it in the earth for future use, after having gorged themselves on the best parts of its flesh and lapped up the warm blood. . . .

The following is from notes of J. W. AUDUBON, made in California in 1849 and 1850: "High up on the waters of the San Joaquin, in California, many of these animals have been killed by the miners now overrunning all the country west of the Sierra Nevada. Greatly as the Grizzly Bear is dreaded, it is hunted with all the more enthusiasm by these fearless pioneers in the romantic hills, valleys, and wild mountains of the land of gold, as its flesh is highly prized by men who have been living for months on salt pork or dry and tasteless deer-meat. I have seen two dollars a pound paid for the leaf-fat around the kidneys. If there is time, and the animal is not in a starving condition, the Grizzly Bear always runs at the sight of man; but should the hunter come too suddenly on him, the fierce beast always commences the engagement. . . ."

GRIZZLY BEAR

Ursus arctos horribilis Ord

The largest carnivore in the world, the grizzly can fell a buffalo weighing more than half a ton and carry off the carcass. One grizzly was reputed to have killed 500 steers and five men. Black bears have been seen to shinny up a tree when this giant arrived on the scene. (Adult grizzlies are too heavy to climb.) Like most bears, the grizzly does not relish the taste of human flesh. For this reason, some men, clawed and bitten, have escaped death by feigning it.

Most grizzly attacks on man have been made by bears that were startled, scared, sick, wounded or defending their young. A hunter who goes into bear habitat with too small a rifle or who can't shoot straight, may wound a bear and be attacked fatally.

In spite of its size, the grizzly catches squirming fish with dexterous paws. It eats much vegetable matter (grass, roots, fruits) and carries off meat and carrion to eat and cache.

Grizzlies mate when three or four years old. The courtship lasts a month or more and involves amorous wrestling, hugging and pawing. Cubs (two or three, rarely one or four) weigh 1½ pounds when they are born in the den during January or February. They stay with the mother until they are 1½ to even 2½ years old, reach full size at eight to 10, and may live in the wild to a ripe old age of 15 to 20 years.

Females and juveniles spend several days preparing their winter den by lining it with grass and leaves. Adult males retire later and usually don't bother to prepare the den. Their winter sleep is not hibernation. The pulse and temperature do not decrease; the mother is active enough to give birth to young and any of the bears may saunter out during warm spells.

There are probably no more than 600 wild grizzlies left in the contiguous United States. The last one in California (whose state emblem is the Golden Bear) was killed in 1922. Only in Alaska, Yukon and British Columbia has the species survived in probably its primeval numbers.

Grizzlies and their subspecies cousins, Alaska brown bears, are 5 to 7½ feet long and 3 to 3½ feet tall at their humped shoulders. Adult males weigh 500 to 650 pounds (sometimes only 300, and a reputed maximum of 1,300 pounds). Females are much smaller than males. The species occurs from the Bering Sea to western Keewatin, south to Wyoming; a small remnant survives in Chihuahua, Mexico.

URSUS MARITIMUS, LINN.

POLAR BEAR.

. . .now, with your permisssion, we will send you with the adventurous navigators of the Polar Seas, in search of the White Bear, for we have not seen this remarkable inhabitant of the icy regions of our northern coast amid his native frozen deserts; and can therefore give you little more than such information as may be found in the works of previous writers on his habits. During our visit to Labrador in 1833, we /John J. Audubon/ coasted along to the north as far as the Straits of Belleisle /Belle Isle/, but it being midsummer, we saw no Polar Bears, although we heard from the settlers that these animals were sometimes seen there; (on one occasion, indeed, we thought we perceived three of them on an ice-berg, but the distance was too great for us to be certain), although the abundance of seals and fish of various kinds on the shores, would have afforded them a plentiful supply of their ordinary food. They are doubtless drifted far to the southward on ice-bergs from time to time, but in our voyages to and from Europe we never saw any, although we have been for days in the ice.

The Polar Bear is carnivorous, in fact omnivorous, and devours with equal voracity the carcases of whales, abandoned, and drifted ashore by the waves; seals, dead fish, vegetable substances, and all other eatable matters obtainable, whether putrid or fresh. Dr. RICHARDSON, in the Fauna Boreali Americana, has given a good compiled account of this animal, and we shall lay a portion of it before our readers. The Dr. says:—"I have met with no account of any Polar Bear, killed of late years, which exceeded nine feet in length, or four feet and a-half in height. It is possible that larger individuals may be occasionally found; but the greatness of the dimensions attributed to them by the older voyagers has, I doubt not, originated in the skin having been measured after being much stretched in the process of flaying.". . .

In BARENTZ's third voyage, a story is told of two Bears coming to the carcass of a third one that had been shot, when one of them, taking it by the throat, carried it to a considerable distance, over the most rugged ice, where they both began to eat it. They were scared from their repast by the report of a musket, and a party of seamen going to the place, found that, in the little time they were about it, they had already devoured half the carcase, which was of such a size that four men had great difficulty in lifting the remainder. . . .

Dr. RICHARDSON says, "They swim and dive well, they hunt seals and other marine animals with great success. They are even said to wage war, though rather unequally, with the walrus. They feed likewise on land animals, birds, and eggs, nor do they disdain to prey on carrion, or, in the absence of this food, to seek the shore in quest of berries and roots. They scent their prey from a great distance, and are often attracted to the whale vessels by the smell of burning *kreng,* or the refuse of the whale blubber." . . .

The Polar Bear is by no means confined to the land, on the contrary he is seldom if ever seen far inland, but frequents the fields of ice, and swims off to floating ice or to icebergs, and is often seen miles from shore. . . .

This species is found farther to the north than any other quadruped, having been seen by Captain /William Edward/ PARRY /British Arctic explorer, later knighted and made rear admiral/ in his adventurous boat-voyage /in 1827/ beyond 82 degrees of north latitude. . . .

Several authors speak of the liver of the Polar Bear as being poisonous. This is an anomaly for which no reason has yet been assigned; the fact seems, however, well ascertained. All the other parts of the animal are wholesome, and it forms a considerable article of food to the Indians of the maritime Arctic regions.

The skin of the Polar Bear is a valuable covering to these tribes, and is dressed by merely stretching it out on the snow, pinning it down, and leaving it to freeze, after which the fat is all scraped off. It is then generally hung up in the open air, and "when the frost is intense, it dries most perfectly; with a little more scraping it becomes entirely dry and supple, both skin and hair being beautifully white." "The time of the year at which the sexes seek each other is not positively known, but it is most probably in the month of July, or of August . ."

POLAR BEAR

Thalarctos maritimus maritimus (Phipps)

The great white bear of the Arctic often swims many miles of open ocean and floats on ice hundreds of miles from land.

Is it a man-killer? Persecuted by airplane hunting, it has become wary and is likely to run away. If, however, it is close enough to sense imminent danger, it is likely to attack immediately. Man's possessions are more appetizing than man himself. Polar bears tear open with teeth and claws many cans of hunters' food and airplane motor oil. Jagged cuts, bleeding gums and jaws do not deter the plunderers. They gobble down weatherproof sheeting, adhesive tape, tobacco, and other materials. One bear eliminated from its intestines a spool of photographic film, intact.

The staple food is seal. Polar bears also kill young walrus, careless or crippled sea birds and spawning fish. Carrion of fish and whale is taken eagerly. During the brief summer, a bear may go ashore, rarely up to 150 miles from the ocean, to graze on green grass or sedge and to plunder bird nests.

Polar bears first mate when three or four years old. After courtship in April or May, the animals go their separate ways. Males and barren females continue to wander through the long dark winter. The pregnant female digs a den in a deep snowdrift. Here twin cubs, male and female, are born in early winter. Only 10 inches long and weighing 1½

pounds, they are blind, deaf and hairless. The mother nurses them (her milk is as rich as cow's cream and tastes like cod liver oil) through much of the summer. She teaches them to hunt and swim; when they get tired, they hang on to her tail or rump. After another winter, she abandons the cubs in order to mate again.

A thousand-pound bear can leap over a six-foot high snowdrift, run 25 miles an hour (for a short distance) and dive 50 feet into the ocean. Experienced hunters know that the high vitamin A content of their liver is poisonous, and that their meat must be frozen or well-cooked because of possible trichinella.

Polar nations are making studies to determine how, through international protection, polar bears may be saved from extinction. Among other research projects are plans to fit 50 bears with radio-equipped collars that will send signals through a Polar orbiting Nimbus satellite. For six months, every two hours, scientists will track the bears' travels.

Fully adult males are 8 to 11 feet long and weigh up to 1,000 pounds; females are 25 to 30% smaller. Cubs are pure white; adults are yellowish-white. The range is circumpolar; in North America, from Labrador west to northwestern Alaska.

BASSARIS ASTUTA, LICHT.
RING-TAILED BASSARIS.

. . . It is a lively, playful, and nimble creature, leaps about on the trees, and has very much the same actions as the squirrel, which it resembles in agility and grace, always having a hole in the tree upon which it resides, and betaking itself to that secure retreat at once if alarmed.

The Bassaris Astuta is shy and retired in its habits, and in the daytime often stays in its hole in some tree, so that we /J.W. Audubon/ were only able to procure about half a-dozen of these animals during our stay in Texas; among which, to our regret, there was not a single female.

The food of this species is chiefly small animals, birds, and insects; they also eat nuts, as we were told, descending from their hiding place and travelling to the pecan and other trees, for the purpose of feeding on the nuts which, if true, is singular, as they are decidedly carnivorous in their dentition.

They are much attached to the tree on which they live, which is generally a post-oak, a live-oak, or other large tree, and they seldom quit the immediate vicinity of their hole, unless when driven out by thrusting a stick at them, when they ascend the trunk of the tree, and jump about among the higher branches so long as the pole is held close to their nest; as soon as this is withdrawn, they descend and at once re-enter their dwelling-place and hide themselves. These animals have a singular habit of eating or gnawing off the bark around the mouth of their holes, and where the bark does not appear freshly peeled off at their hole, you may be certain the animal is not at home, or has deserted the place. Their holes are generally the result of natural decay . . .

They generally select a hole of this kind on the lower side of a leaning tree, probably for better protection from the rain; their holes vary in depth, but are seldom more than about a foot or eighteen inches to the bottom; they are usually furnished with moss or grass, for bedding. Sometimes pecan shells are found in these holes, which no doubt affords presumptive evidence that the Bassaris feeds upon this nut.

When scolding or barking at an intruder, the ring-tailed Raccoon, (as this animal is called by the Texans), holds the tail over its back, bending it squirrel fashion; this animal, however, does not stand upon his hind feet like a squirrel, and cannot jump or leap so far. We have not heard of their springing from one branch to another beyond the distance of about ten feet, and when frightened at the presence of a man, they will sometimes run along a branch even toward him, in order to get within jumping distance of another, evincing more timidity than a squirrel exhibits in springing among the boughs, although they run up the bark with ease, holding on with their claws.

Sometimes the Ring-tailed Bassaris may be seen squatted on the top of a branch, basking in the sun, and half rolled up, appearing almost asleep. On the slightest manifestation of danger, however, he darts into his hole, (which is always within a foot or two of his basking place), and he is seen no more. We have the impression that only one of these singular animals is to be found on a tree at a time — they, therefore, are not very social in their habits, and, as the live-oak and other trees are generally very much scattered, and many of them have no holes suitable for residences for the Bassaris, it is very difficult to procure one. At the foot of many of the trees whereon they dwell, the cactus, brush-wood, and chapperal generally are so thick and tangled, that a man would be pretty well scratched should he attempt to penetrate the thorny, prickly thicket which surrounds the dwelling-place of this solitary and singular animal.

Notwithstanding the shyness and retired habits of this species, it is easily tamed, and when it has been confined in a cage a sufficient length of time, is frequently let loose in the houses of the Mexicans, where it answers the purpose of a playful pet, and catches mice and rats. . . . As far as we could ascertain, the northern limit of the range of this species is somewhere in the neighbourhood of the southern branches of Red river. As you travel south they are more abundant, and probably are found throughout all Mexico . . .

The Bassaris produces three or four young at a birth, as has been ascertained from the animal kept in confinement.

RINGTAIL

Bassariscus astutus astutus (Lichtenstein)

Covered with fine white hair when born in spring or early summer, the one to five (usually three or four) young each weigh about one ounce. When they are three weeks old, the father returns to the den to help bring them bits of meat. Although chiefly carnivorous, ringtails are fond of fruits. Those shells which J. W. Audubon found in tree holes may have been discarded by squirrels or mice. Big-eyed and bushy-tailed, ringtails make excellent mousers as well as delightful pets. Frequently called ringtailed cats, they are no relation to the cat family.

Their fur, beautiful only in life, is sometimes labeled "California mink" and is of little value. Ringtails generally live in cliffs and broken ledges. Where rock shelters are scarce, however, as on the Texas plains where Audubon reported their habits, they often den in hollow trees.

Adults are 24 to 34 inches long, including the 12½- to 17½-inch tail, and weigh 30½ to 38½ ounces. Ringtails occur from southern Oregon and eastern Texas to Oaxaca.

PROCYON LOTOR, CUVIER

RACCOON.

The Raccoon is a cunning animal, is easily tamed, and makes a pleasant monkey-like pet. It is quite dexterous in the use of its fore-feet, and will amble after its master in the manner of a bear, and even follow him into the streets. It is fond of eggs, and devours them raw or cooked with avidity, but prefers them raw of course, and if it finds a nest will feast on them morning, noon and night without being satiated. It will adroitly pick its keeper's pockets of anything it likes to eat, and is always on the watch for dainties. The habits of the muscles (*unios /Unio* sp., the freshwater mussel/) that inhabit our fresh water rivers are better known to the Raccoon than to most conchologists, and their flavour is as highly relished by this animal as is that of the best bowl of clam soup by the epicure in that condiment.

Being an expert climber, the Raccoon ascends trees with facility and frequently invades the nest of the woodpecker, although it may be secure against ordinary thieves, by means of his fore-feet getting hold of the eggs or the young birds. He watches too the soft-shelled turtle when she is about to deposit her eggs, for which purpose she leaves the water and crawling on to the white sand-bar, digs a hole and places them underneath the heated surface. Quickly does the rogue dig up the elastic ova, although ever so carefully covered, and appropriate them to his own use, notwithstanding the efforts of the luckless turtle to conceal them.

Sometimes, by the margin of a pond, shrouded, or crouched among tall reeds and grasses, Grimalkin-like, the Raccoon lies still as death, waiting with patience for some ill-fated duck that may come within his reach. No negro on a plantation knows with more accuracy when the corn (maize) is juicy and ready for the connoisseur in roasting ears, and he does not require the aid of fire to improve its flavour, but attacks it more voraciously than the squirrel or the blackbird . . .

The favourite resorts of the Raccoon are retired swampy lands well covered with lofty trees, and through which are small water-courses. In such places its tracks may be seen following the margins of the bayous and creeks, which it occasionally crosses in search of frogs and muscles which are found on their banks. It also follows the margins of rivers for the same purpose, and is dexterous in getting at the shell-fish, notwithstanding the hardness of the siliceous covering with which nature has provided them. In dry seasons, the receding waters sometimes leave the muscles exposed to the heat of the sun, which destroys their life and causes their shells to open, leaving them accessible to the first animal or bird that approaches.

In the dreary months of winter should you be encamped in any of the great Western forests, obliged by the pitiless storm to remain for some days, as we /presumably J.W. Audubon/ have been, you will not be unthankful if you have a fat Raccoon suspended on a tree above your camp, for when kept awhile, the flesh of this species is both tender and well-flavoured.

The Raccoon when full grown and in good condition we consider quite a handsome animal. We have often watched him with interest, cautiously moving from one trunk to another to escape his view. His bright eye, however, almost invariably detected us ere we could take aim at him, and he adroitly fled into a hollow tree and escaped from us. . . .

The Raccoon usually produces from four to six young at a time, which are generally brought forth early in May, although the period of their littering varies in different latitudes.

When the Indian corn is ripening, the Raccoons invade the fields to feast on the rich milky grain, as we have just stated, and as the stalks are too weak to bear the weight of these marauders, they generally break them down with their fore-paws, tear off the husks from the ears, and then munch them at their leisure. . . .

The Raccoon is not strictly a nocturnal animal; and although it generally visits the corn fields at night, sometimes feeds on the green corn during the day; we have seen it thus employed during the heat of summer, and it will occasionally enter a poultry house at midday, and destroy many of the feathered inhabitants, contenting itself with the head and blood of the fowls it kills. . . .

RACCOON

Procyon lotor lotor (Linnaeus)

Dark, intelligent-looking eyes gleam in the sharp, masked face. Long toes leave footprints that often resemble the hands of a very small child. When water is near — it usually is — the raccoon washes all its food repeatedly before eating. (*Lotor* means "the washer.") Since even muddy water suits the animal, the concensus is that washing is a habit of sensory pleasure rather than a desire for "cleanliness."

Pound for pound, the adult raccoon has few equals in fighting ability. A female with young, if cut off from escape, may attack a human. Few dogs can kill a 'coon "single-handed." In combat, the animal barks, growls and screams savagely; at other times it may whine, churr, or give a quavering call.

Generally solitary in disposition, it is polygamous and necessarily gregarious in good feeding areas. An exceptional pair have been seen now and then living and hunting together with apparent devotion. Immediately after mating, the female usually seeks a separate den. While a hollow tree is preferred, a burrow under a large tree or a cavity in a rock ledge is acceptable. Raccoons sleep on the floor without benefit of nest and are clean. Scat stations are established nearby and en route to their hunting and feeding areas.

Following a gestation of 63 days, the two to seven (usually four) young are born in April to June with yellowish-gray fur covering their black skin. They chitter complaints and protests when hungry or disturbed. At two months they have increased their weight from 2½ ounces to two pounds and accompany the mother on nocturnal hunts. The family stays together at least until November and usually through midwinter. Although the animals sleep through cold weather, they do not truly hibernate since their respiration, temperature and metabolism are not reduced. One raccoon was observed to descend its tree in late winter to look for food. The minute its foot touched snow, it hustled back up again and presumably went back to sleep.

When hunted by dogs, raccoons will frequently tree after a short chase; others will run for miles. Since they are fur-bearers and game animals, they have been subjected to considerable research. Individual toes are cut off in order to identify their tracks, ears are tagged, animals are tracked by radio, their scats analyzed and their dens investigated.

Although young raccoons make entertaining pets, most captives become surly, rough and even vicious as they approach sexual maturity.

Males are 25 to 38 inches long, including the 8- to 16-inch tail; females are an inch or two shorter. Adults weigh 10 to 25 pounds, to a reputed maximum of 49 pounds. Except in the Rockies, raccoons occur from Canada to Panama.

MUSTELA MARTES, LINN.
PINE MARTEN.

Let us take a share of the cunning and sneaking character of the fox, as much of the wide-awake and cautious habits of the weasel, a similar proportion of the voracity (and a little of the fetid odour) of the mink, and add thereto some of the climbing propensities of the raccoon, and we have a tolerable idea of the attributes of the little prowler . . . The Pine Marten, as may be inferred from this compound, is shy, cruel, cunning, and active, and partakes of the habits of the predacious animals above mentioned, with the exception that it is not known to approach the residences of man like the fox, weasel, or mink, but rather keeps in dense woods where it can prey upon birds, their eggs and young, squirrels, the white-footed and other mice, shrews, wood-rats, &c., together with beetles and other insects, larvae of different species, toads, frogs, lizards, water reptiles, and fish. It is also an eater of some kinds of berries and nuts (as we are informed), and is said to be fond of honey like the bear.

It has been supposed that the name Pine Marten was given to this animal because it inhabits the pine forests of the northern parts of this continent, and shows a preference for those trees, in the lofty tops of which it frequently resides. The Pine Marten, however, is often called the America Sable or the Sable, and in fact is more generally known to the country people of our northern States, and also to the furriers, by the latter name than by any other.

Sprightly and agile in its movements, the Pine Marten commonly procures abundance of food. It is prolific, bringing forth from six to eight young at a time, so that notwithstanding the value of its fur and the consequent pursuit of it during the proper season, it is still by no means a scarce animal. We have had several specimens sent to us by friends residing in the State of New York and in the wilder portions of our Canada frontier, which were procured among the woody hills of those districts.

According to Dr. DEKAY (New York Fauna, p. 33), this species is so active as to destroy great quantities of squirrels, the red squirrel (*Sciurus Hudsonius* /*Tamiasciurus hudsonicus*/) only escaping by its superior agility. Dr. GODMAN remarks that the "Pine Marten frequently has its den in the hollows of trees, but very commonly takes possession of the nest of some industrious squirrel, which it enlarges to suit its own convenience, after putting the builder to death."

Sir JOHN RICHARDSON says that "particular races of Martens, distinguished by the fineness and dark colour of their fur, appear to inhabit certain rocky districts." "A partridge's head, with the feathers, is the best bait for the log traps in which this animal is taken. It does not reject carrion, and often destroys the hoards of meat and fish laid up by the natives, when they have accidentally left a crevice by which it can enter. The Marten, when its retreat is cut off, shows its teeth, sets up its hair, arches its back, and makes a hissing noise like a cat. . . ."

The Indians sometimes eat the Pine Marten, but its flesh is rank and coarse. We have seen this species in confinement, when it appeared tolerably gentle, and had lost much of its snappish character.

The Pine Marten burrows in the ground at times, and the female brings forth her young in a fallen hollow log, a hole under rocks, or in a burrow, generally in April or May. These animals are chiefly caught with dead-falls baited with meat of any kind, birds, rabbits, squirrels, &c., and generally a hunter has many traps set, each of which he visits as often as once or twice a week. The Martens are sometimes devoured by larger animals after they have been caught. They are only trapped in the autumn and winter.

The fur of this species has been considered valuable, and when in fashion the skins were worth good prices. It is often palmed off on purchasers as fur of a more costly kind, and for this purpose is dyed any desired colour. /Marten is now one of the most costly furs, a pelt bringing 25 to 50 dollars under average market conditions and around 200 dollars in the boom which followed World War I./

PINE MARTEN

Martes americana americana (Turton)

Usually solitary and silent, the pine marten bounds here and there over its ten-square mile territory by day and night, summer and winter. It sleeps soundly in different places along the way. Once in a while when the hunting is good and martens plentiful, four or five may hunt in the same area. In most cases they keep out of each other's way or meet with bared teeth and snarls.

The favorite method of locating prey is to rush at a windfall or clump of brush hoping to scare it out. If unsuccessful, the predator carefully examines every nook and cranny. Sometimes it tunnels through snow to avoid being seen. It is neither a good digger nor swimmer, nor does it spend as much time in trees as was formerly believed.

Very inquisitive, it can be called from its hiding place by a fake mouse squeak. Experienced woodsmen set their traps conspicuously to call attention and arouse its curiosity.

During breeding season, the promiscuous male fights all rivals. The female has a special clucking voice at this time which is supposed to summon the male in case she has been overlooked. As with other mustelids that breed in July, the cells lie inert until midwinter, then develop to full term by March or April. At birth the young weigh about an ounce and have fine yellow hair. Almost full-grown at three months, they depart but do not mate until their second summer.

Man has been Enemy Number One for a long time. Deforestation and over-trapping practically exterminated the species from the northeastern United States by the 20th century. With regrowth of woodland and enforcement of conservation laws, the marten has begun to come back.

A beautiful fur, the pelt brings 25 to 50 dollars (up to 200 dollars in the boom that followed World War I). Although artificial lighting shortens the marten's gestation by three or four months and reduces the loss of embryos, other factors are adverse.

Males are 23 to 27 inches long, including the 7- to 9½-inch tail, and weigh up to 3 pounds. Females total 21 to 23 inches in length and weigh 1¾ to 2¼ pounds. The species occurs across the continent from the tree limit south (in the mountains) to northern New England and New York, and to New Mexico and the southern Sierra Nevada.

MUSTELA CANADENSIS, LINN.

PENNANTS MARTEN OR FISHER.

Although this species is represented as having been rather common in every part of the Northern and Middle States, in the early periods of our history, and is still met with in diminished numbers, in the thinly settled portions of our country; very little of its history or habits has been written, and much is still unknown. We have occasionally met with it, but it has been to us far from a common species. Even in the mountainous portions of the Northern and Eastern States, the Fisher, thirty years ago, was as difficult to procure as the Bay lynx. It has since become still more rare, and in places where it was then known, scarcely any vestige of the knowledge of its former existence can now be traced. . . .

Whilst residing in the northern part of our native State, (New-York,) thirty-five years ago, the hunters were in the habit of bringing us /Bachman/ two or three specimens of this Marten in the course of a winter. They obtained them by following their tracks in the snow, when the animals had been out in quest of food on the previous night, thus tracing them to the hollow trees in which they were concealed, which they chopped down. They informed us that as a tree was falling, the Fisher would dart from the hollow, which was often fifty feet from the ground, and leap into the snow, when the dogs usually seized and killed him, although not without a hard struggle, as the Fisher was infinitely more dangerous to their hounds than either the gray or the red fox. They usually called this species the Black Fox.

A servant, on one occasion, came to us before daylight, asking us to shoot a raccoon for him, which, after having been chased by his dogs the previous night, had taken to so large a tree that he neither felt disposed to climb it nor to cut it down. On our arrival at the place, it was already light, and the dogs were barking furiously at the foot of the tree. We soon perceived that instead of being a raccoon, the animal was a far more rare and interesting species, a Fisher. As we were anxious to study its habits we did not immediately shoot, but teased it by shaking some grape vines that had crept up nearly to the top of the tree. The animal not only became thoroughly frightened, but seemed furious; he leaped from branch to branch, showing his teeth and growling at the same time; now and then he ran half way down the trunk of the tree . . . He was brought down after several discharges from the gun. He seemed extremely tenacious of life, and was game to the last, holding on to the nose of a dog with a dying grasp. This animal proved to be a male; the body measured twenty-five inches, and the tail, including the fur, fifteen. . . .

The specimen, from which the figure in our plate was drawn, was taken alive in some part of the Alleghany Mountains, in the State of Pennsylvania, and we /J. J. Audubon/ soon afterwards received a letter from our esteemed friend, SPENCER F. BAIRD, Esq., of Carlisle, in that State, informing us of its having been captured, which enabled us, through that gentleman, to purchase it. We received it at New-York, in good condition, in a case tinned inside, with iron bars in front, to prevent the animal from making its escape, as it was so strong and so well supplied with sharp teeth that it could easily have eaten its way out of a common wooden box. . . .

We kept this individual alive for some days, feeding it on raw meat, pieces of chicken, and now and then a bird. It was voracious, and very spiteful, growling, snaring and spitting when approached, but it did not appear to suffer much uneasiness from being held in captivity, as, like many other predacious quadrupeds, it grew fat, being better supplied with food than when it had been obliged to cater for itself in the woods. . . .

The Fisher is represented as following the line of traps set by the trappers, and in the manner of the wolverene, robbing them of their bait. . . .

. . . .It is probable that, by some mistake, the habits of the mink have been ascribed to the Fisher; hence its English name seems to be inappropriate; but as it appears to be entitled to it, by right of long possession, we do not feel disposed to change it. . . .We feel pretty confident that it does not dive after the finny tribes, but it is not improbable that it surprises them in shallow water; and we are well informed that, like the raccoon, it searches under the banks of water-courses for frogs, &c. . . .

FISHER

Martes pennanti pennanti (Erxleben)

Bachman's suspicion that the fisher is not a "fisherman" is essentially correct — although it can swim and may eat fish occasionally. A solitary hunter, it lives largely on snowshoe hares, squirrels, mice and shrews. Frequently it flips over a porcupine, rips it open and feeds down from the unprotected abdomen. (Sometimes a quill proves fatal.) The fisher often eats deer and moose as carrion, although it can readily kill a fawn or starvation-weakened doe.

The one to four (usually three) young are born during April in a hollow tree or rock den and the female mates again within a week or two. Gestation requires almost a year because of delayed implantation of the eggs. The family remains together well into the following winter, hunting chiefly but not entirely by night and traveling a roughly circular route that may be 40 to 100 miles long within the home range of 10 to 20 miles. Fishers prefer old growth forest, and must have extensive wilderness to survive as a species.

Males are 36 to 41 inches long, including the 12- to 16-inch tail; females are 15 percent smaller. The range is boreal America, south to the Adirondacks and Sierra Nevada.

PUTORIUS PUSILLUS, DEKAY.

SMALL WEASEL.

From the form and structure of this species, we might naturally presume that it possesses all the habits of the ermine /long-tailed weasel; see comment below/. It feeds on insects, eggs of birds, and mice, but from its diminutive size we are led to suppose that it is not mischievous in the poultry house, and would scarcely venture to attack a full-grown Norway rat.

/Editor's Comment: In the imperial folio which was issued in 1846, the plate (opposite page) was entitled "Mustela fusca, Little American Brown Weasel." The error was corrected in the text of the octavo (1854) edition of the Quadrupeds.

Audubon and Bachman, in common with other naturalists, had a great deal of trouble classifying the weasels. Much of their difficulty arose from the seasonal color change in many of the animals and from the great difference in size of males and females of the large long-tailed weasels. Erroneously, they established five separate species for

1. The small (short-tailed) weasel, which was brown in summer but white in winter (Putorius pusillus)
2. Large (long-tailed) males which were brown in winter (P. fuscus)
3. Large (long-tailed) males which were white in winter (P. ermineus)
4. Long-tailed females which were brown in winter (P. agilis)
5. Long-tailed weasels which did not fit in the above categories (P. frenatus)

Only catagory 1 has remained a valid species by modern standards — the ermine. Groups 2 to 5 are now recognized as two races of one species, the long-tailed weasel. (However, many (small) individuals of group 4 were actually females of catagory 1.)

Another complication arose from the author's consistent use of ermineus *and "ermine" for male long-tailed weasels which were white in winter (group 3 above). Nearly a century earlier, Linnaeus had applied these names to the small, short-tailed weasel of Europe and Asia. Because the "Small Weasel (pusillus)," category 1 above, has recently been shown to be of the same species (the one species is circumpolar), it must be known as* Mustela erminea, *the ermine. Throughout the five accounts of weasels which are abstracted from the* Quadrupeds, *the modern name "long-tailed weasel" should be read for Audubon and Bachman's "Ermine."*

The old genus name Putorius *is now applied to Old World ferrets and polecats.* Mustela, *the Latin word for weasel, contains five American species: three weasels, the mink and the black-footed ferret./*

ERMINE

Mustela erminea cicognanii Bonaparte

Back arched and eyes glittering, this half-pound weasel kills animals several times its size and does not hesitate to attack a man who stands in the way. A persistent hunter with keen sight, hearing and smell, it lopes and gallops over the hunting territory by day as well as by night. When the quarry comes into sight, the ermine leaps ahead two yards or more at a time. Reaching its prey, it kills with lightning speed and ferocity. Sometimes a rabbit will stop in its tracks, apparently paralyzed with terror, at the mere sight of a weasel.

Also called the short-tailed weasel (to distinguish it from the larger, long-tailed cousin described in following accounts), the ermine eats nothing but meat — including incidental feathers, fur and bones. Rodents (especially mice), shrews, birds, occasional frogs and even earthworms make up the bulk of its diet. Although an awkward swimmer, it will pursue a fleeing victim into a stream or pond.

Different species of mustelids mate at various times of the year, but their progeny always arrive at the same propitious time — spring. Mustelids that, like the ermine, breed in midsummer do not reproduce for nine or ten months. Implantation of the fertilized egg is delayed through the winter. Zoologists believe that the lengthening of daylight stimulates the embryonic development.

Four to 13 young (average six or seven) are born in a burrow nest lined with grass, leaves, the tattered skins and fur of their mother's victims. At birth the kits weigh one-fourteenth of an ounce, are blind and almost naked except for a neck "mane" of very fine white hairs. Both parents bring meat to supplement their milk diet from the time they are two weeks old. In five weeks, the mane has disappeared, the eyes are open and the young are weaned. Young weasels are playful and sometimes the mother romps with them. In mid-summer the family breaks up, and the mating cycle begins again.

The ermine lives in open woodland, thickets or forest borders — never on open grassland. There are several entrances to the tunnel that it digs or appropriates from some other animal. When the food supply is adequate, the home range is usually less than 50 acres. The weasel is active the year round.

The all-white winter coat with its year-round black-tipped tail has been sought for royalty and nobility throughout the centuries. Furriers call the winter coat "ermine" and the brown summer coat, or white winter fur dyed light brown, "summer ermine." Weasels of this species that live in the humid Pacific Coast belt from British Columbia southward, where snow seldom persists on the ground, keep the brown coat throughout the year.

The ermine population fluctuates with the increase and decrease of mice and other prey. Once underway, these changes often are rapid and extreme.

Male ermines measure 9 to 13½ inches in total length and weigh 2½ to 5 ounces, while females are 30 to 35% smaller and about one-half the weight. The tail is 30 to 45% of the length. Range of the species is enormous: all of northern America including northeastern Greenland and the Arctic islands, south to Maryland, Iowa, Alberta, New Mexico and California; also northern Europe and Asia.

PUTORIUS FRENATA, LICHT.

BRIDLED WEASEL.

We have personally no knowledge of the habits of this rare and comparatively new species. The specimen from which Dr. LICHTENSTEIN made his description and figure, was obtained by F. DEPPE, Esq., in the vicinity of the city of Mexico, where the animal was indiscriminately called *Comadreja, Oronzito* and *Onzito*. He was unable to collect any information in regard to its habits. The specimen from which our description and figure were made, was captured by Mr. JOHN K. TOWNSEND. We conversed with an American officer, who informed us that he had occasionally seen it near Monterey in Mexico, that it there bore no better character than its congener the Ermine /long-tailed weasel/ in the more northern parts of America; that it was destructive to poultry and eggs, and very commonly took up its residence in the outhouses on plantations, and under such circumstances was regarded as a great nuisance. Fortunately for them, the species was considered as quite rare in the northern parts of Mexico, as the Mexican who pointed out this animal to our officer stated, this was the first *Comadreja* he had seen in five years.

/Editor's Comment: The "rare and comparatively new species," despite its interesting facial markings, proved to be only a subspecies of the widely distributed long-tailed weasel M. frenata./

LONG-TAILED WEASEL

Mustela frenata frenata Lichtenstein

Larger and longer-tailed than the ermine, this weasel is otherwise similar in appearance and habits. Both species have black tips on their tails the year round. The bridled face (illustration above) occurs only in some races of the long-tailed weasel.

Curiosity and fearlessness are prominent traits of the weasel tribe and this species has a full quota Naturalists who know how to squeak like a mouse or a chipmunk can call it out of its home for inspection. It cranes its neck and moves its head snake-wise to try for a stronger current of scent-laden air. The prominent beady eyes shine — black in daytime but a brilliant deep green in the rays of a flashlight. The animal then rises up on its haunches for a better view and may advance jerkily to within a few inches of an immobile person. Sometimes it rears up again, puts its forepaws on the observer's shoes and sniffs audibly.

A man who was removing a dead snowshoe hare from a trap was startled to see a weasel suddenly appear from a nearby thicket. It ran up within two feet of the man, then reared, moved its head and upper body about and sniffed in search for the game which gave off such a delectable odor. Interested to see what would happen, the trapper permitted the weasel to tug the hare about 15 feet away before he reached to recover his catch. Fortunately for the trapper, this weasel was not aggressively resentful. There have been numerous cases where the long-tailed weasel has attacked and bitten people who have interfered with its hunting or tried to take away prey which it has captured.

Weasels keep no daily or seasonal schedule. They hunt when hungry, in daylight or darkness although they seem to prefer nighttime stalking. The time of activity depends somewhat on the habits of the prey which is most abundant in the weasel's territory. In pattern, the hunting trips are irregular. The male weasel goes further and covers more country — sometimes a mile or two across — while the female may restrict her travels to 30 or 40 acres.

A weasel with a small range can get back easily to a single home den from any part of the territory; otherwise it requires several widely spaced shelters. The burrow need not be deep; after all, few predators deliberately seek a face-to-face quarrel with such a well-armed and ferocious fighter. When a weasel kills a chipmunk or other small mammal, it may like the looks of its victim's tunnel, so it moves in and settles down. In other cases it occupies a natural cavity in a pile of rocks or under a tree stump. In a space about nine inches in diameter, the weasel makes a nest of grass. Because prey is often carried home and eaten there, the nest soon accumulates a good deal of fur and feathers as well as skulls, bones and partially eaten carcasses. Whenever the nest gets too revolting even for a weasel, another layer of grass is placed on top of the mess. Some of its surplus kills are crammed into tunnels. (Continued)

PUTORIUS ERMINEA, LINN.

WHITE WEASEL. STOAT.

The name of Ermine is associated with the pride of state and luxury, its fur having from time immemorial been the favourite ornament of the robes of princes, judges and prelates. From its snowy whiteness it is emblematic of the purity which they *ought* to possess.

To us the Ermine /long-tailed weasel/, in its winter dress, has always appeared strikingly beautiful. On a wintry day, when the earth was covered with a broad sheet of snow, our attention has sometimes been arrested by this little animal peering out from a log heap, or the crevices of a stone fence; its eyes in certain shades of light appearing like sapphires, its colour vieing in whiteness and brilliancy with the snowy mantle of the surrounding land-scape.

Graceful in form, rapid in his movements, and of untiring industry, he is withal a brave and fearless little fellow; conscious of security within the windings of his retreat among the logs, or heap of stones, he permits us to approach him to within a few feet, then suddenly withdraws his head; we remain still for a moment, and he once more returns to his post of observation, watching curiously our every motion, seeming willing to claim association so long as we abstain from becoming his persecutor.

Yet with all these external attractions, this little Weasel is fierce and bloodthirsty, possessing an intuitive propensity to destroy every animal and bird within its reach, some of which, such as the American rabbit, the ruffed grouse, and domestic fowl, are ten times its own size. It is a notorious and hated depredator of the poultry house, and we have known forty well grown fowls to have been killed in one night by a single Ermine. Satiated with the blood of probably a single fowl, the rest, like the flock slaughtered by the wolf in the sheepfold, were destroyed in obedience to a law of nature, an instinctive propensity to kill. We have traced the footsteps of this bloodsucking little animal on the snow, pursuing the trail of the American rabbit /cottontail/, and although it could not overtake its prey by superior speed, yet the timid hare soon took refuge in the hollow of a tree, or in a hole dug by the marmot, or skunk. Thither it was pursued by the Ermine, and destroyed, the skin and other remains at the mouth of the burrow bearing evidence of the fact. We observed an Ermine, after having captured a hare of the above species, first behead it and then drag the body some twenty yards over the fresh fallen snow, beneath which it was concealed, and the snow tightly pressed over it; the little prowler displaying thereby a habit of which we became aware for the first time on that occasion. To avoid a dog that was in close pursuit, it mounted a tree and laid itself flat on a limb about twenty feet from the ground, from which it was finally shot. We have ascertained by successful experiments, repeated more than a hundred times, that the Ermine can be employed, in the manner of the ferret of Europe, in driving our American rabbit from the burrow into which it has retreated. In one instance, the Ermine employed had been captured only a few days before, and its canine teeth were filed in order to prevent its destroying the rabbit; a cord was placed around its neck to secure its return. It pursued the hare through all the windings of its burrow and forced it to the mouth, where it could be taken in a net, or by the hand. In winter, after a snow storm, the ruffed grouse has a habit of plunging into the loose snow, where it remains at times for one or two days. In this passive state the Ermine sometimes detects and destroys it. In an unsuccessful attempt at domesticating this grouse by fastening its feet to a board in the mode adopted with the stool pigeon, and placing it high on a shelf, an Ermine which we had kept as a pet, found its way by the curtains of the window and put an end to our experiment by eating off the head of our grouse.

Notwithstanding all these mischievous and destructive habits, it is doubtful whether the Ermine is not rather a benefactor than an enemy to the farmer, ridding his granaries and fields of many depredators on the product of his labour, that would devour ten times the value of the poultry and eggs which, at long and uncertain intervals, it occasionally destroys. A mission appears to have been assigned it by Providence to lessen the rapidly multiplying number of mice of various species and the smaller rodentia. . . .

Fig. 2

Fig. 1

LONG-TAILED WEASEL

Mustela frenata noveboracensis (Emmons)

The diet of the long-tailed weasel is exclusively animal — preferably at blood-heat and quivering. Small prey is killed by a quick bite through the brain with one or both of the slender, almost needle-like canines. Larger animals are thrown on their side and sometimes the two roll over and over. The weasel holds on tight with both forepaws and feet, and tries to stab the back of the head or jugular vein. Occasionally the larger prey gets free and the weasel is wounded — even fatally. When a weasel is cornered or trapped, it may scream piercingly. If merely annoyed, it stamps its rear feet.

The long-tailed species has amazing strength for its size. It can bound off, carrying in its jaws a victim weighing twice as much as itself, with no apparent strain or slackening of speed. One famous observer, perhaps a little too enthusiastic, compared this to "a terrier loping off with a sheep."

Does the weasel, like the vampire, suck the blood? Audubon and many other naturalists have thought so. In fact, it laps blood flowing from the wound, but does not suck the opening. Flesh is devoured along with fur, skin and bones. (Fur is regurgitated frequently in small pellets.) The weasel's stomach capacity is somewhat limited — captive adults eat only about one-quarter of their weight in 24 hours — and a large part of the carcasses is not touched. Weasels often continue to kill as many victims as are within easy reach at one time. Most of the excess meat, even when stored in the burrow, is not eaten.

The weasel's prey consists largely of small rodents; mice, rats, chipmunks, young cottontails and snowshoe hares. Around buildings, Norway rats and house mice may have high priority. Less often the weasel picks up moles, small birds and their nestlings and eggs, reptiles, amphibians, earthworms and a few insects. (Captive long-taileds may be fussy; those that have been given frogs shook their faces in apparent disgust and refused to eat.)

Although not an expert climber, it chases chipmunks into trees. Usually, if the desperate rodent leaps or falls from a limb to the ground, the weasel rushes down the trunk. In one incident, however, the predator following a chipmunk as it made three leaps in the course of a lengthy chase, jumped from a height of 15 feet directly to the ground. There it caught and killed its quarry.

Sometimes potential prey is ignored. In California, a mother weasel reared a family of young scarcely 30 feet from a bush which contained the nest of a russet-backed thrush. The nest was only 18 inches from the ground and, although the weasels hunted all about and at times passed directly underneath the four young birds, the nursery was never harmed. Small rodents were plentiful at the time and apparently were preferred. (Continued)

233

PUTORIUS AGILIS, AUD & BACH.

LITTLE NIMBLE WEASEL

We preserved a specimen of this little animal during several months in the winter, forty years ago, in the northern part of New York; it had been captured in a box trap, which was set near its hole in a pine forest, whither we had tracked it on the snow, believing from its small foot-prints that it was some unknown species of Rodentia. What was our surprise when on the following morning we discovered the eyes of this little marauder prying through the crevices of the trap. Supposing it to be a young ermine we preserved it through the winter, under the impression that it would become tame, and increasing in size, attain its full growth by the following spring; we were, however, disappointed in our expectations; it continued wild and cross, always printing on our gloves the form of the cutting edges of its teeth whenever we placed our hand within the box. It concealed itself in its nest, in a dark corner of the cage, during the whole day, and at night was constantly rattling and gnawing at the wires in the endeavour to effect its escape. We fed it on small birds, which it carried to its dark retreat and devoured greedily.

Having placed a common Weasel, twice the size of our animal, in the cage with it, the ermine immediately attacked our little fellow, which ensconced itself in a corner at the back of the cage, where with open mouth and angry eyes, uttering a hissing spitting or sputtering noise, he drew back his lips and showed his sharp teeth in defiance of his opponent.

To relieve him from a troublesome companion we /John Bachman/ removed the ermine. Towards spring we placed a Norway rat in his cage in order to test his courage. The rat and the Weasel retreated to opposite corners and eyed each other during the whole day; on the following morning we found the rat had been killed; but the Weasel was so much wounded that he died before evening.

We have no other information in regard to the habits of this Weasel. Its burrow, the entrance to which was very small, and without any hillock of earth at its borders, was situated in a high ridge of pine land.

We have no doubt that, like the ermine, in prowling about it finds its way into the retreats of the meadow-mouse, the little chipping squirrel /chipmunk/, and other small animals, for although the rat above mentioned was too formidable an opponent, we are confident it could easily have mastered the little *Tamias Lysteri* /*T. striatus*/.

/Editor's Comment: Throughout this account, the reader should keep in mind that the authors were misled by the marked difference in size between male and female into describing the latter as a distinct species, the "Little Nimble Weasel." The "Common Weasel, twice the size" of the caged animal, may well have been a male of the same species. See editor's comment, p. 228./

LONG-TAILED WEASEL

Mustela frenata noveboracensis (Emmons)

Like the ermine, long-tailed weasels mate in July and August and, because of delayed implantation, do not have young until the following spring. The female bears only one litter annually but it may contain a round dozen. The average is five to eight. They are pink, wrinkled, blind, nearly hairless and weigh one-ninth ounce. In four weeks they are well-furred; a week later when the eyes open and teeth start to erupt, the weaning begins. Some males help to care for the young, at least in the early stages.

Litter mates play a good deal, tumbling and wrestling with each other. Friendly tussling, however, immediately becomes murderous carnage if one of the litter is injured enough to cause bleeding. The killing instinct in weasels is aroused instantly by the smell of blood, and an injured playmate becomes a meal for its brothers and sisters. Occasionally adults have been seen frolicking together; this may be mating activity.

At about six weeks of age a pair of musk glands located near the base of the tail suddenly begins to function. Throughout life, whenever the weasel becomes excited with rage, fear, or the mating instinct, these glands give off a powerful odor. To most humans, it is much more offensive and nauseating than a skunk. Some persons with a keen sense of smell can detect the weasel scent after an unexcited animal, with glands closed, has gone by. As far as another weasel is concerned, the merest whiff may reveal personal identity, sex, mood and possibly other information. Weasels have been seen to drag their rears on the ground, perhaps to leave a trace of scent from the musk.

Juvenile weasels leave the home den when they are seven or eight weeks old. At this stage, males in the litter are actually larger than their mother. At three months, young weasels are nearly adult size and have acquired their permanent teeth. Females mate about this time but males, in spite of their larger size, do not breed until the following summer.

When contented, weasels purr lightly. They sometimes call "took-took," rapidly repeated. When pursued by an amorous male, the female utters a high-pitched, "reedy," fluttering sound. If startled or annoyed, the weasel hisses.

Audubon and Bachman were far ahead of their time in assessing predation. They recognized that the weasel eliminates Norway rats which destroy poultry, and mice which girdle fruit trees. A weasel that wreaks havoc in a poultry yard or a new litter of pigs must be trapped or shot. As a tribe, however, weasels are an economic asset — both alive and dead. (Continued)

MUSTELA FUSCA, AUD. & BACH.

LITTLE AMERICAN BROWN WEASEL.

/Editor's Comment: Because the account of this "species'" habits contains little of interest, the following description by the senior Audubon of color change in a captive "White Weasel" (actually the same species) is substituted./

. . . The Weasel this evening, the 6th of March /1842/, began to show a change of colour; we were surprised to see that all around its nose, the white hair of its winter dress had changed suddenly to a silky black hue, and this extended to nearly between the ears. Here and there also were seen small spots of black about its rump, becoming more apparent toward the shoulders, and forming as it were a ridge along the back of the animal.

March 10th. By noon the change was wonderfully manifested. The whole upper surface of the head had become black to the eye, as well as the ridge of the back, the latter part having become quite clouded, and showing an indescribable motley mixture of closely-blended white, black, and blackish brown.

18th. This day the change of colour reached the root of the tail, where it formed a ring of about one inch, of the same reddish black colour. All other parts remained white, slightly tinged with pale lemon colour. It fed, as we perceived, more voraciously than ever since we have had it in our possession. No less than three or four mice were devoured to-day, and what is very strange, it left no remains of either hair, skull, feet, or any other part of these animals; and on this day, the 18th of March, it ate a very large piece of fresh beef, weighing nearly half a pound.

19th. Last night our Weasel made great progress, for this morning we found the coloured ridge on the back broader and less mottled. The posterior coloured part of the head had joined the ridge of the back. The posterior part of the hind legs had become brown, and we observed a small spot the size of a sixpence on each upper part of the thighs. At this juncture we think the animal is beautiful.

22d. This morning we found all the white hair on the outward ridge of the back had fallen, and portions of the thighs and shoulders had become broader; the coloured parts were of a rich brown to the very nose, and there existed indications of small dark spots coming from the sides of the belly, somewhat like so many beads strung on a thread, separated from the lower edge of the back ridge by a line of white of about half an inch. The weasel continues as lively as ever. When asleep, it curls its body around, and the tail encircles the whole animal, the end covering the nose. The eyes appear to be kept carefully uncovered. The general tints of the coloured parts of this Weasel were very much darker than in any other specimen which we have in our collection. When angry, it emitted a sharp shrill cry, and snapped with all its might at the objects presented to it. It was very cleanly in its habits, never rendering its sleeping apartment disagreeable.

28th. . . .The purplish brown was now augmented on the thighs and shoulders to the knee joints, no white hairs remaining mixed with those that were coloured. Beneath the jaws, separate small brown spots appeared at equal distances, leaving an intermediate space of white, as was the case along the flanks. The root of the tail had acquired no farther change. Since last week our animal has diffused a very strong disagreeable odour, musky and fetid, which may be attributable to this being its breeding season; we observed that the smell was more disagreeable in the mornings and evenings, than at mid-day.

April. — On paying our accustomed visit to our Weasel this evening, we found it dead, which put a stop to any further observation of its habits. . . .

LONG-TAILED WEASEL

Mustela frenata noveboracensis (Emmons)

Although Audubon did not paint any of the weasels in their white winter pelage for the *Quadrupeds,* he was so intrigued by the seasonal change that he kept a detailed record of the molting progress of a captive weasel. These notes were printed years later in the book (see opposite page).

Modern biologists have made an intensive study of the phenomenon. Weasels that live in regions where the ground in winter is usually snow-covered, become white in autumn and revert to brown on the upper parts in spring. Those weasels that live where snow lies on the ground for only brief periods or not at all, are brown throughout the year.

If a northern weasel is brought south, it continues the change to white at the usual time, while a southern weasel, which is shipped to the northland, stays brown all year. This indicates that the color change is caused by heredity. Date of molt is determined by the amount of light which falls on the animal; in the north, days grow shorter earlier in fall than in the south, so northern weasels change to their winter (white) pelage sooner than more southerly weasels. Warm temperatures in the autumn delay the change a little, while cold weather hastens it. The basic purpose of the color change is, of course, protection for the species. In snow, a white animal is inconspicuous.

In a mid-zone belt about 600 miles wide across the continent, some weasels turn white in winter while the rest remain brown. Evidently this is "nature's" method of insuring that the species will survive regardless of climatic shifts. During a severe winter, white animals stand a better chance; if the weather cycle brings a warmer winter with more bare ground, brown-coated weasels will escape predators.

Even such courageous and able fighters as weasels succumb to enemies other than man. Foxes, raptorial birds, large snakes and house cats do their best. Weasels are very high-strung creatures and may be subject to shock. Large litter size (see p. 235) is an indication of heavy mortality.

Because the fur is soft and durable, weasel pelts are used extensively for trimmings, capes, jackets and coats. The number of black-tipped tails in ceremonial robes at court denoted the rank of the wearer. Like naturalists of Audubon's time, furriers today label this animal "ermine." Zoologists distinguish it from the true ermine by calling it the long-tailed weasel.

The various "kinds" of weasels described in *Quadrupeds* are now grouped into two species. They are easily differentiated by size and relative length of tail. Modern zoologists recognize a third species, the least weasel *(Mustela rixosa).* As its name implies, this is the smallest of the group; it has a very short tail which lacks the black tip.

Long-tailed weasels vary greatly in size. Males are 14 to 23 inches long, of which the tail is 4½ to 7 inches, and weigh 7 to 14 ounces. Females are 11½ to 20 inches long, with a 3½- to 5-inch tail, and weigh 3 to 9 ounces. The species is restricted to the New World, from southern Canada throughout the United States (except the lower Colorado River basin), Mexico (except lower California and adjacent Sonora), Central America and south to northern Bolivia.

PUTORIUS NIGRIPES, AUD. & BACH.

BLACK FOOTED FERRET.

It is with great pleasure that we introduce this handsome new species; it was procured by Mr. /Alexander/ CULBERTSON /partner in the American Fur Company and Bourgeois (chief) of its trading post at Fort Union, eastern Montana/ on the lower waters of the Platte River, and inhabits the wooded parts of the country to the Rocky Mountains, and perhaps is found beyond that range, although not observed by any travellers, from LEWIS and CLARK to the present day. When we consider the very rapid manner in which every expedition that has crossed the Rocky Mountains, has been pushed forward, we cannot wonder that many species have been entirely overlooked, and should rather be surprised at the number noticed by LEWIS and CLARK, and by NUTALL, TOWNSEND, and others. There has never yet been a Government expedition properly organized, and sent forth to obtain *all* the details, which such a party, allowed *time* enough for thorough investigation, would undoubtedly bring back, concerning the natural history and natural resources of the regions of the far west. The nearest approach to such an expedition having been that so well conducted by LEWIS and CLARK. Nor do we think it at all probable that Government will attend to such matters for a long time to come. We must therefore hope that private enterprise will gradually unfold the zoological, botanical, and mineral wealth of the immense territories we own but do not yet occupy.

The habits of this species resemble, as far as we have learned, those of the ferret of Europe. It feeds on birds, small reptiles and animals, eggs, and various insects, and is a bold and cunning foe to the rabbits, hares, grouse, and other game of our western regions.

The specimen from which we made our drawing was received by us from Mr. J. /John/ G. BELL /noted taxidermist, and member of Audubon's party on his Missouri River trip in 1843/, to whom it was forwarded from the outskirts or outposts of the fur traders on the Platte river, by Mr. CULBERTSON. It was stuffed with the wormwood /probably sand sage-brush, *Artemisia filifolia,* which is common along the lower Platte River/ so abundant in parts of that country, and was rather a poor specimen, although in tolerable preservation. We shall have occasion in a future article to thank Mr. BELL for the use of other new specimens, this being only one of several instances of his kind services to us, and the zoology of our country, in this way manifested.

As before stated, the specimen which we have figured and described was obtained on the lower waters of the Platte river. We are not aware that another specimen exists in any cabinet /museum collection/.

BLACK-FOOTED FERRET

Mustela nigripes (Audubon and Bachman)

The black-footed ferret was first described by Audubon and Bachman. For almost a quarter-century after their 1851 publication "introduced" this mammal to its readers, the single specimen on which the account was based remained the only one known to science. When that one pelt vanished, naturalists began to doubt that any such animal had ever existed. It was even rumored that Audubon and Bachman had faked a "new species" in order to enhance their monumental work, *The Quadrupeds of North America.*

Then a piece of skin, covered with the characteristic yellowish-buff fur and with the black-tipped tail attached, was discovered in the U. S. National Museum in Washington where it had lain for years. Appeals for specimens were made in sportsmen's magazines. As a result, several skins were contributed by doctors, army officers and taxidermists living in the Great Plains region. Audubon and Bachman were vindicated. Their names will always be attached to the scientific name of the black-footed ferret. The species, however, is still rare and even today the total number of specimens in all museums hardly exceeds 100.

Only scanty observations have been made of ferrets in the wild and few facts have been gathered during the 126 years since the publication of the *Quadrupeds.* Most live ferrets have been seen in prairie dog towns. The principal food is inferred to be prairie dogs, but positive evidence is lacking. Small rodents such as ground squirrels and mice, rabbits, small birds and their eggs are known prey.

Because it is very inquisitive, the black-footed ferret can be approached if the observer moves slowly. To get a better view, the animal will stand up on its hind legs with its forelimbs hanging down to its abdomen. In this position, the four black feet, for which it received both vernacular and scientific names, are very evident. Although seen mostly in daytime, it is presumed to be in general a nocturnal hunter.

When taken alive, the ferret spits, hisses and scolds angrily. If captured when young, however, it is said to become an interesting pet. Litters containing five young have been found; the juveniles were pale tan and moulted later into the darker adult pelage.

Never common, they have now disappeared from vast areas within their original range (the length of the Great Plains from Alberta and Saskatchewan to Texas and Arizona, and to 10,500 feet elevation in the Rockies). The decline has been ascribed to the widespread poisoning of prairie dogs, resulting in at least some ferrets acquiring lethal doses of poisoned meat. As hundreds of square miles of abandoned burrows filled in, there was less and less food and shelter for surviving ferrets.

Males are 20 to 21½ inches long, including the 4½- to 5-inch tail; females are about 10 percent shorter.

PUTORIUS VISON, LINN.

MINK.

. . .We acknowledge that we have little inclination to say anything in defence of the Mink. We must admit, however, that although he is a cunning and destructive rogue, his next door neighbour, the ermine or common /long-tailed/ weasel, goes infinitely beyond him in his mischievous propensities. Whilst the Mink is satisfied with destroying one or two fowls at a time, on which he makes a hearty meal; the weasel, in the very spirit of wanton destructiveness, sometimes in a single night puts to death every tenant of the poultry-house!

When residing at Henderson, on the banks of the Ohio river, we observed that Minks were quite abundant, and often saw them carrying off rats which they caught like the weasel or ferret, and conveyed away in their mouths, holding them by the neck in the manner of a cat. . . .

We have observed that the Mink is a tolerably expert fisher. On one occasion, whilst seated near a trout-brook in the northern part of the State of New-York, we heard a sudden splashing in the stream and saw a large trout gliding through the shallow water and making for some long overhanging roots on the side of the bank. A Mink was in close pursuit, and dived after it; in a moment afterwards it re-appeared with the fish in its mouth. By a sudden rush we induced it to drop the trout, which was upwards of a foot in length.

We are disposed to believe, however, that fishes are not the principal food on which the Mink subsists. We have sometimes seen it feeding on frogs and cray-fish. In the Northern States we have often observed it with a WILSON's meadow-mouse in its mouth, and in Carolina the very common cotton-rat furnishes no small proportion of its food. We have frequently remarked it coursing along the edges of the marshes, and found that it was in search of this rat, which frequents such localities, and we discovered that it was not an unsuccessful mouser. We once saw a Mink issuing from a hole in the earth, dragging by the neck a large Florida rat /eastern wood rat/. . . .

The Mink, like the musk-rat and ermine /long-tailed weasel/, does not possess much cunning, and is easily captured in any kind of trap; it is taken in steel-traps and box-traps, but more generally in what are called dead-falls. It is attracted by any kind of flesh, but we have usually seen the traps baited with the head of a ruffed-grouse, wild duck, chicken, jay, or other bird The Mink is exceedingly tenacious of life, and we have found it still alive under a dead-fall, with a pole lying across its body pressed down by a weight of 150 lbs., beneath which it had been struggling for nearly twenty-four hours.

This species, as well as the skunk and the ermine /long-tailed weasel/, emits an offensive odour when provoked by men or dogs, and this habit is exercised likewise in a moderate degree whenever it is engaged in any severe struggle with an animal or bird on which it has seized. We were once attracted by the peculiar and well known plaintive cry of a hare, in a marsh on the side of one of our southern rice-fields, and our olfactories were at the same time regaled with the strong fetid odour of the Mink; we found it in possession of a large marsh-hare /marsh rabbit/, with which, from the appearance of the trampled grass and mud, it had been engaged in a fierce struggle for some time.

The latter end of February or the beginning of March, in the latitude of Albany, N.Y., is the rutting season of the Mink. At this period the ground is usually still covered with snow, but the male is notwithstanding very restless, and his tracks may every where be traced, along ponds, among the slabs around saw-mills, and along nearly every stream of water. He seems to keep on foot all day as well as through the whole night. Having for several days in succession observed a number of Minks on the ice hurrying up and down a millpond, where we had not observed any during a whole winter, we took a position near a place which we had seen them pass, in order to procure some of them.

We shot six in the course of the morning, and ascertained that they were all large and old males. As we did not find a single female in a week, whilst we obtained a great number of males, we came to the conclusion that the females, during this period, remain in their burrows. About the latter end of April the young are produced. . . .

MINK

Mustela vison mink Peale and Palisot de Beauvois

Five million ranch mink and another million of the wild species are slaughtered each year to make women feel elegant and glamorous. Mink was first raised commercially before the Civil War. After World War I, the business expanded greatly. Platinum, autumn haze, silver-blue, orchid and other fashionable "shades" have been developed by selective breeding. The value of wild-trapped mink still amounts to millions of dollars annually, offsetting by far the damage that occasional killers may do in poultry runs and fish hatcheries.

Larger than the weasel, the mink is a rapacious hunter both on land and in the water. It often kills a muskrat and then moves into the victim's lodge or bank burrow. It can swim 100 feet under water and dive 18 feet below. Waterfowl, crayfish, frogs and fish are its quarry. On land it devours small rodents, rabbits and other creatures often bigger than itself. Usually it kills with one swift bite in the neck, and often more than it can eat. Feces show feathers, fur, and small but amazingly sharp bones that have passed through its intestines.

During the February-March mating season, the male may serve several females but is likely to remain with the final mate to help hunt for the young until they are half grown. Gestation lasts 39 to 76 (usually about 50) days; late breeders have the shorter period. Generally the litter contains four or five kits but the number varies from three to 10.

At birth, minks are about 3¼ inches long and weigh one-fifth ounce; they are pink, blind and have a scanty covering of fine white hair which is replaced two weeks later by pale, reddish-gray fur. The eyes open at five weeks when the young are weaned.

Although adjacent woodland is desirable to a mink, permanent water is a necessity. It can be fresh, brackish or marine — swift-flowing, lake or swamp. On or near the margin, the mink finds shelters under or in logs, stumps, trees or homes of other animals. The den chamber is about 12 inches in diameter and is floored with grass and leaves.

As a rule the mink is solitary. The female generally uses one den and hunts over a rather limited area — as small as 20 to 40 acres. The male, on the other hand, is a roamer; his hunting trips may take him 15 miles in a single night. The species is active all year but is likely to stay in or close to its den during storms and bitter cold. When the ground is snow-covered, a mink in a hurry (or a playful mood) slides down slopes on its belly. When trapped it hisses, spits, screams, and emits an odor that seems more obnoxious than that of a skunk.

Adult males are 20 to 28 inches long, including the 6- to 8-inch tail, and weigh 1¼ to 3½ pounds. Females are 10 to 20% smaller and one-half that weight. Minks occur throughout most of North America north of Mexico except the Southwest and extreme Arctic Canada.

GULO LUSCUS, LIN.

THE WOLVERINE.

The Wolverene, or Glutton as he is generally called, is one of the animals whose history comes down to us blended with the superstitions of the old writers. Errors when once received and published, especially if they possess the charm of great singularity or are connected with tales of wonder, become fastened on the mind by early reading and the impressions formed in youth, until we are familiarized with their extravagance, and we at length regret to find ideas (however incorrect) adopted in early life, not realized by the sober inquiries and investigations of maturer years.

The Wolverene, confined almost exclusively to Polar regions, where men have enjoyed few advantages of education and hence have imbibed without much reflection the errors, extravagances and inventions of hunters and trappers, has been represented as an animal possessing extraordinary strength, agility, and cunning, and as being proverbially one of the greatest gormandizers among the "brutes.". . . .

In the United States the Wolverene has always existed very sparingly, and only in the Northern districts. About thirty-five years ago, we /Bachman/ saw in the possession of a country merchant in Lansingburg, New-York, three skins of this species, that had as we were informed been obtained on the Green Mountains of Vermont; about the same time we obtained a specimen in Rensselaer county, near the banks of the Hoosack /Hoosick/ river. While hunting the Northern hare, immediately after a heavy fall of snow, we unexpectedly came upon the track of an animal which at the time we supposed to be that of a bear, a species which even then was scarcely known in that portion of the country, (which was already pretty thickly settled.) We followed the broad trail over the hills and through the devious windings of the forest for about five miles, till within sight of a ledge of rocks on the banks of the Hoosack river. . . .we conceived it possible to effect an opening /in the cavern/. . . This was after great labour accomplished by prying away some heavy fragments of the rock. The animal could now be reached with a pole, and seemed very much irritated, growling and snapping at the stick, which he once succeeded in tearing from our hand, all the while emitting a strong and very offensive musky smell. He was finally shot. What was our surprise and pleasure on discovering that we had, not a bear, but what was more valuable to us, a new species of quadruped, as we believed it to be. It was six months before we were enabled, by consulting a copy of BUFFON /the celebrated *Histoire Naturelle;* the first 15 volumes described the world's quadrupeds/, to discover our mistake and ascertain that our highly prized specimen was the Glutton, of which we had read such marvellous tales in the school-books. . . .

There was a large nest of dried leaves in the cavern, which had evidently been a place of resort for the Wolverene we have been speaking of, during the whole winter, as its tracks from every direction led to the spot. It had laid up no winter store, and evidently depended on its nightly excursions for a supply of food. It had however fared well, for it was very fat.

It has been asserted that the Wolverene is a great destroyer of beavers: but we are inclined to think that this can scarcely be the case, unless it be in summer, when the beaver is often found some distance from the water. In such cases we presume that the Wolverene, although not swift of foot, could easily overtake that aquatic animal. . . .

All Northern travellers and writers on the natural history of the Arctic regions, /Henry/ ELLIS /British explorer in Hudson Bay, 1746–7/, PENNANT, HEARNE, /Sir William Edward/ PARRY /British Arctic explorer, 1818–25/, /Sir John/ FRANKLIN /British explorer and leader of the illfated *Erebus-Terror* expedition of 1844–48/, RICHARDSON, &c., speak of the indomitable perseverance of the Wolverene in following the footsteps of the trappers, in order to obtain the bait, or take from the traps the Arctic fox, the marten, beaver, or any other animal that may be caught in them. They demolish the houses built around the dead-falls, in order to obtain the bait, and tear up the captured animals apparently from a spirit of wanton destructiveness. HEARNE (p. 373) gives an account of their amazing strength, one of them having overset the greatest part of a large pile of wood, measuring upwards of seventy yards round, to get at some provisions that had been hid there. . . .

WOLVERINE

Gulo luscus luscus (Linnaeus)

Few mammals have been the subject of more folklore and distorted tales than the wolverine, the largest of the weasel tribe. Although Dr. Bachman had little personal contact with the species in the wild, his account is more factual than some of the stories appearing in popular magazines today.

The wolverine has great endurance and amazing strength for its size. Despite the squat, heavy body on short legs, it climbs trees fairly well. Its fastest gait, a lumbering gallop, does not exceed 10 miles an hour, but it will lope up a 70-degree, boulder-covered mountain side with no apparent effort. Having petted a "tame" wolverine in captivity, the cautious Dr. Bachman thought it "incredible" that the species could kill hoofed animals weighing 10 times as much. Nevertheless, when deer, elk and moose are hampered by deep snow, they sometimes fall prey to this weasel. Even the wolf, cougar and black bear, all with great size advantage, have abandoned their kills when the 12- to 14-inch-high bandit appeared.

Eskimos and Indians of the far north hate and fear the wolverine because it follows their trap lines, destroys the animals caught and may even tear up and hide the traps. It can break into any cache or cabin, create havoc, and foul all food and supplies that it does not take.

Hunting by day or night, the wolverine may cover a home range as great as 50 miles in diameter. Most food is found by remarkable scent and hearing, since its sight is poor. All kinds of living prey, carrion and occasionally berries are taken. Bigger or faster animals such as deer and snowshoe hares are leaped upon from ambush. Surplus food may be cached under earth or rocks, or wedged in the fork of a tree. The enormous consumption of food earned its original vernacular and scientific names of "glutton." Other popular names, "Indian devil" and "skunk bear," are more descriptive than "wolverine," for the animal has no resemblance nor relationship to a wolf.

Wolverines probably mate in mid-summer. Due to delayed implantation, as with most mustelids, the young (one to five, usually two or three) are not born until late winter or early spring. Blind and practically hairless, they grow rapidly and disperse when five or six months of age. A year-old animal is nearly full grown.

Males are 36 to 45 inches long, including the 7½- to 10½-inch tail, and weigh 24 to 40 pounds. Females are 10 percent shorter and 30 percent lighter. The species is circumpolar in range; in America it occurs south to southern Labrador and the southern Sierra Nevada of California.

243

MELES LABRADORIA, SABINE
AMERICAN BADGER.

During our stay at Fort Union, on the Upper Missouri River, in the summer of 1843, we /J. J. Audubon/ purchased a living badger from a squaw, who had brought it from some distance to the Fort for sale; it having been caught by another squaw at a place nearly two hundred and fifty miles away, among the Crow Indians. It was first placed in our common room, but was found to be so very mischievous, pulling about and tearing to pieces every article within its reach, trying to dig up the stones of the hearth, &c., that we had it removed into an adjoining apartment. It was regularly fed morning and evening on raw meat, either the flesh of animals procured by our hunters, or small birds shot during our researches through the adjacent country. It drank a good deal of water, and was rather cleanly in its habits. In the course of a few days it managed to dig a hole under the hearth and fire-place nearly large and deep enough to conceal its body, and we were obliged to drag it out by main force whenever we wished to examine it. It was provoked at the near approach of any one, and growled continuously at all intruders. It was not, however, very vicious, and would suffer one or two of our companions to handle and play with it at times. . . .

On arriving at our residence near New-York, we had a large box, tinned on the inside, let into the ground about two feet and a half and filled to the same depth with earth. The Badger was put into it, and in a few minutes made a hole, in which he seemed quite at home, and where he passed most of his time during the winter, although he always came out to take his food and water, and did not appear at all sluggish or inclined to hibernate even when the weather was so cold as to make it necessary to pour hot water into the pan that was placed within his cage, to enable him to drink, as cold water would have frozen immediately . . .

Our Badger was fed regularly, and soon grew very fat; its coat changed completely, became woolly and of a buff-brown colour, and the fur by the month of February had become indeed the most effectual protection against cold that can well be imagined.

We saw none of these animals in our hunting expeditions while on our journey up the Missouri River, and observed only a few burrowing places which we supposed were the remains of their holes, but which were at that time abandoned. We were informed that these animals had burrows six or seven feet deep running beneath the ground at that depth to the distance of more than thirty feet. The Indians speak of their flesh as being good; that of the one of which we have been speaking, when the animal was killed, looked very white and fat, but we omitted to taste it. . . .

We /John Bachman/ had an opportunity in Charleston of observing almost daily for a fortnight, the habits of a Badger in a menagerie; he was rather gentle, and would suffer himself to be played with and fondled by his keeper, but did not appear as well pleased with strangers; he occasionally growled at us, and would not suffer us to examine him without the presence and aid of his keeper.

In running, his fore-feet crossed each other, and his body nearly touched the ground. The heel did not press on the earth like that of the bear, but was only slightly elevated above it. He resembled the Maryland marmot /woodchuck/ in running, and progressed with about the same speed. We have never seen any animal that could exceed him in digging. He would fall to work with his strong feet and long nails, and in a minute bury himself in the earth, and would very soon advance to the end of a chain ten feet in length. In digging, the hind, as well as the fore-feet, were at work, the latter for the purpose of excavating, and the former, (like paddles,) for expelling the earth out of the hole, and nothing seemed to delight him more than burrowing in the ground . . .

The Badger delights in taking up his residence in sandy prairies, where he can indulge his extravagant propensity for digging. As he lives upon the animals he captures, he usually seeks out the burrows of the various species of marmots, spermophiles, ground-squirrels, &c., with which the prairies abound; into these he penetrates, enlarging them to admit his own larger body, and soon overtaking and devouring the terrified inmates. In this manner the prairies become so filled with innumerable Badger-holes, that when the ground is covered with snow they prove a great annoyance to horsemen. . . .

BADGER

Taxidea taxus taxus (Schreber)

The badger's nightly travels can be followed by its many excavations along the way. If hunting is good, a field may soon be dotted with elliptical-shaped holes and piles of earth. This short, bowlegged, pigeon-toed creature is one of the fastest and most efficient diggers in the animal kingdom. Tremendous strength, flattened body, and long stout claws enable it to follow and out-dig pocket gophers, prairie dogs, other rodents, moles and snakes. Some food is captured above ground — cottontails, lizards, large insects, eggs and young of ground-nesting birds. Surplus kill is buried for future use — "ripening" adds flavor.

This plains dweller can dive and swim if it has the opportunity. It dogpaddles along, holding its short, usually drooping tail straight up. The animal likes to lie in a puddle of water to cool off in hot weather. It licks itself clean frequently — swallowing loose hair in the process.

Few animals dare attack a badger. It can kill a dog or coyote twice its own size, and will put an unarmed man to flight. The dense fur, tough, loose skin and heavy neck muscles usually prevent an enemy from securing a deadly grip. Apparently it is impervious to snake venom, unless the snake happens to strike its nose. Rattles of dead snakes often litter the entrance to the home tunnel, along with bones, bits of fur, and feces.

When fighting, the badger hisses, snarls, growls and sometimes squeals with rage. Its tail is erected and a vile odor is ejected from anal glands. A clumsy, short-winded runner, the badger can only escape underground when it is outnumbered by attackers. If a burrow is handy, it retreats backward, facing the enemies, and then plugs the entrance. If no burrow is available, the fugitive digs one in a hurry. Showers of earth fly into the air, land as much as 10 feet away and the fugitive disappears. Not even a man with a shovel can catch up with him.

The solitary badger mates in autumn. Implantation is delayed and although development may take only nine weeks, the litter does not arrive until late March to early June. The one to five (usually two or three) young, in a grass nest, open their eyes when they are about four weeks old. The mother nurses them for another month and then kills most of their food until fall when they are three-quarters grown and go off to find their own hunting grounds. With luck, an area a mile in diameter will suffice for each one.

Males are 25 to 35 inches long, including the 4- to 6-inch tail; females are 3 to 4 inches shorter. Their weight is 14 to 26 pounds. The range is northern Alberta and southeastern Ontario south through the western United States to central Mexico.

MEPHITIS AMERICANA, DESM.

COMMON AMERICAN SKUNK

There is no quadruped on the continent of North America the approach of which is more generally detested than that of the Skunk: from which we may learn that, although from the great and the strong we have to apprehend danger, the feeble and apparently insignificant may have it in their power to annoy us almost beyond endurance. . . .

The Skunk, although armed with claws and teeth strong and sharp enough to capture his prey, is slow on foot, apparently timid, and would be unable to escape from many of his enemies, if he were not possessed of a power by which he often causes the most ferocious to make a rapid retreat, run their noses into the earth, and roll or tumble on the ground as if in convulsions . . .

This offensive fluid is contained in two small sacs situated on each side of the root of the tail, and is ejected through small ducts near the anus. We have on several occasions witnessed the manner in which this secretion is discharged. When the Skunk is irritated, or finds it necessary to defend himself, he elevates his tail over his back, and by a strong muscular exertion ejects it in two thread-like streams in the direction in which the enemy is observed. He appears to take an almost unerring aim, and almost invariably salutes a dog in his face and eyes. . . .

We /Rev. Bachman/ were once requested by a venerable clergyman, an esteemed friend, who had for many years been a martyr to violent paroxysms of asthma, to procure for him the glands of a Skunk; which, according to the prescription of his medical advisor, were kept tightly corked in a smelling bottle, which was applied to his nose when the symptoms of his disease appeared.

For some time he believed that he had found a specific for his distressing complaint; we were however subsequently informed, that having uncorked the bottle on one occasion while in the pulpit during service, his congregation finding the smell too powerful for their olfactories, made a hasty retreat, leaving him nearly alone in the church. . . .

The Skunk does not support a good character among the farmers. He will sometimes find his way into the poultry-house, and make some havoc with the setting hens; he seems to have a peculiar penchant for eggs, and is not very particular whether they have been newly laid, or contain pretty large rudiments of the young chicken; yet he is so slow and clumsy in his movements, and creates such a commotion in the poultry-house, that he usually sets the watch-dog in motion, and is generally detected in the midst of his depredations; when, retiring to some corner, he is either seized by the dog, or is made to feel the contents of the farmer's fowling piece. . . .

This animal generally retires to his burrow about December, in the Northern States, and his tracks are not again visible until near the tenth of February. He lays up no winter store; and like the bear, raccoon, and Maryland marmot, is very fat on retiring to his winter quarters, and does not seem to be much reduced in flesh at his first appearance toward spring, but is observed to fall off soon afterwards. He is not a sound sleeper on these occasions; on opening his burrow we found him, although dull and inactive, certainly not asleep, as his black eyes were peering at us from the hole, into which we had made an opening, seeming to warn us not to place too much reliance on the hope of finding this striped "weasel asleep."

In the upper districts of Carolina and Georgia, where the Skunk is occasionally found, he, like the raccoon in the Southern States, does not retire to winter quarters, but continues actively prowling about during the night through the winter months. . . .

We doubt not the flesh of the Skunk is well tasted and savoury. We /J. J. Audubon/ observed it cooked and eaten by the Indians. The meat was white and fat, and they pronounced it better than the opossum, — infinitely superior to the raccoon, (which they called rank meat,) and fully equal to roast pig. We now regret that our squeamishness prevented us from trying it.

We have seen the young early in May; there were from five to nine in a litter.

The fur is rather coarse. It is seldom used by the hatters, and never we think by the furriers; and from the disagreeable task of preparing the skin, it is not considered an article of commerce.

STRIPED SKUNK

Mephitis mephitis hudsonica Richardson

The skunk's "terrible weapon" (opposite) of a tablespoon of thick, oily fluid is enough for five or six volleys. A week is needed for replenishment. For warning, the skunk may stamp its feet, growl, spit and click its teeth.

Apiarists dislike this excellent mouser because it also eats insects. In spite of bee stings on tongue, in mouth, throat and on stomach linings, a skunk will crunch and devour bees, if available, night after night. When hibernating, 10 females may occupy a den with one male.

Radio tracking of a skunk, fitted with a collar transmitter, is successful except while it takes a swim. The two to 10 (ordinarily six or seven) young are born between early May and mid-June.

Males are 23 to 32 inches long, including the 7- to 16-inch tail and weigh 3½ to 10 pounds. Females are 15 percent smaller. Striped skunks are found coast to coast, from southern Hudson Bay through the United States to northern Mexico.

MEPHITIS MACROURA, LICHT

LARGE TAILED SKUNK.

In Texas, during the winter of 1845–6, specimens of this skunk were obtained by J. W. AUDUBON; the first he met with was seen on one of the high and dry prairies west of Houston, on the road to Lagrange; this was, however, only a young one. It was easily caught, as these animals never attempt to escape by flight, depending on the fetid discharges which they, like the common skunk, eject, to disgust their assailant and cause him to leave them in safety. By throwing sticks and clods of dirt at this young one, he was induced to display his powers in this way, and teased until he had emptied the glandular sacs which contain the detestable secretion. He was then comparatively disarmed, and by thrusting a forked stick over the back of his head, was pinned to the ground, then seized and thrust into a bag, the mouth of which being tied up, he was considered safely captured, and was slung to one of the pack-saddles of the baggage-mules. The fetor of this young skunk was not so horrid as that of the common species (*Mephitis chinga* /now *M. mephitis*/).

On arriving at the camping ground for the night, the party found that their prisoner had escaped by gnawing a hole in the bag, being unobserved by any one.

This species is described as very common in some parts of Texas, and its superb tail is now and then used by the country folks by way of plume or feather in their hats. . . .

The Large-Tailed Skunk feeds upon snakes, lizards, insects, birds' eggs, and small animals; and it is said that at the season when the pecan (*Carya olivaeformis*) ripens, they eat those nuts, as well as acorns. This is strange, considering their carnivorous formation. They burrow in winter, and live in hollows and under roots. They produce five or six young at a birth.

We are indebted to Col. GEO. A. McCALL, U.S.A., for the following interesting account of an adventure with one of these Skunks . . .

". . . With a hunter's eye, I at once recognized in this shadow /on the front wall of my tent/ the outline of the uplifted tail of a *Mephitis Macroura*, vulgo Large-Tailed *Skunk*, whose body was concealed from my view behind the mess-basket. . . .

. . . just at this moment he succeeded in raising the top of the basket and I heard his descent among the spoons. 'Ha! ha! old fellow, I have you now!' I said to myself; and the next instant I was standing on the top of the mess-basket, whither I had got without the slightest noise, and where I now heard the rascal rummaging my things little suspecting that he was at the time a prisoner. I called my servant—a negro. George made his appearance, and as he opened the front of the tent paused in surprise at seeing me standing *en dishabille* on the top of the mess-basket. 'George,' said I, in a quiet tone, 'buckle the straps of this basket.' George looked still more surprised on receiving the order, but obeyed it in silence. I then stepped gently off, and said, 'Take this basket very carefully, and without shaking it, out yonder, in front, and set it down easily.' George looked still more bewildered; but, accustomed to obey without question, did as he was directed. After he had carried the basket off to a considerable distance, and placed it on the ground, he looked back at the door of the tent, where I still stood, for further orders. 'Unbuckle the straps,' said I; it was done. 'Raise the top of the basket:' he did so; while at the same time, elevating my voice, I continued, *'and let that d----d Skunk out!'* As the last words escaped from my lips the head and tail of the animal appeared in sight, and George, giving vent to a scream of surprise and fear, broke away like a quarter-horse, and did not stop until he had put a good fifty yards between himself and the mess-basket. Meanwhile, the Skunk, with the same deliberation that had marked his previous course (and which, by the way, is a remarkable trait in the character of this animal), descended the side of the basket, and, with tail erect, danced off in a direction down the creek, and finally disappeared in the bushes. I then, having recovered from a good fit of laughter, called to George, who rather reluctantly made his appearance before me. He was still a little out of breath, and with some agitation, thus delivered himself, 'Bless God, massa, if I had known there was a Skunk in the mess-basket, I never would have touched it *in this world!' . . .*"

HOODED SKUNK

Mephitis macroura macroura Lichtenstein

Long white hair often forms a ruff on the back of this skunk's head that resembles a hood (not apparent in illustration). Considerably more active and sprightly than its relative, the slow-moving striped skunk, it has, in spite of Audubon's opinion, a scent no less noxious. The longer tail extends as far as its head and body combined.

The hooded skunk lives mostly on insects, including larvae, and other invertebrates. In addition to Audubon's list, it eats a variety of fruits such as apples, persimmons and manzanita berries. Mice are a staple prey; injured birds are devoured, and carrion is relished. Bachman's doubts were justified; apparently it does not eat such hard-shelled nuts as acorns and pecans. The number of young may be three to eight, with five the average.

Males are 22 to 31½ inches long, including the 11- to 17½-inch tail; females are 10 to 15 percent smaller. Excepting dry deserts and rain forests, hooded skunks occur from west Texas and southern Arizona to western Nicaragua.

MEPHITIS MESOLEUCA, LICHT.

TEXAN SKUNK.

This odoriferous animal is found in Texas and Mexico, and is very similar in its habits to the common skunk of the Eastern, Middle and Southwestern States. A specimen procured by J. W. AUDUBON, who travelled through a portion of the state of Texas in 1845 and 6, for the purpose of obtaining a knowledge of the quadrupeds of that country, was caught alive in the neighbourhood of the San Jacinto; it was secured to the pack saddle of one of his baggage mules, but managed in some way to escape during the day's march, and as the scent was still strong on the saddle, it was not missed until the party arrived at the rancho of Mr. McFADDEN, who kept a house of entertainment for man and beast, which by this time was greatly needed by the travellers.

The almost endless varieties of the *Mephitis chinga /M. mephitis/*, the common /striped/ skunk, many of which have been described as distinct species by naturalists, have, from our knowledge of their curious yet not specific differences, led us to admit any new species with doubt; but from the peculiar characteristics of this animal, there can be no hesitation in awarding to Prof. LICHTENSTEIN the honour of having given to the world the first knowledge of this interesting quadruped.

The *Mephitis Mesoleuca /Conepatus mesoleucus/* is found on the brown, broomy, sedgy plains, as well as in the woods, and the cultivated districts of Texas and Mexico. Its food consists in part of grubs, beetles, and other insects, and occasionally a small quadruped or bird, the eggs of birds, and in fact everything which this carnivorous but timid animal can appropriate to its sustenance.

The retreats of this Skunk are hollows in the roots of trees or fallen trunks, cavities under rocks, &c.; and it is, like the northern species, easily caught when seen, (if any one has the resolution to venture on the experiment,) as it will not endeavour to escape unless it be very near its hiding place, in which case it will avoid its pursuer by retreating into its burrow, and there remaining for some time motionless, if not annoyed by a dog, or by digging after it.

The stomach of the specimen from which our drawing was made, contained a number of worms, in some degree resembling the tape worm at times found in the human subject. /Probably flatworms. All members of the skunk tribe commonly harbor internal parasites./ Notwithstanding this circumstance, the individual appeared to be healthy and was fat. The rainy season having set in (or at least the weather being invariably stormy for some time) after it was killed, it became necessary to dry its skin in a chimney. When first taken, the white streak along the back was as pure and free from any stain or tinge of darkness or soiled colour as new fallen snow. The two glands containing the fetid matter, discharged from time to time by the animal for its defence, somewhat resembled in appearance a soft egg.

This species apparently takes the place of the common American skunk, *(Mephitis chinga, /M. mephitis/)* in the vicinity of the ranchos and plantations of the Mexicans, and is quite as destructive to poultry, eggs, &c., as its northern relative. /There is no evidence, contrary to Audubon's informants that the hog-nosed skunk displaces the striped skunk in the vicinity of ranch buildings. Any poultry killed and eggs broken can be charged to the latter species./ We have not ascertained anything about its season of breeding, or the time the female goes with young; we have no doubt, however, that in these characteristics it resembles the other and closely allied species.

The long and beautiful tail of this Skunk makes it conspicuous among the thickets or in the musquit /mesquite/ bushes of Texas, and it most frequently keeps this part elevated so that in high grass or weeds it is first seen by the hunters who may be looking for the animal in such places.

HOG-NOSED SKUNK

Conepatus mesoleucus mesoleucus (Lichtenstein)

The common name "hog-nosed" was conferred because of the flexible, long, broad, hairless nose. The genus name is derived from two Nahuatl (Uto-Aztecan) words: *conetl* (small) and *epatl* (fox). Largest of our skunks, it is similar in form, color and defense to the striped and hooded skunks. However, it has much bigger front claws, an all-white tail and *no* white on the nose.

More strictly nocturnal than other skunks, it lives almost entirely on insects and larvae. Contrary to Audubon's informants, it apparently does not raid poultry yards. One to four young are born in early spring in the earth den, among broken rocks, or in a hollow tree.

The hog-nosed skunk measures 24 to 33 inches long, including the 9½- to 14½-inch tail. It ranges from eastern Texas, southeastern Colorado and western Arizona south to western Nicaragua.

251

LUTRA CANADENSIS, SABINE.
CANADA OTTER.

. . . we now take up our pen to portray the habits and describe the forms and colours of the species figured in plates 51 to 100 inclusive, and shall, we hope, be able to give our readers tolerably good accounts of them; although, alas! the days of our youth are gone, when, full of enthusiasm, and anxious to examine every object in nature within our reach, the rising sun never found us slumbering away the fresh hours of the morning, but beamed upon our path through the deep forest, or lighted up to joy and gladness the hill side or mountain top . . .

Fresh and pleasant in our mind is the recollection of our early expeditions among the wild woods, and along the unvisited shores of our new country; and although more than forty years of varied and busy life have passed since the Otter was shot and drawn, whose figure we have given, we will try to take you with us to a spot on the eastern banks of the fair Ohio. It is a cold wintry morning: the earth concealed by a slight covering of snow, and the landscape in all its original wildness. Here let us proceed cautiously, followed by that constant companion, our faithful dog. Whilst we are surveying the quiet waters as they roll onward toward the great Mississippi, in whose muddy current they will lose their clear and limpid character, and become as opaque and impetuous as the waves of that mighty river of the West, we see a dark object making its way towards the spot on which we stand, through the swiftly dividing element. It has not observed us: we remain perfectly still, and presently it is distinctly visible; it is an Otter, and now within the range of our old gun "Tear Jacket," we take but one moment to raise our piece and fire; the water is agitated by a violent convulsive movement of the animal, our dog plunges into the river, and swimming eagerly to the Otter, seizes it, but the latter dives, dragging the dog with it beneath the surface, and when they reappear, the Otter has caught the dog by the nose and is struggling violently. The brave dog, however, does not give up, but in a few moments drags the wounded Otter to the shore, and we immediately despatch it. Being anxious to figure the animal, we smooth its disordered fur and proceed homewards with it, where, although at that time we had not drawn many quadrupeds, we soon select a position in which to figure the Otter, and accordingly draw it with one foot in a steel-trap, and endeavour to represent the pain and terror felt by the creature when its foot is caught by the sharp saw-like teeth of the trap. . . .

The American Otter frequents running streams, large ponds, and more sparingly the shores of some of our great lakes. It prefers those waters which are clear, and makes a hole or burrow in the banks, the entrance to which is under water.

This species has a singular habit of sliding off the wet sloping banks into the water, and the trappers take advantage of this habit to catch the animal by placing a steel-trap near the bottom of their sliding places, so that the Otters occasionally put their foot into it as they are swiftly gliding toward the water.

In Carolina, a very common mode of capturing the Otter is by tying a pretty large fish on the pan of a steel-trap, which is sunk in the water where it is from five to ten feet deep. The Otter dives to the bottom to seize the fish, is caught either by the nose or foot, and is generally found drowned. At other times the trap is set under the water, without bait, on a log, one end of which projects into the water, whilst the other rests on the banks of a pond or river; the Otter, in endeavouring to mount the log, is caught in the trap. . . .

/Editor's Comment: Audubon and Bachman each contributed to numerous accounts of habits. Although the literary styles of the two men differed as widely as their personalities, no attempt seems to have been made to revise their manuscripts in order to achieve uniformity. The differences are nowhere better illustrated than in the above excerpts from their account of habits of the otter. The first two paragraphs were written by Audubon in his flowery, rambling style, the remainder by Bachman in more concise, factual manner.

Audubon's plaintive cry that he was no longer physically able to hunt and "examine every object in nature" was all too true; he was very near the end of his effective working life as a partner in the Quadrupeds *project./*

RIVER OTTER

Lutra canadensis canadensis (Schreber)

Unlike other mustelids, otters enjoy each other's company. Either in groups, or singly, the animals roll and tumble in the water and toss bright pebbles or bits of shell with their noses. The greatest fun seems to be sliding. Families and small groups rush "belly-bump" fashion in single file down snow or wet, slick earth slopes. The slides may be a few yards long, or up to 20 yards on ice or snow. On the following page, the authors vividly describe this pastime, but it is not, as they thought, limited to the mating season.

The river otter is a restless animal and, when not held down by family cares, will often travel 25 or even 100 miles on a foraging trip lasting several days. In winter it makes a few leaps, then humps up its back with an extra effort and gives itself a mighty push with hind legs that propel it perhaps 25 feet over the snow. Sliding along in this manner, it goes as much as 17 miles an hour; on bare ground, with its short legs and awkward gait, it can travel approximately half as fast.

With streamlined form, valved ears and nostrils, webbed hind feet and dense oily fur, the otter undulates through the water rather like a porpoise. A thick blanket of fat under the skin keeps the animal warm. It swims with head, neck and shoulders above the water line, or completely submerged, at about six miles an hour (even faster if in a hurry). An otter may dive 60 feet deep, stay below the surface nearly five minutes and swim under water for a quarter of a mile. By using air bubbles trapped in pockets under the ice, the animal can travel farther without being seen by enemies or its prey. When looking for food, an otter paddles along slowly using the relatively small forepaws. Its snake-like head swivels this way and that while the beady, black eyes search. On spotting prey, the animal's hind feet take hold and drive fast while the tail acts as scull and rudder.

Audubon's caption of "Canada Otter," is an alternate name still in use today. "River Otter" is more descriptive because the animal lives on rivers and large creeks (also ponds and lakes) and is by no means limited to Canada. Rather secretive and usually nocturnal, the river otter is occasionally active in the daytime but is seldom seen. Unmistakable signs are tracks of webbed hind feet, large droppings crammed with fish scales and crayfish scutes, and the conspicuous slides. (Continued)

LUTRA CANADENSIS, SABINE, VAR.

LATAXINA MOLLIS, GRAY.

CANADA OTTER

. . . /Earlier/ we promised to give a figure of this variety of the Canada Otter . . .

Mr. GRAY, we presume, thought that a larger and different species existed near Hudson's Bay, and named his specimen *Lataxina Mollis,* calling the animal the Great Northern Otter.

The figure /Plate 122, painted by J. W. Audubon, is reproduced on opposite page/ now before you was published, notwithstanding our doubts as to the specific differences Mr. GRAY thinks are observable between the Otters of Hudson's Bay and those of Canada and the United States, for the purpose of giving a correct drawing of the identical specimen named and described by that gentleman, in order that it might be seen that it is only a large variety of the common American Otter.

/Editor's Comment: Following is a continuation of the discussion by J. J. Audubon and John Bachman which was opened on page 252./

. . . The Otters ascend the bank at a place suitable for their diversion, and sometimes where it is very steep, so that they are obliged to make quite an effort to gain the top; they slide down in rapid succession where there are many at a sliding place. On one occasion we /J. J. Audubon/ were resting ourself on the bank of Canoe Creek, a small stream near Henderson, which empties into the Ohio, when a pair of Otters made their appearance, and not observing our proximity, began to enjoy their sliding pastime. . . .

This habit of the Otter of sliding down from elevated places to the borders of streams, is not confined to cold countries, or to slides on the snow or ice, but is pursued in the Southern States, where the earth is seldom covered with snow, or the waters frozen over. Along the reserve-dams of the rice fields of Carolina and Georgia, these slides are very common. From the fact that this occurs in most cases during winter, about the period of the rutting season, we are inclined to the belief that this propensity may be traced to those instincts which lead the sexes to their periodical associations.

RICHARDSON says that this species has the habit of travelling to a great distance through the snow in search of some rapid that has resisted the severity of the winter frosts, and that if seen and pursued by hunters on these journeys, it will throw itself forward on its belly and slide through the snow for several yards, leaving a deep furrow behind it . . .

The Otter is a very expert swimmer, and can overtake almost any fish, and as it is a voracious animal, it doubtless destroys a great number of fresh water fishes annually. . . . About twenty-five years ago we /John Bachman/ went early one autumnal morning to study the habits of the Otter at Gordon and Spring's Ferry, on the Cooper River, six miles above Charleston, where they were represented as being quite abundant. They came down with the receding tide in groups or families of five or six together. In the space of two hours we counted forty-six. They soon separated, ascended the different creeks in the salt marshes, and engaged in capturing mullets *(Mugil* /presumably *M. cephalus/).* . . . They returned up the river to their more secure retreats with the rising tide. In the small lakes and ponds of the interior of Carolina, there is found a favourite fish with the Otter, called the fresh-water trout *(Grystes salmoides* /*Micropterus salmoides,* the large-mouthed bass/). . . .

Otters when caught young are easily tamed, and although their gait is ungainly, will follow their owner about, and at times are quite playful. We /John Bachman/ have on two occasions domesticated the Otter. The individuals had been captured when quite young, and in the space of two or three days became as tame and gentle as the young of the domestic dog. . . .

The American Otter has one litter annually, and the young, usually two and occasionally three in number, are brought forth about the middle of April, according to Dr. RICHARDSON, in high northern latitudes. In the Middle and Southern States they are about a month earlier, and probably litter in Texas and Mexico about the end of February. . . .

RIVER OTTER

Lutra canadensis canadensis (Schreber)

River otters breed in the water from December to early April. Males serve several females but stay near a favorite for months afterward. Although the female mates again soon after the birth of a litter, she does not permit the male to approach the young until they are three months old. The gestation period, due to delayed implantation, may last nine to 12 months. Sparsely furred and only eight inches long at birth, the young do not open their eyes for five weeks nor leave the den for three months. During this time the mother nurses them, plays with them, and they all groom each other's fur. When the male joins the family, he appears to take much pleasure in helping to train the young and leading the family on hunting trips. Surprisingly the pups are often afraid of water and have to be taught to swim. The mother may get them on her back and then dive as a rather drastic form of persuasion.

Ordinarily a family hunts up or down a main stream but may cross between drainages at well-known places. They use regular landings where they shake off water, dry their fur by rolling on the ground, and leave scent from their anal glands. To the human nose, otter musk is much less offensive than that of the weasel. Two or more otters, when traveling together, keep in touch by chirping like birds. Adult otters are savage fighters and can beat off most dogs. When angry, they growl or hiss; if frightened or hurt, they whistle and scream; while contented they purr and chirp. When they are a year old, the young look for their own territories, but most of them do not mate until they are two years old.

The complaints of fishermen that otters eat quantities of game fish have been so vociferous that a great deal of study has been made of the otter diet. Otters can and at times do capture the fastest trout, but most of their finned prey are slower, non-game species. The head is gobbled down first, body follows, and the tail is discarded. A major food, crayfish, is supplemented by frogs, salamanders, snails, mussels, turtles and other aquatic life. The teeth of those otters whose diet is largely shellfish do not decay but are badly worn and often chipped.

Otter fur is one of the most durable and beautiful; during the early 19th century an otter pelt was worth at least two beaver skins. In Audubon's time, the hunting of otters with trained dogs was considered top sport. Depletion of the game brought an end to this type of hunting. Today, enforcement of conservation laws has restored this interesting animal to parts of eastern America where it had been extirpated.

Male otters measure 35½ to 48 (rarely 55) inches long, including the 12- to 19-inch tail, and weigh 10 to 25 or even 30 pounds. Females are 10 to 20% smaller. The range includes virtually all of the Canadian mainland and the United States excepting the extreme southwest.

ENHYDRA MARINA, ERXLEBEN.
SEA OTTER.

Next to the seals the Sea Otter may be ranked as an inhabitant of the great deep: it is at home in the salt waves of the ocean, frequently goes some distance from the "dull tame shore," and is sometimes haunted in sailboats by the men who live by catching it, even out of sight of land.

But although capable of living almost at sea, this animal chiefly resorts to bays, the neighbourhood of islands near the coast, and tide-water rivers, where it can not only find plenty of food, but shelter or conceal itself as occasion requires. . . .

Hunting the Sea Otter was formerly a favourite pursuit with the few sailors or stray Americans that lived on the shores of the Bay of San Francisco, but the more attractive search for gold drew them off to the mines when SUTTER's mill-race had revealed the glittering riches intermixed with its black sands. . . .

The boat was manned with four or five hands and a gunner, and sailed about all the bays, and to the islands even thirty or forty miles from the coast, and sometimes north or south three or four hundred miles in quest of these animals. On seeing an Otter the boat was steered quietly for it, sail being taken in to lessen her speed so as to approach gently and without alarming the game. When within short gun-shot, the marksman fires, the men spring to the oars, and the poor Otter is harpooned before it sinks by the bowsman. Occasionally the animals are sailed up to while they are basking on the banks, and they are sometimes caught in seines. The man who gave this information stated that he had known five Otters to be shot and captured in a day, and he had obtained forty dollars apiece for their skins. At the time J. W. AUDUBON was in California he was asked a hundred dollars for a Sea Otter skin . . .

Only one of these Otters was seen by J. W. AUDUBON whilst in California: it was in the San Joaquin river, where the bulrushes grew thickly on the banks all about. The party were almost startled at the sudden appearance of one, which climbed on to a drift log about a hundred yards above them. Three rifle balls were sent in an instant towards the unsuspecting creature, one of which striking near it, the alarmed animal slided into the water and sunk without leaving, so far as they could see, a single ripple. It remained below the surface for about a minute, and on coming up raised its head high above the water, and having seen nothing to frighten it, as they judged, began fishing. . . .

In the accounts of this species given by various authors we find little respecting its habits, and it is much to be regretted that so remarkable an animal should be yet without a full "biography." . . .

GODMAN states that "its food is various, but principally cuttle-fish, lobsters, and other fish. The Sea Otter, like most other animals which are plentifully supplied with food, is entirely harmless and inoffensive in its manners, and might be charged with stupidity, according to a common mode of judging animals, as it neither offers to defend itself nor to injure those who attack it. But as it runs very swiftly and swims with equal celerity it frequently escapes, and after having gone some distance turns back to look at its pursuers. In doing this it holds a fore-paw over its eyes, much in the manner we see done by persons who in a strong sunshine are desirous to observe a distant object accurately. It has been inferred that the sight of this animal is imperfect; it sense of smelling, however, is said to be very acute."

The latter part of the above paragraph at least, may be taken as a small specimen of the fabulous tales believed in olden times about animals of which little that was true had been learned.

Dr. GODMAN relates farther that the female Sea Otter brings forth on land after a pregnancy of eight or nine months, and but one at a birth, and states that the extreme tenderness and attachment she displays for her young are much celebrated. According to his account the flesh is eaten by the hunters, but while it is represented by some as being tender, juicy, and flavoured like young lamb, by others it is declared to be hard, insipid, and tough as leather. We advise such of our readers as may wish to decide which of these statements is correct, and who may be so fortunate as to possess the means and leisure, to go to California and taste the animal — provided they can catch or kill one. . . .

SEA OTTER

Enhydra lutris lutris (Linnaeus)

Audubon and Bachman were doubtful, but the sea otter actually stands upright in the water and shades its eyes with both forepaws, just like a person. It does not live in the open sea but stays usually within a mile of shore. Anchored by a strand of kelp around its middle, it sleeps in calm water. During storms, however, it hauls out on land just beyond the waves. There it is very clumsy and a poor runner if it needs to escape. Vision is good, and hearing exceptional.

Bands of sea otters stay together and are active both in daylight and in moonlight. Unlike seals, they lack a blubber coat for insulation against cold water. Instead, they are protected by a blanket of air held among the waterproof fibers of the gossamer fine fur.

Fish and octopus are eaten but most food consists of bottom-dwelling invertebrates such as urchins, mussels, crabs and, in California, abalones. When necessary to break hard shells such as mollusks, the otter brings up a three- to five-inch rock from the sea bottom. Floating on its back, the animal places the rock on its chest and then, with both paws, brings the shell down hard in a series of rapid blows, until it breaks. The otter often keeps the rock in an armpit for later need — indicating that the species is learning to use tools!

The single young is born after a nine-month gestation. It has dense, gray fur, a set of milk teeth and open eyes. About 17 inches long, it weighs 3½ pounds. The mother cares for it with great affection, keeping it on her chest except when diving briefly for food. If in danger, she carries it under her arm and dives frantically. She nurses it for a year and keeps it with her — sometimes even after the next pup is born and swimming. It is full grown when four years old. Otters express themselves with barks, squeals and growls. They appear amiable with seals and sea lions, occasionally even touching noses. Great white (man-eating) sharks are deadly enemies.

After Cook's expedition to the North Pacific in 1779, sea otters were hunted almost to extinction. By 1922, the rare pelts sold for nearly $2,500. Only a small nucleus survived among the Aleutian Islands, but with strict protection by international treaty, part of the range has been restocked — possibly 50,000 animals. A few of the southern race escaped on the California coast and have increased to several hundred.

Adult males are 40 to 60 inches long, including the 10- to 11-inch tail, and weigh up to 85 pounds. Females weigh at most 65 pounds.

FELIS ONCA, LINN.

THE JAGUAR.

Alike beautiful and ferocious, the Jaguar is of all American animals unquestionably the most to be dreaded, on account of its combined strength, activity, and courage, which not only give it a vast physical power over other wild creatures, but enable it frequently to destroy man.

Compared with this formidable beast, the cougar need hardly be dreaded more than the wild cat; and the grizzly bear, although often quite as ready to attack man, is inferior in swiftness and stealthy cunning. To the so much feared tiger of the East he is equal in fierceness; and it is owing, perhaps, to his being nocturnal in his habits to a great extent, that he seldom issues from the deep swamps or the almost impenetrable thickets or jungles of thorny shrubs, vines, and tangled vegetation which compose the chaparals of Texas and Mexico, or the dense and untracked forests of Central and Southern America, to attack man. From his haunts in such nearly unapproachable localities, the Jaguar roams forth towards the close of the day, and during the hours of darkness seizes on his prey. During the whole night he is abroad, but is most frequently met with in moonlight and fine nights, disliking dark and rainy weather, although at the promptings of hunger he will draw near the camp of the traveller, or seek the almost wild horses or cattle of the ranchero even during daylight, with the coolest audacity.

The Jaguar has the cunning to resort to salt-licks, or the watering-places of the mustangs and other wild animals, where, concealing himself behind a bush, or mounting on to a low or sloping tree, he lies in wait until a favorable opportunity presents itself for springing on his prey. Like the cougar and the wild cat, he seeks for the peccary, the skunk, opossum, and the smaller rodentia; but is fond of attacking the larger quadrupeds, giving the preference to mustangs or horses, mules, or cattle. The colts and calves especially afford him an easy prey, and form a most important item in the grand result of his predatory expeditions.

Like the lion and tiger, he accomplishes by stealth or strategem what could not be effected by his swiftness of foot, and does not, like the untiring wolf, pursue his prey with indomitable perseverance at top speed for hours together, although he will sneak after a man or any other prey for half a day at a time, or hang on the skirts of a party for a considerable period, watching for an opportunity of springing upon some person or animal in the train. . . .

. . . When lying in wait at or near the watering-places of deer or horses, this savage beast exhibits great patience and perseverance, remaining for hours crouched down, with head depressed, and still as death. But when some luckless animal approaches, its eyes seem to dilate, its hair bristles up, its tail is gently waved backwards and forwards, and all its powerful limbs appear to quiver with excitement. The unsuspecting creature draws near the dangerous spot; suddenly, with a tremendous leap, the Jaguar pounces on him, and with the fury of an incarnate fiend fastens upon his neck with his terrible teeth, whilst his formidable claws are struck deep into his back and flanks. The poor victim writhes and plunges with fright and pain, and makes violent efforts to shake off the foe, but in a few moments is unable longer to struggle, and yields with a last despairing cry to his fate. The Jaguar begins to devour him while yet alive, and growls and roars over his prey until his hunger is appeased. . . .

In a conversation with General HOUSTON at Washington city, he informed us /John J. Audubon/ that he had found the Jaguar east of the San Jacinto river, and abundantly on the head waters of some of the eastern tributaries of the Rio Grande, the Guadaloupe, &c.

These animals, said the general, are sometimes found associated to the number of two or more together, when they easily destroy horses and other large quadrupeds. On the head waters of the San Marco, one night, the general's people were aroused by the snorting of their horses, but on advancing into the space around could see nothing, owing to the great darkness. The horses having become quiet, the men returned to camp and lay down to rest as usual, but in the morning one of the horses was found to have been killed and eaten up entirely, except the skeleton. The horses on this occasion were hobbled and picketed; but the general thinks the Jaguar frequently catches and destroys wild ones, as well as cattle. The celebrated BOWIE caught a splendid mustang horse, on the rump of which were two extensive scars made by the claws of a Jaguar or cougar. Such instances, indeed, are not very rare. . . .

JAGUAR

Felis onca onca Linnaeus

The jaguar's ferocity and murderous attacks on man make hair-raising reading in "Quadrupeds" but they are exaggerated. This big spotted cat has learned to fear firearms and avoids man whenever possible. Fact-finding biologists who have traveled extensively in Mexico and Central America during the twentieth century have been unable to verify any rumor that a jaguar had become a man-eater.

Although the jaguar is a formidable killer of all kinds of domestic stock, it rather seldom "specializes" at man's expense. Unlike the cougar, which prefers deer, the jaguar preys on all types of animals: peccaries, deer, tapirs and agoutis, rabbits and other small mammals (even mice), birds, lizards, fish, snakes and turtles and their eggs. Most of its hunting is done on the ground by stealth, in the manner of other cats, but it is said that the jaguar may also go into the trees after monkeys.

Some individuals (generally old males) may wander hundreds of miles from their home range, but normally the hunting territory is astonishingly small — only two or three miles in extent.

The mating period of the jaguar is brief but noisy, with much roaring, screaming and snarling. The males soon resume their solitary lives. The young (usually two, sometimes three and rarely four) are born in a cave 99 to 105 days later. During their long adolescence while the young are learning to hunt, the mother is a fierce and zealous protector. In most areas the female probably breeds at irregular intervals and not more frequently than every two years.

In developed areas, particularly where livestock raising is important, jaguars are hunted (usually with packs of dogs) — often until exterminated. However in deep rainforest or jungle habitat, this majestic cat is holding its own and probably is as numerous there as in primitive times.

In Aztec mythology, the sun-god, Texcatlipoca who ripened crops, appeared in the form of a jaguar. Today, Indians of the upper Amazon believe that the jaguar is the patron of all medicine men.

Larger than cougars, male jaguars measure: head and body, 44 to 72 inches; tail, 21 to 36 inches, height at shoulders, 28 to 30 inches; weight 175 to 300 pounds. The measurements of females are one-fifth less. The races north of Panama are relatively small, few individuals exceed 6 feet including tail. Color may range from gray to tawny, with black spots. Although a number of jaguars have been taken as far north as central Texas, northern New Mexico and southern California, the usual range extends from the mouth of the Rio Grande and extreme southeastern Arizona to 40 degrees south in south-central Argentina.

FELIS CONCOLOR, LINN.

THE COUGAR.

The Cougar is known all over the United States by the name of the panther or painter, and is another example of that ignorance or want of imagination, which was manifested by the "Colonists," who named nearly every quadruped, bird, and fish, which they found on our continent, after species belonging to the Old World, without regard to more than a most slight resemblance, and generally with a total disregard of propriety. /See opposite page/ ....the Cougar ... is but little more like the true *panther* than an opossum is like the kangaroo! Before, however, entirely quitting this subject, we may mention that for a long time the Cougar was thought to be the lion; the supposition was that all the skins of the animal that were brought into the settlements by the Indians were skins of females; and the lioness, having something the same colour and but little mane, it occurred to the colonists that the skins they saw could belong to no other animal!

The Cougar is found sparsely distributed over the whole of North America up to about latitude 45°. /In western Canada, to 60°./ In former times this animal was more abundant than at present, and one was even seen a few miles from the city of New-York within the recollection of Dr. DEKAY, who speaks of the consternation occasioned by its appearance in Westchester County, when he was a boy. /James Ellsworth DeKay, zoologist of the New York natural history survey, was born in 1792./

The Cougar is generally found in the very wildest parts of the country, in deep wooded swamps, or among the mountain cliffs and chasms of the Alleghany range. In Florida he inhabits the miry swamps and the watery everglades; in Texas, he is sometimes found on the open prairies, and his tracks may be seen at almost every cattle-crossing place on the sluggish bayous and creeks with their quick-sands and treacherous banks. . . .

This species at times attacks young cattle, and the male from which our drawing was made, was shot in the act of feeding upon a black heifer which he had seized, killed, and dragged into the edge of a thicket close adjoining the spot. The Cougar, is however, generally compelled to subsist on small animals, young deer, skunks, raccoons, &c., or birds, and will even eat carrion when hard pressed by hunger. His courage is not great, and unless very hungry, or when wounded and at bay, he seldom attacks man.

J.W. AUDUBON was informed, when in Texas, that the Cougar would remain in the vicinity of the carcase of a dead horse or cow, retiring after gorging himself, to a patch of tall grasses, or brambles, close by, so as to keep off intruders, and from which lair he could return when his appetite again called him to his dainty food. In other cases he returns, after catching a pig or calf, or finding a dead animal large enough to satisfy his hungry stomach, to his accustomed haunts . . .

Dr. DEKAY mentions, that he was told of a Cougar in Warren County, in the State of New-York, that resorted to a barn, from whence he was repeatedly dislodged, and finally killed. "He shewed no fight whatever, His mouth was found to be filled with the spines of the Canada porcupine, which was probably the cause of his diminished wariness and ferocity, and would in all probability have finally caused his death."

The panther, or "painter," as the Cougar is called, is a nocturnal animal more by choice than necessity, as it can see well during the day time It steals upon its intended prey in the darkness of night, with a silent, cautious step, and with great patience makes its noiseless way through the tangled thickets of the deepest forest. When the benighted traveller, or the wearied hunter may be slumbering in his rudely and hastily constructed bivouac at the foot of a huge tree, amid the lonely forest, his fire nearly out, and all around most dismal, dreary, and obscure, he may perchance be roused to a state of terror by the stealthy tread of the prowling Cougar; or his frightened horse, by its snortings and struggles to get loose, will awaken him in time to see the glistening eyes of the dangerous beast glaring upon him like two burning coals. Lucky is he then, if his coolness does not desert him, if his trusty rifle does not miss, through his agitation, or snap for want of better flint; or well off is he, if he can frighten away the savage beast by hurling at him a blazing brand from his nearly extinguished camp-fire. For, be sure the animal has not approached him without the gnawing hunger — the desire for blood, engendered by long fasting and gaunt famine. . . .

MOUNTAIN LION, or COUGAR

Felis concolor couguar Kerr

The cougar, panther, puma, painter and catamount are all one animal — mountain lion. Its plain-colored, lion-coat and long tail explain the name. Only ancestral spots and rings on the kittens' fur indicate a possible relationship to the panther (Asiatic leopard) millions of years ago.

Probably no large American mammal has inspired more tall tales and has been seen less than the cougar. Throughout the colonial era and much of the 19th century, this animal was feared, hated and misrepresented. Audubon and Bachman showed exceptional restraint and good judgment in winnowing truth from fiction when writing their account.

Notably, they refused to accept a common belief that the mountain lion is an habitual man-eater (see next page). In some of the few unprovoked attacks on man that have been authenticated, the animal had rabies, or was crippled and starving.

There is one proven case of a man-eater in this century. It happened 40 years ago. Curious, like all wild cats, a mountain lion had followed a 13-year-old boy. Footprints in the snow showed that the boy had started to run, which probably sparked the attack. The boy's body was found that evening, partially eaten. Three weeks later, a young, healthy female cougar was trapped. Its stomach contained a small hard mass of undigested human hair wound around bits of blue denim and a flattened cartridge shell that the boy was used to carrying.

Although the cougar sometimes preys on beaver, porcupine, skunk and mice, its principal food is deer. When the first settlers developed livestock industries, predation was extended to sheep, pigs, calves, colts and even adult cattle and horses. As a result of this, cougars were destroyed ruthlessly.

Hunting night or day in wilderness country, the "lion" cannot depend on speed to catch a deer. Too restless to lie in ambush, it stalks its prey. When within rushing distance, it makes tremendous leaps — perhaps 25 feet or more at a time — and hurls itself on the deer. If neck or back are not broken by the impact, the prey is killed by bites on the neck. Remnants of carcasses are covered with litter and the cat may return later. It much prefers warm meals (freshly killed) to cold leftovers.

In violent, all-out charges, the mountain lion is sometimes injured or even killed. Bones of the nose and face are broken, or the cat may impale itself on a tree limb or the sharp tine of a victim's antler. Apparently the only disease to which it is susceptible is rabies. (Continued)

FELIS CONCOLOR, LINN.

THE COUGAR

. . . .at long intervals, and under peculiar circumstances, when perhaps pinched with hunger, or in defence of its young, the Cougar sometimes attacks men. These instances, however, are very rare, and the relations of an affrightened traveller must be received with some caution, making a due allowance for a natural disposition in man to indulge in the marvellous.

Our own experience in regard to the habits of this species is somewhat limited, but we are obliged to state that in the only three instances in which we /Bachman/ observed it in its native forests, an impression was left on our minds that it was the most cowardly of any species of its size belonging to this genus. In our boyhood, whilst residing in the northern part of New-York, forty-eight years ago, on our way to school through a wood, a Cougar crossed the path not ten yards in front of us. We had never before seen this species, and it was, even at that early period, exceedingly rare in that vicinity. When the Cougar observed us he commenced a hurried retreat; a small terrier that accompanied us gave chase to the animal, which, after running about a hundred yards, mounted an oak and rested on one of its limbs about twenty feet from the ground. We approached and raised a loud whoop, when he sprang to the earth and soon made his escape. He was, a few days afterwards, hunted by the neighbours and shot. Another was treed at night, by a party on a raccoon hunt; supposing it to be a raccoon, one of the men climbed the tree, when the Cougar leaped to the ground, overturning one of the young hunters that happened to be in his way, and made his escape. A third was chased by cur-dogs in a valley in the vicinity of the Catskill mountains, and after half an hour's chase ascended a beech-tree. He placed himself in a crotch, and was fired at with duck-shot about a dozen times, when he was finally killed, and fell heavily to the ground. . . .

From all the conversations we have had with hunters who were in the habit of killing the Cougar, we have been brought to the conviction that a man of moderate courage, with a good rifle and a steady arm, accompanied by three or four active dogs, a mixture of either the fox-hound or grey-hound, might hunt the Cougar with great safety to himself, and with a tolerable prospect of success.

This animal, which has excited so much terror in the minds of the ignorant and timid, has been nearly exterminated in all our Atlantic States, and we do not recollect a single well authenticated instance where any hunter's life fell a sacrifice in a Cougar hunt. . . .

According to the relations of old hunters, the Cougar has three or four young at a litter. We have heard of an instance of one being found, a very old female, in whose den there were five young, about as large as cats, we believe, however, that the usual number of young, is two. . . .

The tales related of the cry of the Cougar in the forest in imitation of the call of a lost traveller, or the cry of a child, must be received with much caution, and may in many of their exaggerations be set down as vulgar errors. In a state of captivity, we have never heard the male uttering any other note than a low growl; the female, however, we have frequently heard uttering a kind of mewing like that of a cat, but a more prolonged and louder note, that could be heard at the distance of about two hundred yards. All the males, however, of the cat kind, at the season when the sexes seek each other, emit remarkable and startling cries as is evidenced by the common cat, in what is denominated caterwauling. We have observed the same habit in the leopard, the ocelot, and in our two species of lynx. It is not impossible, therefore, that the male Cougar, may at the rutting season have some peculiar and startling notes. The cries, however, to which persons have from time to time directed our attention, as belonging to the Cougar, we were well convinced were uttered by other animals. . . .

The female Cougar is a most affectionate mother, and will not leave her young cubs, unless occasionally to procure food to support her own strength; she therefore often becomes very lean and poor. The female we have figured, was in this condition; we procured one of her cubs and figured it, presenting its beautiful spots, seldom before noticed. The other made its escape. . . .

MOUNTAIN LION, or COUGAR

Felis concolor couguar Kerr

The "lion" may walk 25 miles or more without lying down to rest when it is seeking food. Its home range often extends over many square miles. In arid regions the animal goes for some time without drinking. Although disliking to get wet, it crosses streams more than a mile wide when hunting. Up to three years of age, it plays with others, romps by itself and rolls and bats "toy" objects back and forth. Catnip oil lures it into traps. There are a few instances of a "cannibal" cougar attacking, killing and eating one of its own kind.

Although generally silent, the mountain lion has a repertoire of sounds for various occasions. It hisses, trills and even whistles. When young and contented, it purrs. Cougars in a mating mood growl, yowl, scream and roar. Males will not tolerate a competitor at this time, and a fight may be to the finish.

The young are born in a rock den or dense thicket three months later with no special preparations. North of Mexico, most litters arrive from May to September but breeding may take place at any season. The spotted kittens, one to a rare six (average three), are eight to 12 inches long and weigh eight to 16 ounces. Their eyes open at eight to 14 days and they are weaned when two to three months old. At five or six months they weigh 30 to 45 pounds and most of the black spots of their baby coats have faded. Only a rare male helps with rearing the young; it is more likely to eat them.

Cubs hunt with the mother until they are at least one and usually two years old, when she goes forth to look for a mate. Some females may have kittens as often as 12 to 15 months. In the wild, cougars live about 10 years or sometimes longer.

Males are 68 to 110 inches long, of which the tail accounts for 26½ to 31 inches; they stand 26 to 30 inches high at the shoulder. The weight is generally 100 to 175 pounds, to a maximum of 275 pounds. Females weigh about 40% less. The one species of cougar has the most extensive range of any native American mammal — northern British Columbia to Tierra del Fuego. In North America, cougars once occurred from Nova Scotia to southern Florida and west to the Pacific Coast. Today they have been extirpated from the continent east of the 100th meridian except for minor remnants in New Brunswick and central and south Florida. The number in the western United States has been estimated roughly at about 5,000, with a similar population in Canada.

FELIS PARDALIS, LINN.

OCELOT, OR LEOPARD-CAT.

... Our animal is quite well known in Texas as the Leopard-Cat, and in Mexico is called the Tiger-Cat, it is in the habit of concealing itself in hollows in trees, and also by squatting upon the larger branches. It is rather nocturnal, and preys upon the smaller quadrupeds, and on birds, eggs, &c., when they can be seized on the ground.

The activity and grace of the Leopard-Cat, are equal to the beauty of its fur, and it leaps with ease amid the branches of trees, or runs with swiftness on the ground. These Cats seldom stray far from woods, or thickets bordering on rivers, streams, or ponds, very rarely lying on the hill-sides, or out on the plains.

They run like foxes, or wild-cats, when chased by the hunters with hounds or other dogs, doubling frequently, and using all the stratagems of the gray fox, before they take a straight course, but when hard pressed and fatigued, they always ascend a tree, instead of running to earth.

Like all the cat tribe, the Ocelot is spiteful when confined in a cage, and snarls and spits at the spectator when he draws near; but we have never seen it strike through the bars like the leopard, which sometimes inflicts severe wounds on the incautious or fool-hardy person, who, to see it better, approaches too closely its prison.

According to our information, the Ocelot only has two young at a litter, but we have not had an opportunity of ascertaining this point ourselves.

The specimen from which our figure was drawn, was procured by Gen. /William Selby/ HARNEY, who sent it fresh killed to J.W. AUDUBON, then at San Antonio on an expedition in search of the quadrupeds of Texas, for our work. We here give an extract from his journal.

"But for the kindness of Col. HARNEY, I might ever have made the drawing of this most beautiful of all the North American feline race. /Harney's promotion in rank came shortly after Audubon's stay in Texas, November, 1845 to April, 1846./ . . . .

I was invited out to the camp, and as I talked of the animals I was most anxious to procure, all seemed desirous to aid me. Col. HARNEY, fond of field sports, as active and industrious as he was tall and magnificent-looking waked at day light the lone prairies and swamps with shouts of encouragement to his small pack of well-chosen dogs, till they in turn burst forth in full cry on the hot trail of a magnificent specimen of this most interesting species. I had just returned from an examination of all my steel-traps; some were sprung, yet nothing but fur was left, showing that a strong wolf or lynx had been caught, but had pulled away; thus preventing perhaps, the capture of some smaller animal that I wanted; and rats, mice, skunks, or other little quadrupeds, were eaten nightly whilst fast in the steel teeth, by these prowlers. I sat down, to think of spring-guns, and long for means to prevent this robbery of my traps, when a sergeant came in, with the result of Col. HARNEY's morning's chase, the beautiful Ocelot, from which my drawing was made.

This was a new animal to me, as, though I knew of its existence, I had never seen one, so that my delight was only equalled by my desire to paint a good figure of it. Its beautiful skin makes a most favourite bullet pouch, and its variegated spots are only surpassed by the rich glossy coat and fur of the far famed 'black otter.' "

OCELOT

Felis pardalis pardalis Linnaeus

Is it a leopard or tiger cat? Bedazzled naturalists have called it both. Black spots, blotches, rings and short, narrow stripes are splashed haphazardly; the patterns vary with individuals, even from side to side on the same animal. This tropical cat is Mexican and is twice as big as a house cat.

Ocelots frequently hunt in pairs (male and female) and meow back and forth to each other. Some naturalists conclude that they live together for years and that the male helps raise the offspring.

When hunting in trees, a tiger cat may catch a dozing monkey. At other times it stretches out on a limb and goes to sleep itself. Once it was seen stalking an ocellated turkey that was roosting on the large branch of a tree. When the rush came, the ocelot lost its balance and both creatures came tumbling down through the leaves. Most of their food is found on the ground. Snakes, frogs, small turtles, crustaceans, iguanas and other lizards, and birds provide a varied diet. The cats are frequently seen along the margins of rivers and lakes, presumably seeking fish. Animals relished besides monkeys are pacas, nutria, rabbits and other species up to the size of a brocket deer. Occasionally an ocelot learns that smaller types of domestic stock, such as poultry and young pigs, goats and sheep, are easy and delectable prey.

The two, sometimes three or four, young are born in a rock den or hollow tree, apparently at any time of year. Learning to climb, swim and hunt, they soon fend for themselves. Regular defecating places are used, which probably serve as scent posts.

As Audubon and Bachman wrote, the tiger cat, when chased by dogs, sometimes practices several tricks of the fox before taking final refuge in a tree. Not wary of traps, it is easily caught and, despite conservation laws, the pelt is regularly bought and sold in Mexico. Some hunters claim that the meat is not only delicious but that the warm blood has medicinal and perhaps supernatural qualities.

Males measure 36 to 54 inches long, including the 11- to 15-inch tail, and weigh up to 25 pounds. Females are about 10% smaller. The range extends from Texas and Arizona over the eastern and western lowlands of Mexico through Central America into South America.

Lynx Canadensis, GEOFF.

Canada Lynx.

. . . .The Canada Lynx is more retired in its habits than our common wild cat, keeping chiefly far from the habitations of even the settlers who first penetrate into the depths of the wilderness. Its fine long fur enables it to withstand the cold of our northern latitudes, and it is found both in the wooded countries north of the great lakes, and as far south as the Middle States, dispersed over a great many degrees of longitude; even occasionally approaching the sea-coast. The specimen from which we /J.J. Audubon/ drew the figure of this animal was sent to us from Halifax, Nova Scotia. It had been taken in a wolf-trap, after having (as we supposed) destroyed several sheep. We kept it alive for a few weeks, feeding it on fresh raw meat; it ate but a small quantity at a time and like all predacious animals, appeared able to support a long fast without inconvenience. . . .

It has been stated that the Canada Lynx "is easily destroyed by a blow on the back with a slender stick;" this we are inclined to think a mistake, never having witnessed it, and judging merely by the activity and strength manifested by the animal, although we agree with the farther remarks of the same writer, "that it never attacks man." This indeed is a remark applicable to nearly all the beasts of prey in our country, except in extreme cases of hunger or desperation. It is said by Dr. RICHARDSON, that the Canada Lynx "swims well, and will cross the arm of a lake two miles wide" — this is a habit which is also shared by the more southern species, *(Lynx rufus.)*

The Canada Lynx, like all other animals of its general habits, breeds but once a year, generally having two young; we have heard of an instance, however, of three whelps being littered at a time.

The skin of this animal is generally used for muffs, collars, &c., and is ranked among the most beautiful materials for these purposes. It varies somewhat in colour, and the best are much lighter, when killed in good season, than the specimen from which our drawing was made. . . .

The Indians, we /J.J. Audubon/ are told, regard its flesh as good eating, which may perhaps be ascribed to the excellence of their appetites. HEARNE, (see Journey, p. 366,) who ate of it in the neighbourhood of York Fort /York Factory, Manitoba, on Hudson Bay/, says, "the flesh is white, and nearly as good as that of the rabbit." We think we would give the preference, however, to a buffalo-hump well roasted, for either dinner or supper.

The stories told of the great cunning of this species, in throwing mosses from the trees in order to entice the deer to feed on them, and then dropping on thier backs and tearing their throats, may as well be omitted here, as they fortunately require no refutation at the present day.

The food of the Canada Lynx consists of several species of grouse and other birds, the northern hare, gray rabbit /eastern cottontail/, chipping squirrel /chipmunk/, and other quadrupeds. It has been mentioned to us, that in the territories to the north of the Gulf of St. Lawrence they destroy the Arctic fox, and make great havoc among the lemmings, (GEORYCHUS.) /now two genera, *Lemmus and Dicrostonyx*/ HEARNE informs us, that in Hudson's Bay they "seldom leave a place which is frequented by rabbits till they have killed nearly all of them." They are said to pounce on the wild goose at its breeding places, and to destroy many marmots and spermophiles /ground squirrels/, by lying in wait for them at their burrows. At a public house in Canada we were shown the skin of one of these Lynxes, the animal having been found quite helpless and nearly dead in the woods It appears, that leaping on to a porcupine, it had caught a Tartar, as its head was greatly inflamed, and it was nearly blind. Its mouth was full of the sharp quills of that well-defended animal, which would in a day or two have occasioned its death. We have heard one or two accounts of the Canada Lynx having killed a deer; we are somewhat sceptical in regard to this being a general habit of the species, although when pressed by hunger, which renders all creatures desperate at times, it may occasionally venture to attack a large animal. . . .

LYNX

Lynx canadensis canadensis Kerr

Rabbits and especially snowshoe hares make up nine-tenths of the lynx's food. About every 10 years the snowshoe hare population is almost wiped out, and the lynx are nearly eliminated. After the "crash" the carnivores slowly breed back again as the hare population recovers. Fur-trade records show that these 10-year cycles of drastic reductions have occurred regularly for over 200 years. Scientists disagree strongly on causes and interrelationships of this and other cyclic declines. Most agree that the "shock disease" of rabbits, which affects liver and spleen, is a factor in the hare-lynx decline.

Grouse, squirrels, red foxes, porcupines and rarely deer make up the other tenth of the lynx's diet. It will take carrion if not putrid, but it prefers its meat fresh. Vegetable matter, if any, is limited to a few spears of grass. Like most, if not all, cats the lynx is neither a strong nor a fast runner. Occasionally it goes into a clumsy gallop of 12 miles an hour. Usually it ambushes or creeps up on its quarry, and then, with a mighty leap that may cover 15 feet or more, it attempts a kill. If this fails, the predator seldom continues pursuit for more than a couple of further bounds. The large, especially broad and heavily furred feet keep the lynx from sinking deep into the snow.

Generally solitary, the lynx is most active at night, but if hungry it comes out in daylight. It enters water readily, swims well and is often so buoyant that the upper three or four inches of its back does not get wet. Although it climbs with agility, it hunts on the ground. If it lies in wait for prey, it usually chooses a log or rock rather than a tree limb. This species is intensely curious; sometimes it trails a woodsman for miles with no intention of attacking.

Mating is in January to March, when the animals may do considerable screaming and yowling. (Listeners usually call it "blood-curdling" or "hair-raising.") The young, one to four or rarely five, are born after a gestation of about 62 days. They are well-furred for the cold climate in which they have arrived, and in 10 days their eyes open. The kittens stay with the mother until fall or sometimes late winter when they are sexually mature.

The lynx inhabits extensive tracts of woodland, thickets and swamps which are chiefly coniferous. The mother with young does not hunt more than five miles from the home den, but the male may range up to 50 miles if food is scarce.

The lynx measures 34 to 40 inches long including the 4-inch tail, and weighs 16 to 35 pounds (rarely more). The species is scarce north of the tree line, ranging from there south to New England and, in the mountains, to Colorado and Oregon.

Lynx Rufus. Guldenstaed.

Common American Wild Cat.

. . .The Wild Cat pursues his prey with both activity and cunning, sometimes bounding suddenly upon the object of his rapacity, sometimes with stealthy pace, approaching it in the darkness of night, seizing it with his strong retractile claws and sharp teeth, and bearing it off to his retreat in the forest. . . .

The Wild Cat not only makes great havoc among the chickens, turkeys, and ducks of the planter, but destroys many of the smaller quadrupeds, as well as partridges, and such other birds as he can surprise roosting on the ground. The hunters often run down the Wild Cat with packs of fox-hounds. When hard pressed by fast dogs, and in an open country, he ascends a tree with the agility of a squirrel, but the baying of the dogs calling his pursuers to the spot, the unerring rifle brings him to the ground, when, if not mortally wounded, he fights fiercely with the pack until killed. . . .

An individual that was kept alive at Charleston, and afterwards for a short time at our /Audubon's/ house, in the city of New-York, showed its affinity to the domestic cat, by purring and mewing at times loud enough to be heard at some distance. At the former place its cry was several times mistaken for that of the common house-cat. . . .

Although this species may perhaps be designated as nocturnal in its habits, it is, by no means, exclusively so. . . . We have, in fact, in several instances, seen this Cat engaged in some predatory expedition in full sunshine, both in winter and summer.

It is not a very active swimmer, but is not averse to taking the water. We witnessed it on one occasion crossing the Santee river when not pursued, and at another time saw one swimming across some ponds to make its escape from the dogs. It has been observed, however, that when it has taken to the water during a hard chase, it soon after either ascends a tree or is caught by the hounds.

The domicile of the Wild-Cat is sometimes under an old log, covered with vines such as the *Smilax, Ziziphus volubilus /Berchemia scandens,* supple-jack/, *Rubus,* &c., but more commonly in a hollow tree. Sometimes it is found in an opening twenty or thirty feet high, but generally much nearer the ground, frequently in a cavity at the root, and sometimes in the hollow trunk of a fallen tree, where, after collecting a considerable quantity of long moss and dried leaves to make a comfortable lair, it produces from two to four young. These are brought forth in the latter end of March in Carolina; in the Northern States, however, the kittens appear later, as we have heard of an instance in Pennsylvania where two young were found on the 15th day of May, apparently not a week old. . . . On four occasions, we have had opportunities of counting the young, either in the nest or having been very recently taken from it. In every case there were three young ones. In one instance the nest was composed of long moss, *(Tillandsia /Dendropogon/ usneoides,)* which seem to have been part of an old, deserted, squirrel's nest.

We once made an attempt at domesticating one of the young of this species, which we obtained when only two weeks old. It was a most spiteful, growling, snappish little wretch, and showed no disposition to improve its habits and manners under our kind tuition. We placed it in a wooden box, from which it was constantly striving to gnaw its way out. It, one night, escaped into our library, where it made sad work among the books, (which gave us some valuable lessons on the philosophy of patience, we could not have so readily found among our folios,) and left the marks of its teeth on the mutilated window-sashes. Finally, we fastened it with a light chain, and had a small kennel built for it in the yard. Here it was constantly indulging its carnivorous propensities, and catching the young poultry, which it enticed within reach of its chain by leaving a portion of its food at the door of its house, into which it retreated until an opportunity offered to pounce on its unsuspecting prey. Thus it continued, growing, if possible, more wild and vicious every day, growling and spitting at every servant that approached it, until at last, an unlucky blow, as a punishment for its mischievous tricks, put an end to its life, and with it to one source of annoyance.

The Bay Lynx is generally in fine order, and often very fat. The meat is white, and has somewhat the appearance of veal. Although we omitted to taste it, we have seen it cooked, when it appeared savoury, and the persons who partook of it pronounced it delicious. . . .

BOBCAT

Lynx rufus rufus (Schreber)

Often called wildcat, this 20-pound predator can kill a 200-pound deer. Like a small fury, it springs at the jugular vein of its prey, and the struggle is soon over. Usually smaller, but occasionally larger than a lynx, its ear tufts, neck ruff and feet are much less conspicuous. In the northern states and extreme southern Canada where both animals may inhabit the same wilderness area, the bobcat can be further distinguished by its shorter, more slender legs, and the tail tip which is never all-black like that of the lynx. Its abbreviated tail, and perhaps the bobbing motion of its body as it gallops, account for the most commonly used name. Audubon and Bachman's title of "bay lynx" is still current — based on the backwoods belief that the bobcat was an offspring of the lynx.

A shy, solitary, usually silent hunter, the bobcat creeps furtively through the forest and brushland — seldom seen by humans. It "signs itself" by long scratches on tree trunks and characteristic footprints on the soil as it walks along on its toes. It does not make odor posts.

Although it ordinarily prefers rocky country, in the East the animal is often found in dense swamps or, particularly in winter, on wooded ridges. The usual territory of about five square miles is greatly enlarged when the wildcat is looking for a mate, or when food is scarce. It often walks 25 miles in a single night. Different areas are hunted over on successive nights. Each morning the animal finds a new shelter, such as a hollow tree, a rock cavern, thicket or windfall, in which to spend the day. If none of these are handy, it rests on a tree limb.

During mating season (generally March, but occasionally January to August) the normally quiet bobcat vocalizes like a domestic cat, although more loudly and higher in pitch. Three or four (even one to six) kittens are born about two months later. They are blind, about 10 inches long, weigh five to 10 ounces, and their fur is spotted rather than barred like the mother. If danger threatens, she grabs each kitten by its neck and hustles it up a tree. Although they are weaned when two months old, they stay with her until mid-winter when they are two-thirds grown. A particularly fecund female may bear a second litter in late summer.

Young bobcats may be killed by coyotes, foxes and great horned owls. Man and his hunting dogs are the chief and greatly feared enemies. Life expectancy in the wild probably does not exceed 10 years. The bobcat is worthy of protection as a game animal and for its recreational-aesthetic value as a symbol of the wild. (Continued)

269

LYNX RUFUS, VAR MACULATUS,

HORSFIELD & VIGORS.

TEXAN LYNX.

This variety of Lynx /bobcat/ may be called the Common Wild-Cat of Texas, where it is occasionally found even on the prairies, although it generally confines itself to the neighbourhood of woods and chaparal.

The Texan Wild-Cat is, like the *Lynx rufus* /the typical subspecies, *L.r. rufus*/, a wily and audacious depredator — he steals the fowls from the newly-established rancho, or petty farm; follows the hares, rats, and birds, and springs upon them in the tall rank grass, or thick underbrush, and will sometimes even rob the ranger of a fine turkey; for should the Wild-Cat be lurking in the dense thicket, when the crack of the rifle is heard, and the wild gobbler or hen falls slanting to the earth, he will, instead of flying with terror from the startling report of the gun, dart towards the falling bird, seize it as it touches the ground, and bear it off at full speed, even if in sight of the enraged and disappointed marksman who brought down the prize. In general, however, the Southern Lynx (as this species is sometimes called) will fly from man's presence, and will only come abroad during the day when very hard pressed by hunger, when it may be occasionally seen near little thickets, on the edges of the prairies, or in the open ground, prowling with the stealthy sneaking gait observed in the domestic cat, when similarly employed. This species of Wild-Cat is better able to escape from an ordinary pack of dogs, than the Common Lynx, being accustomed to the great distances across the high dry prairies, which it must frequently cross at full speed. We have known one chased, from 11 o'clock in the morning till dark night, without being "treed." The animal, in fact, prefers running, to resorting to a tree at all times, and will not ascend one unless it be nearly exhausted, and hard pressed by the hounds. . . .

We have admitted this as a variety of the Bay Lynx /bobcat/ with some doubt and hesitation, and not without misgivings that it might yet be proved to be a distinct species. The permanency of its colours, together with the smaller size of our specimens, and their softer fur, may afford sufficient characters to entitle it to the name of *Maculatus,* as given by HORSEFIELD and VIGORS. Aware, however, of the many varieties in the Bay Lynx, we have not felt authorised to regard it as positively distinct.

/Editor's Comment: A total of 11 races of bobcats have been distinguished, but only a single species. The authors' scientific caution in retaining Horsefield and Vigors' "variety," instead of declaring it a separate species, has been justified.

The bobcats which Audubon and Bachman discussed under the name "Common American Wild Cat" or "Bay Lynx" (see p. 268) were those of the eastern half of the continent. Since that time they have been separated into at least three subspecies. The typical form, L.r. rufus, occupies the region from central New England to Virginia and west to the 100th meridian. Their "Texan Lynx," now L.r. texensis, is found from northwestern Louisiana and southwestern Oklahoma south into northeastern Mexico. It is a little larger and darker colored than the eastern bobcat./

WAPITI or ELK

Cervus canadensis canadensis Erxleben

Originally named wapiti by the Shawnee Indians, this animal was called elk by early English settlers. (Elk is used in Europe for the animal we call the moose!) To be on the safe side, Audubon and Bachman ran the two names together. Today, "wapiti" is more correct; "elk" is more popular.

An exceptional elk may collect a harem of over 60 cows during the rutting season. Bugling through the woods, rushing back and forth to keep the cows from wandering off, collecting an additional one now and then and fighting any rival that appears, the bull has hardly time to eat. A single battle may wound, dispossess or possibly kill him.

By the end of the season, all successful bulls are exhausted. Winter is approaching and the vast herds of elk, forced by instinct and deepening snow, leave the mountain meadows and trek to the lower valley bottoms. There they paw down through the crusted snow for dried grass, and browse on sage, juniper and willow. Because they often concentrate in large numbers and each animal requires a great deal to eat, they are likely to run out of food.

By spring, many of the wapiti may have starved or died of disease. The survivors follow the retreating snowline back to the mountain pastures. In late May or June the cow is in her zenith and has a bugle of her own. She usually drives off the yearling. (Unlike the moose calf, the young wapiti is not completely rejected but is still a member of the herd.)

The new calf (rarely twins) weighs 30 to 40 pounds and its tawny coat is speckled with white. After a week of concealment, the calf joins the mother and others in "nursery herds." Some of the cows seem to take regular guard duty. When fording a river, the mothers form a line so that the young will not be swept downstream. Adults are strong swimmers. Both old and young acquire their heavy, long-haired, gray winter coats in August. Coyotes, grizzlies, black bears, wolves and cougars are enemies, but the first three can kill only young and cripples. With flailing hoofs, dams will sometimes join forces to beat off a kidnapper. A healthy adult can outrun any predator at a top speed of 35 miles an hour.

Audubon lamented the destruction of game; even in his time wapiti were all but extirpated outside of the Rockies and Pacific Northwest. Many of these were slaughtered for their two canine teeth alone and the bodies left to rot. (These teeth were formerly in demand for a fraternal organization.) During the 20th century, however, the species has been re-established where practicable throughout east-central North America.

Male wapiti are 81 to 119 inches long, including the 3- to 8½-inch tail. They stand 49 to 60 inches high at the shoulder, weighing about 650 pounds, to a maximum of 1,100 pounds. Cows seldom weigh over 550 pounds. The species is restricted chiefly to the Rocky Mountains and areas on the Pacific slope from British Columbia south to central California.

CERVUS RICHARDSONII, AUD & BACH.

COLUMBIAN BLACK-TAILED DEER.

This beautiful Deer is found variously dispersed over the western portions of the North American continent, where it was first noticed by LEWIS and CLARK, near the mouth of the Columbia River; but not until the discovery of the golden treasures of California did it become generally known to white men. In that country, along the hill sides and in the woody dells and "gulches," the hardy miners have killed hundreds, nay thousands, of Black-tailed Deer; and it is from the accounts they have given that it is now known to replace, near the great Sierra Nevada, the common or Virginian Deer which is found east of the Rocky Mountains; all the hunters who have visited California, and whom we have seen, tell us that every Deer they shot there was the Black-tailed species.

J. W. AUDUBON killed a good many of these Deer, and describes them as tender and of good flavour; and during the time his party encamped on the Tuolome River, and in the "dry diggings" near Stockton, when he kept two of his men busy shooting for the support of the others, they generally had one or two Deer brought into camp every day. The mode of hunting them was more similar to what is called Deer-stalking in Scotland than to the methods used for killing Deer in the eastern part of the Union. Sometimes the hunters (who had no dogs) would start before day, and, gaining the hills, anxiously search for fresh tracks in the muddy soil (for it was then the rainy season, and the ground everywhere wet and soft), and, having found a trail, cautiously follow; always trying to keep the wind in such a direction as not to carry the scent to the animals. After discovering a fresh track, a search of a most tedious and toilsome nature awaited them, as the unsuspecting Deer might be very near, or miles off, they knew not which . . . at last they gain the next summit: the object of their chase is at hand; suddenly they see him — a fine buck — he is yet on the declivity of the hill, and they cautiously observe his motions. Now they see some broken ground and rocky fragments scattering towards the left; they redouble their caution; locks are ready cocked; and, breathing rapidly, they gain the desired spot One instant — the deadly rifle has sent its leaden messenger and the buck lies struggling in his gore.

Short work is made of the return to camp if no more Deer signs are about; and a straight cut may bring the hunters home in less than an hour, even should they have been two or three in following their prize.

Sometimes the Deer start up suddenly, quite near, and are shot down on the instant; occasionally, after a long pursuit, the crack of a rifle from an unknown hunter deprives the others of their chance; and — must we admit it — sometimes they miss; and not unfrequently they see no game at all.

Mr. J. G. BELL informed us that while he was digging gold in a sequestered and wild cañon, in company with a young man with whom he was associated in the business, they used to lie down to rest during the heat of the day, and occasionally he shot a Black-tailed Deer, which unsuspectingly came within shooting distance down the little brook that flowed in the bottom of the ravine. He also used to rise very early in the mornings occasionally, and seek for the animals in the manner of still-hunting, as practised in the United States. One morning he killed three in this manner, before his breakfast-time, and sold them, after reserving some of the best parts for himself and companion, for eighty dollars apiece! He frequently sold Deer subsequently, as well as hares and squirrels, birds, &c., which he shot at different times, for enormous prices. Many of the miners, indeed, turned their attention to killing Deer, elk, bear, antelopes, geese, ducks, and all sorts of game and wild fowl, by which they realized considerable sums from selling them at San Francisco and other places. We have heard of one person who, after a luckless search for gold, went to killing Deer and other game, and in the course of about eighteen months had made five thousand dollars by selling to the miners at the diggings.

The gait of this species is not so graceful as that of the Virginian /white-tailed/ Deer, it bounds rather more like the roebuck of Europe than any other of our Deer except the Long-tailed /Columbian white-tailed/ Deer, and is reported to be very swift. The season of its breeding is earlier than that of the common /white-tailed/ Deer, and it no doubt brings forth the same number of young at a time.

BLACK-TAILED DEER

Odocoileus hemionus columbianus (Richardson)

More than a million — possibly 20 million — years ago, the primitive ancestors of our present-day deer ventured across the Alaskan land bridge from Asia into the New World. From that ancestral stock evolved a number of species all the way to South America. Two that inhabit the part of North America which Audubon and Bachman took as their field, are the mule deer and the white-tailed deer. The first remained in the western half of the continent while the second spread from coast to coast.

The humid forests of the North Pacific Coast have deer which for a long time were regarded (by Bachman and others) as a distinct species — the coastal blacktail. More recently it was found that, wherever the ranges adjoin, blacktails and mule deer interbreed regularly. Accordingly, the two are classified as one species — the mule deer.

Excepting some differences due to its environment, the habits and behavior of the blacktail are similar to those of the mule deer. (See following pages.) Apparently blacktails have tender mouths and avoid feeding on thorny shrubs.

Lumbermen dislike the species because they prefer the foliage and twigs of trees which produce the best timber. If food is ample, these deer are content to live on a surprisingly small area — within a radius of 200 to 300 yards. However, the animals that summer at upper elevations must move down when snow is more than three feet deep. Their migration routes remain the same year after year and hunters camp along the way for easy shooting.

The blacktail swims not only large rivers but ocean channels several miles wide. The most important enemies, aside from man, are the cougar, domestic dog, wolf (where still present), coyote, black bear (which hunts newborn fawns) and bobcat.

Blacktail bucks measure 54 to 71 inches in total length, including the 4- to 9-inch tail. Height at shoulder is about 3 feet; weight is up to 456 pounds. Does average 4 or 5 inches less in length. This subspecies inhabits the Pacific Slope from central British Columbia to Monterey County, California.

CERVUS MACROTIS, SAY.

BLACK-TAILED DEER.

The first opportunity was afforded us /John J. Audubon/ of observing this magnificent animal, on the 12th of May /1843/ as we were ascending the Missouri, about eleven hundred miles above Fort Leavenworth. On winding along the banks, bordering a long and wide prairie, intermingled with willows and other small brush wood, we suddenly came in sight of four Mule or black-tailed Deer /see opposite page/, which after standing a moment on the bank and looking at us, trotted leisurely away, without appearing to be much alarmed. After they had retired a few hundred yards, the two largest, apparently males, elevated themselves on their hind legs and pawed each other in the manner of the horse. They occasionally stopped for a moment, then trotted off again, appearing and disappearing from time to time, when becoming suddenly alarmed, they bounded off at a swift pace, until out of sight. They did not trot or run as irregularly as our Virginian /white-tailed/ Deer, and they appeared at a distance darker in colour, as the common /white-tailed/ Deer at this season is red. On the 25th of the same month, we met with four others, which in the present instance did not stop to be examined; we saw them at a distance rapidly and gracefully hurrying out of sight. On the evening of the same day, one of our hunters brought to us a young Buck of this species, the horns of which, however, were yet too small to enable us to judge what would be their appearance in the adult animal. When on the Upper Missouri, near Fort Union, we obtained through the aid of our hunters, the female Black-tailed Deer, from which our figure, description and measurements have been made. We regret exceedingly that we were so unfortunate as not to have been able to procure a male, the delineation of which we must leave to our successors.

The habits of this animal approach more nearly those of the Elk, than of either the long-tailed /Columbian white-tailed/ or Virginian /eastern white-tailed/ Deer. Like the former they remove far from the settlements, fly from the vicinity of the hunter's camp, and when once fairly started, run for a mile or two before they come to a pause.

The female produces one or two young, in the month of June.

We /John W. Audubon/ have figured a female in summer pelage, and have represented the animal in an exhausted state, wounded through the body, and about to drop down, whilst the hunter is seen approaching, through the tall grass, anticipating the moment when she will reel and fall in her tracks.

MULE DEER

Odocoileus hemionus hemionus (Rafinesque)

Life begins for the deer with "mule ears" when, as twins (sometimes one or three), they are dropped by their mother, often hundreds of yards apart. She wanders away grazing, and may let 10 hours go by before she returns to feed them. Her milk is very rich and she lets the fawns nurse from four to 15 minutes, depending on their hunger and her supply. As the days go by, the spotted young move about and she must call them to her with a soft bleat that is barely audible to a human being. They are eating grass, chewing their cud, and accompanying their parent long before being weaned at five months.

With excited clamor, birds warn a deer of the approach of man, coyote, bear or mountain lion. Scared themselves, the birds are then silent until the predator passes. When all is clear, their normal chatter resumes, the deer relaxes and scratches itself with a hind leg. Birds sometimes peck along the back of a deer, apparently looking for ectoparasites. Eagles are different. Fond of carrion, they may go off with a dead fawn — possibly sometimes with a live one. An extraordinarily voracious (perhaps playful or plain bumptious?) eagle may attack an adult deer repeatedly as it stands on its hind legs and angrily strikes back.

From May to the end of July much of the buck's vigor goes into growing a set of antlers. (The velvet is often eaten with relish when shed.) By early October, with swollen neck, head lowered, at times with ears laid back and face contorted with curled upper lip, he is restlessly roaming the woods looking for does. Sometimes he gathers small temporary harems of two, three or perhaps four females, whose offspring of the year tag along. (Mothers don't mind their presence but the buck threatens them from time to time as a nuisance.) Females are in estrus for only 24 hours but the condition returns after 28 days if she is not successfully bred. Should there be no buck around when this period occurs, she sets out to find one.

Fighting between bucks is seldom fatal but ears are often torn, and sometimes bodies are gored and antlers are locked. Evenly matched males may wrestle for two hours with their antlers, and then give up — both exhausted. Toward the end of the season, many lusty bucks which have been most active, lose interest, depart and leave the field to the younger ones.

As the snow deepens, the mating urge is forgotten and the deer move gradually down toward the valley. Here the bucks drop their antlers and become meek members of the deer community. Oregon herd statistics show that there, in spite of hunting, the buck lives twice as long as the doe.

The typical mule deer is a little larger than the black-tailed subspecies (previous account). The range is vast, extending from southern Yukon to Durango and from the Pacific Coast east to western Manitoba, Minnesota and Oklahoma.

CERVUS LEUCURUS, DOUGLASS

LONG-TAILED DEER.

In its general appearance this Deer greatly resembles the European roebuck, and seems to be formed for bounding along in the light and graceful manner of that animal. The species has been considered of doubtful authenticity, owing to the various lengths of tail exhibited by the common deer, many specimens of which we collected near the Rocky Mountains, not differing from *C. /Odocoileus/ Virginianus* /the eastern white-tail/ in any other particular, but with long tails . . . At one time we examined the tails of some common /white-tailed/ deer in Fulton market, New York, and found that the longest exceeded nineteen inches, while the average length does not go beyond nine. The different form of the light, springy animal described by Mr. DOUGLAS /David Douglass, the Scottish botanist/ will, however, at once separate it from *C. Virginianus* on comparison.

Sir JOHN RICHARDSON says: "This animal, from the general resemblance it has in size, form, and habits, to the *Cervus capreolus* /the roe deer/ of Europe, has obtained the name of *Chevreuil* from the French Canadians, and of Roebuck from the Scottish Highlanders employed by the Hudson's Bay Company. /Richardson used for his description the yearling male which J. W. Audubon figured in his painting above. The antlers as depicted have a superficial resemblance to those of the roe deer. The latter, however, is a much smaller and very different animal./ These names occur in the works of several authors who have written on the fur countries, and UMFREVILLE gives a brief, but, as far as it goes, a correct description of it." "This species does not, on the east side of the Rocky Mountains, range farther north than latitude 54°, nor is it found in that parallel to the eastward of the 105th degree of longitude."

Mr. DOUGLAS speaks of it as "the most common deer of any in the districts adjoining the river Columbia, more especially in the fertile prairies of the Cowalidske and Multnomah rivers, within one hundred miles of the Pacific Ocean. It is also occasionally met with near the base of the Rocky Mountains on the same side of that ridge. Its favourite haunts are the coppices, composed of *Corylus* /hazel/, *Rubus* /thimble berry/, *Rosa* /rose/, and *Amelanchir* /service berry/, on the declivities of the low hills or dry undulating grounds. Its gait is two ambling steps and a bound exceeding double the distance of the steps, which mode it does not depart from even when closely pursued. In running, the tail is erect, wagging from side to side, and from its unusual length is the most remarkable feature about the animal. The voice of the male calling the female is like the sound produced by blowing in the muzzle of a gun or in a hollow cane. The voice of the female calling the young is *mae, mae,* pronounced shortly. This is well imitated by the native tribes, with a stem of *Heracleum lanatum* /cow parsnip/, cut at a joint, leaving six inches of a tube: with this, aided by a head and horns of a full grown buck, which the hunter carries with him as a decoy, and which he moves backwards and forwards among the long grass, alternately feigning the voice with the tube, the unsuspecting animal is attracted within a few yards in the hope of finding its partner, when instantly springing up, the hunter plants an arrow in his object. The flesh is excellent when in good order, and remarkably tender and well flavoured." "They go in herds from November to April and May, when the female secretes herself to bring forth. The young are spotted with white until the middle of the first winter, when they change to the same colour as the most aged."

LEWIS and CLARK considered it the same animal as the common deer, with the exception of the length of the tail. They found it inhabiting "the Rocky Mountains, in the neighbourhood of the Chopunnish, and about the Columbia, and down the river as low as where the tide-water commences." These travellers in another passage observe that "the common Fallow Deer with long tails (our present species), though very poor, are better than the black-tailed fallow deer of the coast, from which they differ materially."

We did not see any Deer of this species on our journey up the Missouri, nor do we think it is to be found east of the Rocky Mountains. The Virginian deer, on the contrary, disappears to the north and west, as RICHARDSON says he has not been able to discover the true *Cervus Virginianus* /eastern white-tail/ within the district to which the Fauna Boreali Americana refers.

COLUMBIAN WHITE-TAILED DEER

Odocoileus virginianus leucurus (Douglas)

A little smaller than the blacktail, this "long-tailed deer" had become scarce in Audubon's time. His son was able to find only one museum specimen in this country from which to paint a picture for the *Quadrupeds*. The skin and skull in the Philadelphia Academy of Sciences was of a young male, leading the authors to conclude (wrongly) that the species resembled a long-tailed roe deer of Europe. Later determined to be a subspecies of the native whitetail, the total population even today is probably less than a thousand animals. They are in two groups — one around the mouth of the Columbia River and the other in a state refuge in southwestern Oregon.

How do you distinguish between the three deer whose ranges sometimes overlap? The tail of the white-tailed deer is large, spreading and all-white on the edges and underside; the mule deer's smaller white tail is rounded and black-tipped, while that of the black-tailed deer is smallest; it is black (or brownish) on the upper surface and white beneath.

There are 30 subspecies of whitetails ranging from the big northern and most common, to the tiny Florida Key deer that is less than two feet high at the shoulders and whose hoofs are no bigger than a man's thumbnail. At one time

there were only 40 Key deer left alive; there may be 200 now under better protection. They mate at any time of year.

How old is a deer? The typical whitetail buck grows a pair of spike antlers during his second summer. Each set thereafter is larger with more tines, until there are about 12 when the animal is five years old. From then until past maturity (seven or eight years old) the antlers are heavier but have about the same number of points. Later the antlers decrease until a rare 14-year-old may have only spikes. The weight and size of antlers, however, depend not only on age but on the individual and his heredity, health and diet. (Only one buck in about 5,000 will have as many as 17 points.)

A deer's age is best estimated by its teeth. The whitetail's eight lower incisors are cut before it is born. (Ruminants have no upper incisors.) At six months, permanent incisors replace the baby teeth, and milk molars are coming in. All permanent teeth have erupted by 19 months and, after that, age can be calculated only by the degree of stain and wear. A 10-year-old deer (most do not live that long) has loose or no incisors, and the molars are smooth and worn nearly to the roots. For laboratory research, the age is determined by the number of rings in the cementum of incisors. (Continued)

CERVUS VIRGINIANUS, PENNANT.

COMMON OR VIRGINIAN DEER.

Perhaps no species of wild animal inhabiting North-America, deserves to be regarded with more interest than the subject of our present article, the Common or Virginian Deer; its symmetrical form, graceful curving leap or bound, and its rushing speed, when, flying before its pursuers, it passes like a meteor by the startled traveller in the forest, exciting admiration, though he be ever so dull an observer.

The tender, juicy, savoury, and above all, digestible qualities of its flesh are well known; and venison is held in highest esteem from the camp of the backwoodman to the luxurious tables of the opulent, and, when not kept too long (a common error in our large cities by the way) a fat haunch with jelly and chafing dishes is almost as much relished, as a "hunter's steak," cooked in the open air on a frosty evening far away in the west. The skin is of the greatest service to the wild man, and also useful to the dweller in towns; dressed and smoked by the squaw, until soft and pliable, it will not shrink with all the wettings to which it is exposed. In the form of mocasins, leggings, and hunting shirts, it is the most material part of the dress of many Indian tribes, and in the civilized world is used for breeches, gloves, gaiters, and various other purposes.

From the horns are made beautiful handles for various kinds of cutlery.

The timidity of the Deer is such, that it hurries away, even from the sight of a child, and it is but seldom that the hunter has any danger to apprehend, even from a wounded buck; it does but little injury to the fields of the planter, and is a universal favourite with old and young of both sexes in our Southern States.

The Virginian, or as we wish to designate it, the Common Deer, is the only large animal, if we except the bear, that is not driven from the vicinity of man by the report of the deer-driver's gun, or the crack of the hunter's rifle; the buffalo and the elk are now rarely seen east of the Mississippi. . . .

The young are, in Carolina, produced in the month of April; young does, however, seldom yean till May or June. In the Northern States, they bring forth a little later, whilst in Florida and Texas the period is earlier. It is a remarkable, but well ascertained fact, that in Alabama and Florida, a majority of the fawns are produced in November. /An error; fawns in the Southeast are born in April-May./ The doe conceals her young under a prostrate tree-top, or in a thick covert of grass, visiting them occasionally during the day, especially in the morning, evening, and at night. The young fawns, when only a few days old, are often found in so sound a sleep that we have, on several occasions, seen them taken up in the arms before they became conscious that they were captives. They are easily domesticated, and attach themselves to their keepers in a few hours. A friend possesses a young deer that, when captured, during the last summer, was placed with a she goat, which reared it, and the parties still live in habits of mutual attachment. We have seen others reared by a cow. A goat, however, becomes the best foster-mother. They breed in confinement, but we have found them troublesome pets. A pair that we had for several years, were in the habit of leaping into our study through the open window, and when the sashes were down they still bounced through, carrying along with them the shattered glasses. They also seemed to have imbibed a vitiated and morbid taste, licked and gnawed the covers of our books, and created confusion among our papers. No shrub in the garden, however valuable to us, was sacred to them; they gnawed our carriage harness, and finally pounced upon our young ducks and chickens . . .

The doe does not produce young until she is two years old, when she has one fawn. If in good order, she has two the following year. A very large and healthy doe often produces three, and we were present at Goose Creek when an immense one, killed by J. W. AUDUBON, was ascertained, on being opened, to contain four large and well formed fawns. . . .

The wild doe is attached to her young, and its bleat will soon bring her to its side, if she is within hearing. The Indians use a stratagem, by imitating the cry of the fawn, with a pipe made of a reed, to bring up the mother, which is easily killed by their arrows. We have twice observed the doe called up by this imitation of the voice of the young. She is, however, so timid that she makes no effort in defence of her captured offspring, and bounds off at the sight of man. . . .

WHITE-TAILED DEER
Odocoileus virginianus virginianus (Zimmermann)

Some whitetail fawns breed when six or seven months old. They have ample milk for their six to seven-and-a-half pound offspring, but they have only one young while their mothers have two or three (very rarely four). Whitetail milk has three times as much fat and protein as that of a Jersey cow. If in good condition, a doe can nurse four fawns at the same time. Some does adopt an orphan; others will butt or kick it away. Most fawns of this species are weaned at four months.

A mother does not stay with the spotted, almost scentless young lest her adult odor and size call attention to the hiding places. She often remains within 200 yards but may have to go farther for browse and water. Her ears are constantly moving and she frequently looks in the direction of the fawns. When she sees a predator in the neighborhood, she may try to lead it away. Disliking and sometimes terrified of snakes, she has been known to jump with all fours on a rattler and stamp it to death — probably when near a fawn.

From the time they are born, the doe frequently washes her young with her rough tongue from stem to stern — sometimes knocking them off their feet in her zeal. (She may even give her yearlings an automatic swipe.) During a very hard rainstorm, she often shelters the fawns under her belly and tries to lick them dry afterward. When discipline is necessary, she butts them or gives them an angry whack with a foreleg. This brings a surprised, hurt bleat and immediate obedience.

Unfortunately, or perhaps necessarily, the mother instinct wanes during winter. Although the fawn cannot reach nearly as high as an adult, the mother keeps the best for herself, and when a fawn becomes too weak to follow, she abandons it.

A healthy deer can run 35 miles an hour, jump 8½ feet high and clear a ravine of 30 feet. Young adults as well as fawns enjoy games and splashing in water. They play tag, follow-the-leader and sometimes leapfrog. When pushed by fear, they can swim up to 12 miles an hour.

Although whitetails are rarely heard, they are not mute. They murmur (to call the young), "ba" to attract a mate, bleat (fawn when hungry or lost), blow violently through the nose (to startle an unidentified object into betraying itself), and bawl loudly when badly hurt. Deer communicate with each other through scent glands in their hind legs and in each foot, and the raised tail which is an involuntary alarm. (Continued)

CERVUS VIRGINIANUS, PENNANT.

COMMON AMERICAN DEER.

.... The localities selected by /white-tailed/ Deer as places of rest and concealment during the day are various, such as the season of the year and the nature of the country and climate. may suggest to the instincts of the animal. Although we have occasionally in mountainous regions, especially in the higher mountains of Virginia and the Green Mountains of Vermont, detected a Deer lying without concealment on an elevated ledge of bare rock, like the ibex and chamois on the Alps, yet as a general habit, the animal may be said to seek concealment, either among clumps of myrtle or laurel bushes, *(Kalmia),* in large fallen tree-tops, briar-patches, clusters of alder bushes, *(alnus),* or in tall broom-grass, *(Andropogon dissitiflorus /A. virginicus,* broom-sedge/). In cold weather it prefers seeking its repose in some sheltered dry situation, where it is protected from the wind, and warmed by the rays of the sun; and on these occasions it may be found in briar-patches which face the south, or in tufts of broom-grass in old uncultivated fields. In warm weather it retires during the day to shady swamps, and may often be started from a clump of alder or myrtle bushes near some rivulet or cool stream. To avoid the persecution of moschetoes /mosquitoes/ and ticks, it occasionally, like the moose in Maine, resorts to some stream or pond and lies for a time immersed in the water, from which the nose and a part of the head only project. We /John Bachman/ recollect an occasion, when on sitting down to rest on the margin of the Santee river, we observed a pair of antlers on the surface of the water near an old tree, not ten steps from us. The half-closed eye of the buck was upon us . . . Anxious to observe the cunning he would display, we turned our eyes another way, and commenced a careless whistle, as if for our own amusement, walking gradually towards him in a circuitous route, until we arrived within a few feet of him. He had now sunk so deep in the water that an inch only of his nose, and slight portions of his prongs were seen above the surface. We again sat down on the bank for some minutes . . . At length we suddenly directed our eyes towards him, and raised our hand, when he rushed to the shore, and dashed through the rattling canebrake, in rapid style.

The food of the common Deer varies at different periods of the year. . . .

Possessing such a choice of food, we might suppose this animal would be always fat: this, however, is not the case, and, except at certain seasons of the year, the Deer is rather poor. The bucks are always in fine order from the month of August to November, when we have seen some that were very fat. One which we killed weighed one hundred and seventy-five pounds. We have been informed that some have reached considerably over two hundred pounds. In November, and sometimes a little earlier, the rutting season commences in Carolina, when the neck of the buck begins to dilate to a large size. He is now constantly on foot, and nearly in a full run, in search of the does. On meeting with other males, tremendous battles ensue, when, in some rare instances, the weaker animal is gored to death; generally, however, he flies from the vanquisher, and follows him, crest fallen, at a respectful and convenient distance, ready to turn on his heels and scamper off at the first threat of his victorious rival. In these rencontres, the horns of the combatants sometimes become interlocked in such a manner that they cannot be separated, and the pugnacious bucks are consigned to a lingering and inevitable death by starvation. We have endeavoured to disengage these horns, but found them so completely entwined that no skill or strength of ours was successful. We have several times seen two, and on one occasion, three pairs of horns thus interlocked, and ascertained that the skulls and skeletons of the Deer had always been found attached. These battles only take place during the rutting season, when the horns are too firmly attached to be separated from the skull. Indeed, we have seen a horn shot off in the middle by a ball, whilst the stump still continued firmly seated on the skull. The rutting season continues about two months, the largest and oldest does being earliest sought for, and those of eighteen months at a later period. About the month of January, the bucks drop their horns, when, as if conscious of having been shorn of their strength and honours, they seem humbled, and congregate peaceably with each other, seeking the concealment of the woods, until they can once more present their proud antlers to the admiring herd. . . .

WHITE-TAILED DEER

Odocoileus virginianus virginianus (Zimmermann)

Males and most females do not breed until 18 months old. The buck begins the October-November rut by stamping, pawing, slashing the brush, and working himself into top form. The fact that he becomes less wary is one of the reasons for scheduling legal hunting at this time. Two rival bucks come together with a clash of horns that can be heard 65 yards away.

Whitetails do not collect harems. A buck may stay with a doe a few days before and after the 24 hours that she is receptive — but then departs for further conquests. Occasionally a mating seems to have permanence; the same pair with new young each spring have been seen together year after year.

The rapid multiplication of both whitetails and mule deer has long been a serious problem. In overpopulated areas, the deer denude and kill all new growth. Standing on their hind legs, they eat all the foliage within reach so that an eight-foot high deer-line extends throughout the woods. Besides damaging the forests in which they live, they destroy truck crops, grape vineyards, orchards, ornamental trees and shrubs. (Unimportant tidbits are snails, fish, acorns and beechnuts.)

A whitetail's individual range in the fall is about three or four square miles. The rest of the year it may be only a square mile, and that of a nursing mother much less. Circling its home area, the deer becomes very attached regardless of shortcomings. Animals in badly depleted habitat have been live-trapped, ear-tagged and released amid a lush supply of food. Within a few days each deer was back on its original range and starving. (This strong homing instinct is baffled when the deer are moved more than 20 miles.)

The only practical way to restore the forests and to save the deer from themselves is to have adequate, regulated hunting. Every autumn about 15 million hunters "harvest" more than half a million animals — 10% of the estimated five million deer population. This "take" of nearly 40 million pounds of venison (worth at least 20 million dollars) could be doubled without reducing the basic stock of deer which has an annual reproduction potential of nearly 40%. In overpopulated and over-browsed areas, does also have to be taken if either deer or forests are to survive.

Size varies with the subspecies, generally decreasing from north to south: total length from 41 to 96 inches, including the 7- to 15-inch tail; height at shoulders, 21 to 42 inches; weight up to 300 pounds, or rarely 400 pounds. Whitetails occur from Nova Scotia and central British Columbia south into South America (except the Great Basin, California and Baja California.)

CERVUS ALCES, LINN

MOOSE DEER.

We were favoured by Mr. KENDALL, of the Literary Society of Quebec, with the following account of the Moose Deer, with which we will begin our article on this noble quadruped.

"The Moose are abundant to the north of Quebec and in the northern parts of the state of Maine. In the neighbourhood of Moose River and the lakes in its vicinity, they are very abundant. In the summer they are fond of frequenting lakes and rivers, not only to escape the attacks of insects which then molest them, but also to avoid injuring their antlers, which during their growth are very soft and exquisitely sensitive, and besides, such situations afford them abundance of food.

"They there feed on the water-plants, or browse upon the trees fringing the shores. In the winter they retire to the dry mountain ridges, and generally 'yard', as it is termed, on the side facing the south, where there are abundance of maple and other hard-wood trees upon which to feed, either by browsing on the tender twigs or peeling the bark from the stems of such as are only three or four inches in diameter. Their long, pendulous upper lip is admirably adapted for grasping and pulling down the branches, which are held between the fore legs until all the twigs are eaten. They peel off the bark by placing the hard pad on the roof of the mouth against the tree, and scraping upwards with their sharp, gouge-like teeth, completely denuding the tree to the height of seven or eight feet from the surface of the snow. . . .

"The antlers begin to sprout in April, and at first appear like two black knobs. They complete their growth in July, when the skin which covers them peels off and leaves them perfectly white; exposure to the sun and air, however, soon renders them brown. When we consider the immense size to which some of them grow in such a short period of time, it seems almost incredible that two such enormous excrescences could be deposited from the circulating system alone; the daily growth is distinctly marked on the velvety covering by a light shade carried around them. . . . The old and vigorous animals invariably shed them in December; some of four and five years old I have known to carry them as late as March, but this is not often the case.

"The rutting season commences in September; the males then become very furious, chasing away the younger and weaker ones. They run bellowing through the forest, and when two of equal strength meet, have dreadful conflicts, and do not separate until one or both are severely injured. I bought a pair of antlers from a Penobscot Indian, with one of the brow antlers and the adjoining prong broken short off. The parts were at least 1½ inches in diameter, and nearly as hard as ivory. At that season they are constantly on the move, swimming large lakes and crossing rivers in pursuit of the female.

"The female brings forth in May. The first time she produces one fawn, but ever afterwards two. It is supposed by hunters that these twins are always one a male and the other a female. . . .

"Their flesh is very coarse, though some people prefer it to any other; it is apt to produce dysentery with persons unaccustomed to use it. The nose or *moufle,* as it is generally called, if properly cooked is a very delicious morsel. The tongue is also considered a delicacy; the last entrail (called by hunters the bum-gut) is covered with round lumps of suety fat, which they strip off and devour as it comes warm from the animal, without any cooking. Also the marrow warm from the shanks is spread upon bread, and eaten as butter. I must confess that the disgusting luxury was rather *too rich* to tempt me to partake of it. I have seen some officers of the Guards enjoy it well enough! . . .

"In September, two persons in a bark canoe paddle by moonlight along the shore of the lake imitating the call of the male, which, jealous of the approach of a stranger, answers to the call and rushes down to the combat. The canoe is paddled by the man in the stern with the most death-like silence, gliding along under the shade of the forest until within short shooting distance, as it is difficult to take a sure aim by moonlight; the man in the bow generally fires, when if the animal is only wounded, he makes immediately for shore, dashing the water about him into foam; he is tracked by his blood the next day to where he has lain down, and where he is generally found unable to proceed any further. . . ."

MOOSE

Alces alces americana (Clinton)

Largest of all deer, the moose stands on its hind legs and reaches 10 to 12 feet to chew tender branches. When aggravated, it chases black bears and hunters up into the trees. On the other hand, an irate sandhill crane may beat the huge animal's face, ears and neck with its wing and send the moose snorting and crashing into the woods. Because of its long legs, it has to get down on its knees to eat grass.

Both bull and cow call to each other during the fall rutting season. When hunters imitate the respective bellow or "moo," a bull moose comes running. During this period, the calf stays with its mother, but no other moose is permitted to come around. The cow will not tolerate any potential female competitor. Hair rising on her hump, she lays back her ears, rears up on her hind legs and threatens the interloper with flying hoofs. The bull fights all rivals, sometimes to the death.

The bull stays with the cow for about 10 days and then moves on to a second and later a third and perhaps a fourth mate. After a gestation of about 240 days, the mother drives the last year's calf away. Bewildered, the young animal tries to return but is repeatedly repulsed. Although it weighs 300 or 400 pounds, it still feels dependent.

By late May or June the new calf is born, weighing 20 to 30 pounds. Light-reddish, unspotted, with a dark dorsal stripe and long legs, the wobbly calf tries to follow its mother the first day. Calves are usually single; twins and rare triplets may occur more frequently when food is abundant. If hungry or hurt, the young whimpers and sobs, and the mother comforts it with food and grunts.

During the summer, moose scatter over the uplands. They wade and submerge in ponds and lakes to feed on aquatic plants, and stalk through swamps, bogs, quicksands and forests to eat herbs and hardwood twigs. An adult moose needs up to 60 pounds of food a day. It is a powerful swimmer and can cross eight or 10 miles of cold water with apparent ease. Although its sight is not good, its hearing and smell are excellent.

Moose are 80 to 115 inches long and 66 to 81¾ inches high at the shoulders. Bulls weigh 600 to 800 pounds (1,177 pounds has been verified, 1,800 pounds is presumed possible). Cows are 25% smaller. Record antler spreads are: eastern moose, 65⅝ inches; Alaskan moose, 77⅝ inches. The single species occurs in the boreal evergreen forest zone around the world; in North America — Maine and Nova Scotia west to western Alaska, below the tundra south to northwestern Colorado.

TARANDUS FURCIFER, AGASSIZ.

CARIBOU OR AMERICAN REIN-DEER

The Caribou, or American Reindeer, is one of the most important animals of the northern parts of America, and is almost as graceful in form as the elk *(Elaphus /Cervus/ Canadensis),* to which it is nearly equal in size; but it has never, we believe, been domesticated or trained to draw sledges in the manner of the Reindeer of the old world, although so nearly allied to that species that it has been by most authors considered identical with it.

Whilst separating the Caribou found in Maine and the States bordering on the St. Lawrence, and in Canada, Labrador, &c., from the Reindeer of Europe, we are inclined to think that the Reindeer found within the polar circle may be the European species, domiciled in that part of America, and that they sometimes migrate farther south than even Hudson's Bay. . . .

This species /now the eastern woodland caribou, a subspecies/ . . . is not abundant near Quebec; it is mostly found in the swamps, wherever these are well supplied with moss-covered dead trees and bushes; the moss the animals prefer is a long and black species, and forms their chief subsistence during the winter months; but towards spring these animals remove to the sides of the hills or mountains, and even ascend to their summits occasionally, feeding on the newly swollen buds of different shrubs. Like the moose deer they shed their antlers about this period, and renew them in the summer months.

The Caribou is famous for its swiftness, and has various gaits, walking trotting or galloping alike gracefully and rapidly. By many people these animals are in fact thought to be much fleeter animals than the moose, and they are said to take most extraordinary leaps.

When pursued the Caribou immediately makes for a swamp and follows the margin, taking at times to the water and again footing it over the firm ground, and sometimes turning towards the nearest mountain crosses it to another morass. If hard pressed by the hunters (who now and then follow up the chase for four or five days) the animal ascends to the loftiest peaks of the mountains for greater security, and the pursuit becomes very fatiguing and uncertain. Upon one occasion two men followed several Caribou for a whole week, when, completely tired out they gave up the chase, which was then continued by two other hunters who at last succeeded in killing a couple of the animals at long shot. Sometimes, however, fresh tracks are found and the Caribou is surprised whilst lying down or browsing, and shot on the spot. When the snow is not deep and the lakes are covered with ice only, the animal if closely pushed makes for one of them and runs over the ice so fast that it is unable to stop if struck with alarm at any object presenting itself in front, and it then suddenly squats down on its haunches and slides along in that ludicrous position until, the impetus being exhausted, it rises again and makes off in some other direction. . . .

When overtaken by dogs in chase, the Caribou stand at bay and show fight, and when thus brought to a stand will not pay much attention to the hunter, so that he can approach and shoot them with ease.

During our /John J. Audubon's/ expeditions in Labrador we saw many trails of Reindeer through the deep and stiff moss; they are about as broad as a cowpath, and many times the fatigues of a long day's hunt over the sterile wilds of that country were lightened by following in these tracks or paths, instead of walking on the yielding moss. . . .

We were informed that the Caribou are sometimes abundant on the island of Newfoundland, to which they cross on the ice from the mainland, and as the fishermen and French trappers at St. George's Bay told us, sometimes the herds stay so late in the spring that by the occasional early breaking up of the ice, they are prevented from leaving the island. /Audubon was misinformed. The caribou of Newfoundland are a separate subspecies. With relatively minor exceptions, the animals remain on the island throughout their lives./

The horns of the Caribou run into various shapes, and are more or less palmated. The female of this species has also horns, which are not dropped until near the month of May. No two individuals of this species have the horns alike, nor do the horns of any grow into the same number of prongs, or resemble those of the last season. . . .

CARIBOU

Rangifer tarandus caribou (Gmelin)

Every spring vast herds of barren ground caribou walk, trot, gallop and run 600 to 800 miles on their annual migration from the winter forest habitat to the tundra. Grunts, snorts, clicking of tendons against foot bones, and the ammoniate odor of glands in massed bodies mark their passage. First come the does, then the yearlings, the bucks and last of all the packs of wolves scavenging for the weak, the sick and the dying. By June the females that are carrying young are hurrying to reach the fawning grounds.

The single fawn (twins are rare) is very precocious. A mother was seen to urge her newborn to hop, walk and run for several miles within an hour and a half of birth. During this time it was allowed to nurse only twice — briefly. One fawn, still trailing its umbilical cord, managed to stay 20 feet out of reach except for the times it advanced to be sure that the pursuing game warden was not its mother! When a fawn gets far behind, the parent waits and beckons with her head to hurry. During a stampede or blizzard, the young may be separated permanently from their mothers, bawl desperately, starve, die of exposure, be gored by strange mothers, or devoured by wolves.

By July the impetus of the migration is slowing down, and the herds begin to swing back. The animals are harried from place to place by warble flies, nose flies and hordes of swarming mosquitoes. In autumn, the rut begins. The bucks of some barren ground herds do not collect harems; in other herds and in woodland caribou groups, harems of five to 10 are defended. Some remain on the tundra during the winter; most are back in the forests by December.

The woodland caribou, southern subspecies of caribou, is pictured above and described on the opposite page. Somewhat larger than the barren ground caribou (northern subspecies), it makes relatively short seasonal trips between elevations rather than long migrations. Otherwise it is similar in appearance and habits. Both caribou are entirely white in certain habitats. The spectacular antlers of the buck may be taller than the animal's height at the shoulders. The antlers worn by both sexes are eagerly chewed for calcium when shed.

In Canada alone there were an estimated two million caribou in 1900. With the advent of firearms, resulting wasteful slaughter, and forest fires that destroy browse and lichens, the population has been reduced by perhaps 90%.

Subspecies vary widely in size: length, 55 to 102 inches, including the 4- to 9-inch tail; shoulder height, 40 to 60 inches; bulls weigh 200 to 700 (average 275) pounds. Cows are 30% smaller. The single species is circumpolar in distribution; in America, south to Lake Superior and southern British Columbia.

ANTILOPE AMERICANA, ORD.

PRONG - HORNED ANTELOPE.

Reader, let us carry you with us to the boundless plains over which the prong-horn speeds. Hurra for the prairies and the swift antelopes, as they fleet by the hunter like flashes or meteors, seen but for an instant, for quickly do they pass out of sight in the undulating ground, covered with tall rank grass. Observe now a flock of these beautiful animals; they are not afraid of man — they pause in their rapid course to gaze on the hunter, and stand with head erect, their ears as well as eyes directed towards him, and make a loud noise by stamping with their forefeet on the hard earth; but suddenly they become aware that he is no friend of theirs, and away they bound like a flock of frightened sheep — but far more swiftly do the graceful antelopes gallop off . . . Sometimes, eager with curiosity and anxious to examine the novel object which astonishes as well as alarms them, the antelopes on seeing a hunter, advance toward him, stopping at intervals, and then again advancing, and should the hunter partly conceal himself, and wave his handkerchief or a white or red rag on the end of his ramrod, he may draw the wondering animals quite close to him and then quickly seizing his rifle send a ball through the fattest of the group . . . .

The Indians, we were told, sometimes bring the antelope to within arrow-shot (bow-shot), by throwing themselves on their backs and kicking up their heels with a bit of a rag fastened to them, on seeing which moving amid the grass the antelope draws near to satisfy his curiosity. . . .

The rutting season of this species commences in September, the bucks run for about six weeks, and during this period fight with great courage and even a degree of ferocity. When a male sees another approaching, or accidentally comes upon one of his rivals, both parties run at each other with their heads lowered and their eyes flashing angrily, and while they strike with their horns they wheel and bound with prodigous activity and rapidity, giving and receiving severe wounds, — sometimes like fencers, getting within each others "points." and each hooking his antagonist with the recurved branches of his horns, which bend considerably inwards and downwards.

The Prong-horned Antelope usually inhabits the low prairies adjoining the covered woody bottoms during spring and autumn, but is also found on the high or upland prairies, or amid broken hills, and is to be seen along the margins of the rivers and streams: it swims very fast and well, and occasionally a herd when startled may be seen crossing a river in straggling files, but without disorder, and apparently with ease.

Sometimes a few of these animals, or even only one or two by themselves may be seen, whilst in other instances several hundreds are congregated in a herd. They are remarkably shy, are possessed of a fine sense of smell, and have large and beautiful eyes, which enable them to scan the surface of the undulating prairie and detect the lurking Indian or wolf . . .

It was supposed by the hunters at Fort Union, that the prong-horned antelope dropped its horns; but as no person had ever shot or killed one without these ornamental and useful appendages, we /John J. Audubon/ managed to prove the contrary to the men at the fort by knocking off the bony part of the horn, and showing the hard, spongy membrane beneath, well attached to the skull and perfectly immoveable.

. . .Their walk is a slow and somewhat pompous gait, their trot elegant and graceful, and their gallop or "run" light and inconceivably swift; they pass along, up or down hills, or along the level plain with the same apparent ease, while so rapidly do their legs perform their graceful movements in propelling their bodies over the ground, that like the spokes of a fast turning wheel we can hardly see them, but instead, observe a gauzy or film-like appearance where they should be visible. . . .

Whilst on our journey in the far west, in 1843, on one occasion, we /John J. Audubon/ had the gratification of seeing an old female, in a flock of eight or ten antelopes, suckling its young. The little beauty performed this operation precisely in the manner of our common lambs, almost kneeling down, bending its head upwards, its rump elevated, it thumped the bag of its mother, from time to time, and reminded us of far distant scenes, where peaceful flocks feed and repose under the safeguard of our race . . .

PRONG-HORNED ANTELOPE, or PRONGHORN

Antilocapra americana americana (Ord)

The fastest of all American animals, the pronghorn may race a car at 45 miles an hour — and then suddenly cross in front of it. When pressed, the animal can spurt ahead briefly at 60 miles an hour. With a good start, it can leap across a 27-foot gully. The antelope's leg bones have seven times the breaking strength of a domestic cow. When hungry coyotes come around, the pronghorn tries to outrun or outwit them. It can go much faster than the predators but a pack running in relay may wear it down and it can only strike at them with flailing hoofs. When coyotes are hunting a kid, the mother tries to decoy them.

The hollow hairs of the pronghorn's outer coat are controlled by muscles which pull them down tightly to hold in body heat, or raise them to let in the breeze on a hot day. Also by muscular control, the twin rosettes of white hair on the rump set up a flashing signal that can be seen miles away.

Every winter both sexes grow new horn sheaths from permanent bony cores that project from the skull; these are shed after the August rut. The short two-week mating period is featured by much odd posturing and some fighting by the bucks as they gather harems of two to a dozen females. After a gestation of about eight months, the normally gregarious does go off individually for the birth of twins. (Usually only the firstborn is single.) As a safety precaution, each kid is dropped from 50 to 400 feet apart. The mother tries to lick them dry, but in cold, rainy weather they may die of exposure. Covered with wavy, grayish hair, they weigh four to five pounds each. Hard to locate by sound, their bleats seem to be ventriloquial. The mother's milk is as thick as undiluted evaporated milk, but less sweet. From five weeks to six months of age, the kids play games, race around and sometimes jump on the backs of reclining mothers.

Eyes of the pronghorn are as large as those of the horse which is 10 times its size. They not only have a very wide angle of vision but can see moving objects three or four miles away. In addition to Audubon's suggested methods of attracting their attention, crawling under a bedsheet has been successful!

Prong-horned antelopes live on open, rolling plains in bands of five to 25 animals. They eat grass, leaves, twigs and even prickly cactus. Although "antelope" is the most commonly used name, the animal is not one of that group. True antelopes have solid horns and are limited to Africa and Eurasia. This New World genus has only one species.

Our smallest-hoofed animal, the pronghorn buck is 50 to 59 inches long, 35 to 41 inches high at the shoulder, and weighs 100 to 138 (average 115) pounds. A doe weighs 80 to 105. Range: southern Saskatchewan to northern Durango, and the Dakotas and Texas to central Oregon and Baja California, in Mexico.

291

BOS AMERICANUS, GMEL.

AMERICAN BISON OR BUFFALO.

. . . In the days of our boyhood and youth, Buffaloes roamed over the small and beautiful prairies of Indiana and Illinois, and herds of them stalked through the open woods of Kentucky and Tennessee; but they had dwindled down to a few stragglers, which resorted chiefly to the "Barrens," towards the years 1808 and 1809, and soon after entirely disappeared. Their range has since that period gradually tended westward, and now you must direct your steps "to the Indian country," and travel many hundred miles beyond the fair valleys of the Ohio, towards the great rocky chain of mountains which forms the backbone of North-America, before you can reach the Buffalo, and see him roving in his sturdy independence upon the vast elevated plains, which extend to the base of the Rocky Mountains. . . .

The American Bison is much addicted to wandering, and the various herds annually remove from the North, at the approach of winter, although many may be found, during that season, remaining in high latitudes, their thick woolly coats enabling them to resist a low temperature, without suffering greatly. During a severe winter, however, numbers of them perish, especially the old, and the very young ones. The breeding season is generally the months of June and July, and the calves are brought forth in April and May; although occasionally they are produced as early as March or as late as July. The Buffalo most frequently has but one calf at a time, but instances occur of their having two. The females usually retire from the herd either singly or several in company, select as solitary a spot as can be found, remote from the haunt of wolves, bears, or other enemies that would be most likely to molest them, and there produce their young.

Occasionally, however, they bring forth their offspring when the herd is migrating, and at such times they are left by the main body, which they rejoin as soon as possible. The young usually follow the mother until she is nearly ready to have a calf again. The Buffalo seldom produces young until the third year, but will continue breeding until very old. When a cow and her very young calf are attacked by wolves, the cow bellows and sometimes runs at the enemy, and not unfrequently frightens him away; this, however, is more generally the case when several cows are together . . .

The Bison bulls generally select a mate from among a herd of cows and do not leave their chosen one until she is about to calve.

When two or more males fancy the same female, furious battles ensue and the conqueror leads off the fair cause of the contest in triumph. Should the cow be alone, the defeated lovers follow the happy pair at such a respectful distance, as will ensure to them a chance to make their escape, if they should again become obnoxious to the victor, and at the same time enable them to take advantage of any accident that might happen in their favour. But should the fight have been caused by a female who is in a large herd of cows, the discomfited bull soon finds a substitute for his first passion. It frequently happens, that a bull leads off a cow, and remains with her separated during the season from all others, either male or female.

When the Buffalo bull is working himself up to a belligerent state, he paws the ground, bellows loudly, and goes through nearly all the actions we may see performed by the domesticated bull under similar circumstances, and finally rushes at his foe head foremost, with all his speed and strength. Notwithstanding the violent shock with which two bulls thus meet in mad career, these encounters have never been known to result fatally, probably owing to the strength of the spinous process commonly called the hump, the shortness of their horns, and the quantity of hair about all their fore-parts. . . .

During the rutting season, or while fighting, (we are not sure which,) the bulls scrape or paw up the grass in a circle, sometimes ten feet in diameter, and these places being resorted to, from time to time, by other fighting bulls, become larger and deeper, and are easily recognized even after rains have filled them with water.

In winter, when the ice has become strong enough to bear the weight of many tons, Buffaloes are often drowned in great numbers, for they are in the habit of crossing rivers on the ice, and should any alarm occur, rush in a dense crowd to one place; the ice gives way beneath the pressure of hundreds of these huge animals, they are precipitated into the water, and if it is deep enough to reach over their backs, soon perish. . . .

AMERICAN BISON

Bison bison bison (Linnaeus)

Fifty million bison once thundered over the prairies of North America. By 1889, only 541 animals were left in the United States.

Without guns and horses, the Indians had utilized the buffalo (bison) but had had little effect on the vast populations. Sometimes they swam after the herds and killed stragglers with knives. More often a large band of howling warriors, vigorously waving blankets, would stampede frightened herds into a "surround" (natural compound) or to a cliff where the animals plunged over the edge and were either killed or crippled by the fall. One of these natural traps is the famed Jump-off on the Yellowstone River about 25 miles north of the Montana-Wyoming boundary. A layer of buffalo hair, bones and other remains several feet thick, with occasional spear points and stone tools, is age-old evidence of the red man's "jumping-pound."

Feverish expansion after the Civil War and the building of transcontinental railroads brought doom to the vast herds. Buffaloes were killed by professional hunters to supply meat for the armies of construction workers. "Buffalo Bill" Cody brought down 4,280 animals in 18 months. In two days Grand Duke Alexis of Russia and his party shot 1,500 bison. Millions of hides were shipped on freight cars. Tourists fired at buffalo from train windows just to see them drop. Many animals were killed for their tongues alone and the bodies left to rot. (Tongues were considered a great delicacy by gourmets "back East.")

When the bison was almost exterminated in 1890, conservationists rushed to the rescue. Small nuclei of bison were established on national wildlife refuges and in national parks. Today there are over 6,000 "wild" bison in the United States and at least 25,000 in Canada. Nearly all of the former live behind fences but they are spread over wide areas and most controls, except necessary cropping, have ceased. Over 400 ranches from coast to coast raise buffaloes commercially for exhibit, sportsmen's banquets, gourmet restaurants and even "buffalo burgers."

Sporadic attempts to breed bison with cattle and yaks with buffaloes have not proved practical. Too many cows died and too many of the hybrids (cattalo and yakalo) were infertile.

Audubon observed buffalo during several months in 1843 and obtained much information from others. Most of it was accurate; errors that have been discovered during the intervening century will be mentioned in discussion of life history under the next painting. (Continued)

BOS AMERICANUS, GMEL.

AMERICAN BISON OR BUFFALO.

... The gaits of the Bison are walking, cantering, and galloping, and when at full speed, he can get over the ground nearly as fast as the best horses found in the Indian country. In lying down, this species bends the forelegs first, and its movements are almost exactly the same as those of the common cow. It also rises with the same kind of action as cattle.

When surprised in a recumbent posture by the sudden approach of a hunter, who has succeeded in nearing it under the cover of a hill, clump of trees or other interposing object, the Bison springs from the ground and is in full race almost as quick as thought, and is so very alert, that one can scarcely perceive his manner of rising on such occasions.

The bulls never grow as fat as the cows, the latter having been occasionally killed with as much as two inches of fat on the boss or hump and along the back to the tail. The fat rarely exceeds half an inch on the sides or ribs, but is thicker on the belly. The males have only one inch of fat, and their flesh is never considered equal to that of the females in delicacy or flavour. In a herd of Buffaloes many are poor, and even at the best season it is not likely that all will be found in good condition ...

A large Bison bull will generally weigh nearly two thousand pounds, and a fat cow, about twelve hundred. We weighed one of the bulls killed by our party and found it to reach seventeen hundred and twenty seven pounds, although it had already lost a good deal of blood. This was an old bull and was not fat; it had probably weighed more at some previous period. We were told that at this season a great many half-breed Indians were engaged in killing Buffaloes and curing their flesh for winter-use, on Moose river, about 200 miles north of us.

When these animals are shot at a distance of fifty or sixty yards, they rarely, if ever, charge on the hunters. Mr. CULBERTSON told us he had killed as many as nine bulls from the same spot, unseen by these terrible animals. There are times, however, when they have been known to gore both horse and rider, after being severely wounded, and have dropped down dead but a few minutes afterwards. ...

Although large, heavy, and comparatively clumsy, the Bison is at times brisk and frolicksome, and these huge animals often play and gambol about, kicking their heels in the air with surprising agility, and throwing their hinder parts to the right and left alternately, or from one side to the other, their heels the while flying about and their tails whisking in the air. ...

The Mandan Indians chase the Buffalo in parties of from twenty to fifty, and each man is provided with two horses, one of which he rides, and the other being trained expressly for the chase, is led to the place where the Buffaloes are started. The hunters are armed with bows and arrows, their quivers containing from thirty to fifty arrows according to the wealth of the owner. When they come in sight of their game, they quit the horses on which they have ridden, mount those led for them, ply the whip, soon gain the flank or even the centre of the herd, and shoot their arrows into the fattest, according to their fancy. When a Buffalo has been shot, if the blood flows from the nose or mouth, he is considered mortally wounded; if not, they shoot a second or a third arrow into the wounded animal. ...

The scrapings of the skins, we were informed, are sometimes boiled with berries, and make a kind of jelly which is considered good food in some cases by the Indians. The strips cut off from the skins are sewed together and make robes for the children, or caps, mittens, shoes, &c. The bones are pounded fine with a large stone and boiled, the grease which rises to the top is skimmed off and put into bladders. This is the favourite and famous marrow grease, which is equal to butter. The sinews are used for stringing their bows, and are a substitute for thread; the intestines are eaten, the shoulder-blades made into hoes, and in fact (as we have already stated) nothing is lost or wasted ....

There exists a singular variety of the Bison, which is however very scarce, and the skin of which is called by both the hunters and fur traders a "beaver robe." These are valued so highly that some have sold for more than three hundred dollars. ...

AMERICAN BISON

Bison bison bison (Linnaeus)

Although it looks slow and lethargic, the buffalo will suddenly, swiftly and without provocation, kill a man on foot or horseback. (An automobile is probably safe.) Weighing sometimes over a ton, the largest animal in the New World is amazingly fast and agile when aroused. Although the bull is 40% longer and 60% heavier than the cow, it is the cow that leads the herd. Around her are several generations of offspring and, in a less stable relationship, a bull. Only during the July-August mating season does the bull become master. He is neither sagacious nor satisfied with one mate, as Audubon was told. Instead, he tries to maintain a harem of perhaps 20 or more. (Audubon's term for the cows at this point as the "fair ones" illustrates the flowery phrase of another day.) After all of the cows are mated, most of the mature bulls retire and form little "clubs" somewhat apart from the main herd.

Most of the bright yellowish-red calves are born the following May; others arrive late in April or at any time in June. Twins are rare. In two or three days, each calf accompanies the cow when she leaves the birthing spot and returns to the herd.

Usually protected by her, sometimes by the bull and entire herd, the calf is likely to stay near the mother until it is three years old. Females do not breed until that age and they continue to grow until they are about six. Males try to mate at four and achieve full growth at nine or 10. Cows do not produce young every year but have been known to have healthy young at the very old age of 26. Most captive bison do not last that long; in the wild they seldom live longer than 15 years.

Bison have poor sight but good hearing and smell. They graze on grass and some herbs. In olden times the herds wandered erratically but, contrary to Audubon's informant, they did not make annual migrations between north and south. Neither did they use the dusting places and wallows merely in the mating period or when fighting. Both cows and bulls, but especially the latter, do considerable rolling and twisting to relieve themselves of insects and itching.

Adult bulls are 10 to 12 2/3 feet long, including the 2-foot tail; 5½ to 6 feet high at the massive humped shoulder and weigh up to 2,000 pounds or more. Cows are considerably smaller: 7 to 9½ feet long and 5 feet high at the shoulder; weight usually 700 to 900 pounds but occasionally 1,200 pounds. Wild bison now occur only in Yellowstone National Park in the United States and Wood Buffalo National Park in Canada.

CAPRA AMERICANA, BLAINVILLE.
ROCKY MOUNTAIN GOAT.

. . . In the vast ranges of wild and desolate heights, alternating with deep valleys and tremendous gorges, well named the Rocky Mountains . . . we may find the savage grizzly bear, the huge bison, the elegant and fleet antelope, the large-horned sheep of the mountains, and the agile fearless climber of the steeps — The Rocky Mountain Goat.

This snow-white /slightly yellowish/ and beautiful animal appears to have been first described, from skins shown to LEWIS and CLARK, as "the Sheep," in their general description of the beasts, birds, and plants found by the party in their expedition. They say, ". . . .We have only seen the skins of these animals, which the natives dress with the wool, and the blankets which they manufacture from the wool. The animal from this evidence appears to be of the size of our common sheep, of a white colour. The wool is fine on many parts of the body, but in length not equal to that of our domestic sheep. On the back, and particularly on the top of the head, this is intermixed with a considerable portion of long straight hairs. From the Indian account these animals have erect pointed horns."

The Rocky Mountain Goat wanders over the most precipitous rocks, and springs with great activity from crag to crag, feeding on the plants, grasses, and mosses of the mountain sides, and seldom or never descends to the luxuriant valleys, as the Big-Horn does. /Goats go into dense timber at times and cross grassy valley bottoms./ This Goat indeed resembles the wild Goat of Europe, or the chamois, in its habits, and is very difficult to procure. Now and then the hunter may observe one browsing on the extreme verge of some perpendicular rock almost directly above him, far beyond gun-shot, and entirely out of harm's way. At another time, after fatiguing and hazardous efforts, the hungry marksman may reach a spot from whence his rifle will send a ball into the unsuspecting Goat; then slowly he rises from his hands and knees, on which he has been creeping, and the muzzle of his heavy gun is "rested" on a loose stone, behind which he has kept his movements from being observed, and now he pulls the fatal trigger with deadly aim. The loud sharp crack of the rifle has hardly rung back in his ear from the surrounding cliffs when he sees the Goat in its expiring struggles reach the verge of the dizzy height: a moment of suspense and it rolls over, and swiftly falls, striking perchance here and there a projecting point, and with the clatter of thousands of small stones set in motion by its rapid passage down the steep slopes which incline outward near the base of the cliff, disappears, enveloped in a cloud of dust in the deep ravine beneath; where a day's journey would hardly bring an active man to it, for far around must he go to accomplish a safe descent, and toilsome and dangerous must be his progress up the gorge within whose dark recesses his game is likely to become the food of the ever prowling wolf or the solitary raven. . . .

Notwithstanding these difficulties, as portions of the mountains are not so precipitous, the Rocky Mountain Goat is shot and procured tolerably easily, it is said, by some of the Indian tribes, who make various articles of clothing out of its skin, and use its soft woolly hair for their rude fabrics.

According to Sir JOHN RICHARDSON, this animal has been known to the members of the Northwest and Hudson's Bay Companies from the first establishment of their trading posts on the banks of the Columbia River and in New Caledonia, and they have sent several specimens to Europe. The wool being examined by a competent judge, under the instructions of the Wernerian Society of Edinburgh, was reported to be of great fineness and fully an inch and a half long. "It is unlike the fleece of the common sheep, which contains a variety of different kinds of wool suitable to the fabrication of articles very dissimilar in their nature, and requires much care to distribute them in their proper order. The fleece under consideration is wholly fine. That on the fore part of the skin has all the apparent qualities of wool. On the back part it very much resembles cotton. . . ."

The flesh of this species is hard and dry, and is not so much relished as that of the Big-Horn, the Elk, &c., by the hunters or travellers who have journeyed towards the Pacific across the wild ranges of mountains inhabited by these animals.

MOUNTAIN GOAT

Oreamnos americanus americanus (Blainville)

Generally living above timberline, among precipices and rock slides, this goat-antelope can climb higher and farther than any other animal its size. With less desirable trophy horns, less delicious meat, and not subject to the epizootic diseases of the mountain sheep, the species has kept its primitive numbers. When not hunted, mountain goats are quite unwary and will investigate anything unusual.

In November the billies slash their sharp nine-inch horns against brush and each other. A large gland at the rear base of each horn leaves a signature of musk When fighting, some animals are badly wounded and others are killed. Males may be monogamous for the season or not — depending on the individual and the opportunity.

By late April most of the adult males have gone into small bachelor clubs and the yearlings are being driven off to fend for themselves. Kids (usually one, frequently two) are born between early May and mid-June. Covered with a warm wool coat, they stand 13 inches high and weigh about 6½ pounds. Precocious, they follow their mother on spindly legs almost immediately. They nurse vigorously, wiggling their tails constantly. The nanny is extremely watchful and drives off any would-be intruders, even her own yearlings, with angry thrusts of horns.

Kids gambol and play together but adults do not join in. Sometimes an absentminded mother may go off without her offspring. When she remembers, she returns, nuzzles and licks it thoroughly to be sure it is all right. Before long it is so big that it has to get down on its knees to nurse. Goats are generally silent but kids bleat for a missing nanny and adults growl when angry. Grazers and browsers, the animals take a bite here and a nip there as they wander along perhaps a couple of miles daily.

Snow slides may cause more fatalities than predation. Bears, coyotes, cougars, bobcats, wolverines, and golden and bald eagles are potential but probably not important enemies. The small kids occasionally seen carried off in the talons of eagles may have been ill, crippled or already dead.

The mountain goat is much more closely related to the chamois than the domestic goat. There is only one species. Billies are 48 to 66 inches long, including the 3½- to 5½-inch tail, and measure up to 43½ inches tall at the humped shoulders. A large male in fine condition may weigh 300 pounds. Females are about 4 inches lower and 35 pounds lighter. Goats occur irregularly on the Rockies and Cascade-Coast ranges from Colorado (by introduction) and Oregon to northern Yukon and the Chugach Mountains of Alaska.

OVIBOS MOSCHATUS, GMEL

MUSK OX

For our description and account of the habits of this very peculiar animal we have resorted to other authors, never having ourselves had an opportunity of seeing it alive, and in fact knowing it only from the specimen in the British Museum, from which our /J. W. Audubon's/ figures were drawn, and which is the only one hitherto sent to Europe, so difficult is it to procure the animal and convey the skin, with the skull, leg bones, &c., in a tolerable state of preservation, from the barren lands of the northern portions of British America, where it is found, and where an almost perpetual winter and consequent scarcity of food make it very difficult to prevent the Indians, or white hunters either, from eating (we should say devouring) everything that can by any possibility serve to fill their empty stomachs — even skins, hoofs, and the most refuse parts of any animal they kill. . . .

Sir GEORGE SIMPSON, of the Hudson's Bay Fur Company, most kindly promised some years ago that he would if possible procure us a skin of the Musk-Ox . . . We have not yet received this promised skin, and therefore feel sure that the hunters failed to obtain or to preserve one . . .

"The country frequented by the Musk-Ox is mostly rocky, and destitute of wood except on the banks of the larger rivers, which are generally more or less thickly clothed with spruce trees. Their food is similar to that of the caribou — grass at one season and lichens at another; and the contents of their paunch are eaten by the natives with the same relish that they devour the 'nerrooks' of the reindeer. . . .

"When this animal is fat, its flesh is well tasted, and resembles that of the caribou, but has a coarser grain. The flesh of the bulls is highly flavoured, and both bulls and cows, when lean, smell strongly of musk, their flesh at the same time being very dark and tough . . .

"The carcase of a Musk-Ox weighs, exclusive of the offal, about three hundred weight, or nearly three times as much as a barren ground caribou, and twice as much as one of the woodland caribou.

"Notwithstanding the shortness of the legs of the Musk-Ox, it runs fast, and climbs hills or rocks with great ease. One, pursued on the banks of the Coppermine, scaled a lofty sand cliff, having so great an acclivity that we were obliged to crawl on hands and knees to follow it. Its foot-marks are very similar to those of the carbou, but are rather longer and narrower. These oxen assemble in herds of from twenty to thirty, rut about the end of August and beginning of September, and bring forth one calf about the latter end of May or beginning of June.

"HEARNE, from the circumstance of few bulls being seen, supposed that they kill each other in their contests for the cows. If the hunters keep themselves concealed when they fire upon a herd of Musk-Oxen, the poor animals mistake the noise for thunder, and, forming themselves into a group, crowd nearer and nearer together as their companions fall around them; but should they discover their enemies by sight or by their sense of smell, which is very acute, the whole herd seek for safety by instant flight. The bulls, however, are very irascible, and particularly when wounded will often attack the hunter and endanger his life, unless he possess both activity and presence of mind. The Esquimaux, who are well accustomed to the pursuit of this animal, sometimes turn its irritable disposition to good account; for an expert hunter having provoked a bull to attack him, wheels round it more quickly than it can turn, and by repeated stabs in the belly puts an end to its life. The wool of the Musk-Ox resembles that of the bison, but is perhaps finer, and would no doubt be highly useful in the arts if it could be procured in sufficient quantity." — *Richardson, F.B.A.* /Fauna Boreali-Americana/, p. 277. . . .

According to PARRY, this animal weighs about seven hundred pounds. The head and hide weigh about one hundred and thirty pounds. "The horns are employed for various purposes by the Indians and Esquimaux, especially for making cups and spoons. From the long hair growing on the neck and chest the Esquimaux make their musquito wigs, to defend their faces from those troublesome insects. The hide makes good soles for shoes and is much used for that purpose by the Indians."

MUSKOX

Ovibos moschatus moschatus (Zimmermann)

The muskox lives where it is night four months of the year and the temperature goes down to 65 degrees below zero. The sparse diet of the barren land is supplemented by vitamin B manufactured in its rumen (first stomach) and perhaps nitrogen which may be recycled through the body instead of being excreted.

Even the single calf born in alternate years is on short rations. Its mother's milk has only one-fourth the amount of fat and one-half of the protein that caribou and reindeer have. Within a week, the youngster begins to eat the scanty grass available but continues to nurse for a year or even 18 months. Born in April or May, sometimes at 30 below zero, its wet fur coat soon dries as it huddles under its mother's fur "skirt."

When a herd of muskoxen, usually led by a cow, sights an approaching enemy, they crowd together in a rough circle. Adults face outward and the calves press against flanks or under their elders. Any wolf that dashes within snapping distance risks being slashed open or impaled on a sharp, thrusting horn. Nevertheless, a calf is sometimes snatched away. The defense circle was nearly perfect for the open Arctic barrens until man came with firearms. This formation made slaughter easy and possibly 90% of the muskoxen population was destroyed. Since 1917, Canada has given the species complete protection and will continue to do so because of the rigorous environment and slow reproduction. There are probably about 10,000 muskoxen living in the Canadian Arctic today.

Muskoxen are unpredictable and sometimes attack man. Besides excellent hearing and vision, the eye has a slit pupil which can close completely when sun glare on the snow is too intense. Named for the glands which presumably emitted a musky secretion under stress of mating and fighting, the animal apparently has only a bovid odor.

Muskoxen live in small bands which are usually widely spaced because of the scarcity of food. They eat grasses and many other herbs, dwarf woody shrubs and moss-lichens — a variety which conserves the sparse, slow-growing vegetation. Tall plants are stripped of leaves and foliage with the long tongue.

Adult bulls are 81 to 97 inches long and 54 to 60 inches at the shoulders; they weigh 500 to 900 pounds. (In confinement, a 51-month-old bull weighed 1,450 pounds.) Cows are considerably smaller. During the most southerly glaciation, the species occupied a broad area from New York and Pennsylvania west to Iowa and Kansas; the present-day range is northeast Mackenzie and adjacent Keewatin districts of Canada to northern Greenland.

OVIS MONTANA, DESM

ROCKY MOUNTAIN SHEEP.

It was on the 12th of June, 1843, that we /J. J. Audubon/ first saw this remarkable animal; we were near the confluence of the Yellow Stone river with the Missouri, when a group of them, numbering twenty-two in all, came in sight. This flock was composed of rams and ewes, with only one young one or lamb among them. They scampered up and down the hills much in the manner of common sheep, but notwithstanding all our anxious efforts to get within gun-shot, we were unable to do so, and were obliged to content ourselves with this first sight of the Rocky Mountain Ram.

The parts of the country usually chosen by these animals for their pastures, are the most extraordinary broken and precipitous clay hills or stony eminences that exist in the wild regions belonging to the Rocky Mountain chain. They never resort to the low lands or plains except when about to remove their quarters, or swim across rivers, which they do well and tolerably fast. Perhaps some idea of the country they inhabit (which is called by the French Canadians and hunters, "mauvaise terres") may be formed by imagining some hundreds of loaves of sugar of different sizes, irregularly broken and truncated at top, placed somewhat apart, and magnifying them into hills of considerable size. Over these hills and ravines the Rocky Mountain Sheep bound up and down among the sugar loaf shaped peaks, and you may estimate the difficulty of approaching them, and conceive the great activity and sure-footedness of this species, which, together with their extreme wildness and keen sense of smell, enable them to baffle the most vigorous and agile hunter. /Until modern times, loaf sugar was made in cone-shaped molds./

They form paths around these irregular clay cones that are at times from six to eight hundred feet high, and in some situations are even fifteen hundred feet or more above the adjacent prairies, and along these they run at full speed, while to the eye of the spectator below, these tracks do not appear to be more than a few inches wide, although they are generally from a foot to eighteen inches in breadth. In many places columns or piles of clay, or hardened earth, are to be seen eight or ten feet above the adjacent surface, covered or coped with a slaty flat rock, thus resembling gigantic toad stools, and upon these singular places the big horns are frequently seen, gazing at the hunter who is winding about far below, looking like so many statues on their elevated pedestals. One cannot imagine how these animals reach these curious places, especially with their young along with them, which are sometimes brought forth on these inaccessible points, beyond the reach of their greatest enemies, the wolves . . .

"ι..The Rocky Mountain Sheep are gregarious, and the males fight fiercely with each other in the manner of common rams. Their horns are exceedingly heavy and strong, and some that we have seen have a battered appearance, showing that the animal to which they belonged must have butted against rocks or trees, or probably had fallen from some elevation on to the stony surface below. We have heard it said that the Rocky Mountain Sheep descend the steepest hills head foremost, and they may thus come in contact with projecting rocks, or fall from a height on their enormous horns. /See opposite page./

As is the case with some animals of the deer tribe, the young rams of this species and the females herd together during the winter and spring, while the old rams form separate flocks, except during the rutting season in December.

In the months of June and July the ewes bring forth, usually one, and occasionally, but rarely, two. /See opposite page./

Dr. RICHARDSON, on the authority of DRUMMOND, states that in the retired parts of the mountains where the hunters had seldom penetrated, he (DRUMMOND) found no difficulty in approaching the Rocky Mountain Sheep, which there exhibited the simplicity of character so remarkable in the domestic species; but that where they had been often fired at, they were exceedingly wild . . . He lost several that he had mortally wounded, by their retiring to die among the secluded precipices." They are, we are farther informed on the authority of DRUMMOND, in the habit of paying daily visits to certain caves in the mountains that are encrusted with saline efflorescence. The same gentleman mentions that the horns of the old rams attain a size so enormous, and curve so much forwards and downwards, that they effectually prevent the animal from feeding on the level ground. . . .

BIGHORN, or MOUNTAIN SHEEP

Ovis canadensis canadensis Shaw

During the rutting season the clanging horns of battling rams can be heard a mile away. More often than not the bighorns silhouetted against the skies are not fighting for mates, for no ewe is present. At other times, however, when two rams have been pursuing the same female, the combat has a specific goal. Standing 20 feet apart, the rams rush headlong at each other, meeting on their horns with a resounding crash. These collisions are repeated — occasionally 40 times in two hours. Between assaults, the ritual is to eat grass and keep an eye on each other. Suddenly, without warning, one of the contenders may rear on his hind legs, lower his head and hurl himself at the other. In the meantime a third ram can come along, serve the waiting female and depart unnoticed. Horns of the combatants are chipped, splintered, or possibly broken off. (This permanent damage is usually caused by fighting, not by falling down mountains, as Audubon was told.) Very rarely during the battle, a skull is fractured or one of the rivals is pushed over a cliff.

The most promiscuous big game animal in America, the bighorn does not collect a harem. It stalks along from one band to another, searching for receptive females. It curls its lip and licks its nose excitedly. Locating a ewe in estrus, the ram dashes toward her. In his eager pursuit, he pushes other sheep aside, falls down, scrambles along and gets up again. The object of his chase may run a long distance and then wait to let him catch up to her. A reluctant female, that

does not get away, may be beaten by the shank of his leg, nipped in the flank or bunted.

After a gestation of about six months, the usually single lamb is born in a damp fur coat which the mother licks fondly. It is soon playing with other lambs and even some adults — kicking up its heels, rushing around in circles, playing follow-the-leader — or climbing precipices at dizzying heights. In the desert mountains, bighorns become dehydrated, look emaciated and ready for death. After drinking long at a water hole and resting a half hour, their bodies fill out so that they act and look in the best of health.

Man's persistent hunting for trophies and meat, the competitive foraging with domestic stock, insufficient winter food, and mortality from sheep scabies, lungworms and privation-induced diseases have decimated the original population of one or two million to only 15,000 to 18,000 animals. The badlands race, which Audubon studied in eastern Montana, is extinct.

Adult rams are 53 to 78 inches long and 38 to 42 inches in shoulder height; they weigh about 200 to (rarely) 320 pounds. Ewes are about 10% smaller and weigh 100 to 120 pounds (occasionally 160 pounds). The species occurs in many mountain ranges and "badlands" from British Columbia and southwestern Alberta to Baja California and Coahuila. Dall's sheep *(Ovis dalli)* live in Alaska and northwestern Canada.

INDEX

The index includes major proper and common names found in the book. Scientific names appear in italic type, common names of mammals in upright type and names of the principal individuals and places in capital letters. The names of Audubon and Bachman have not been included, as it was felt that the frequency with which their names appeared rendered it unnecessary.

REFERENCES CITED IN TEXT

Bartram, William. 1794. *Travels through North and South Carolina, Georgia, East and West Florida, etc.* 527 pages, illus. Philadelphia and London.

Buffon, G. G. L. de. 1749–1804. *Histoire Naturelle, general et particulière avec la description du cabinet du roi.* 44 volumes, illus. Paris.

DeKay, James Ellsworth. 1842. *Zoology of New York.* Part I, Mammals. (6 volumes of Natural History of New York). 146 pages, illus. New York.

Geoffroy-Saint-Hilaire, Étienne. 1815–32. *Memoires,* volumes 1–20, Museum National d'Histoire Naturelle, Paris.

Hearne, Samuel. 1795. *A journey from Prince of Wales' Fort in Hudson's Bay, to the Northern Ocean . . . . in the year 1769, 1770, 1771, 1772.* 458 pages, illus. London.

Kendall, George Wilkins. 1844. *Narrative of the Texan Santa Fe Expedition.* 585 pages. Harper & Bros., New York.

Lewis, Meriwether, and Clark, W. 1814. *History of the expedition under the commands of Captains Lewis and Clark to the sources of the Missouri, etc. during 1804–6.* 4 volumes. Philadelphia.

Morton, Thomas. 1637. *The new English Canaan, or New Canaan.* 188 pages. J. F. Stam, Amsterdam.

Richardson, John. 1829. *Fauna Boreali-Americana.* Part First, Quadrupeds. 346 pages, illus. London.